PHYSICAL
GEOGRAPHY:

Selected Readings

PHYSICAL
GEOGRAPHY:

Selected Readings

edited by FRED E. DOHRS
Wayne State University

and LAWRENCE M. SOMMERS
Michigan State University

THOMAS Y. CROWELL COMPANY
New York
Established 1834

910.02
D65

First Printing, March, 1967
Second Printing, September, 1967

PREFACE

In compiling this volume of readings, we have sought materials from the rich literature available that would be especially suitable for introductory geography courses. We have endeavored to cover each of the main topics discussed in the majority of introductory texts, and although our organization is systematic, we have included articles pertaining to all of the major regions of the earth, thus making the collection suitable for courses of the regional type.

Physical Geography: Selected Readings is divided into the traditional subsections of physical geography, and the introductions to these sections relate the unit as well as the individual selections not only to the narrower field of physical geography, but to the larger field of geography as well. Student geographers, whether in a course that may be essentially cultural, physical, or regional in character, have much to learn about the elements of the physical earth. A particular course may or may not stress the importance of the elements of the physical environment, but it certainly will not—indeed, cannot—ignore them. This volume is designed to reinforce as well as illuminate and broaden the understanding of physical geography, whether it be of major or minor concern in the particular course itself. A number of the selections in this volume were written by nongeographers, usually by specialists in the allied sciences concerned. In a few instances, they are by writers whose ability to portray these elements is more important than their depth of understanding, and it is their style that enhances these selections and aids in comprehension and understanding.

To make this volume as useful as possible for teacher and student alike, several distinctive features have been included. Each section is preceded by a brief introduction that suggests the breadth and scope of the subject covered within the section, and its place within the field of geography as a whole. In addition, preceding each selection there are headnotes that place each article in relation to the topic being covered, as well as to the other articles in that section. We have also provided bibliographical notes on the opening page of each selection, which serve to identify the author and the source from which the selection was taken. Finally, to aid the instructor in making assignments, a table has been included that correlates chapters in selected introductory geography texts with the articles in this volume.

Footnotes, graphs, photographs, and tables that originally appeared in the articles, as a rule, have been omitted; only when we have deemed that they are vital to the meaning have they been retained.

Physical Geography: Selected Readings is the second of three volumes in the series. The first volume, *Introduction to Geography: Selected Readings*, and the third, *Cultural Geography: Selected Readings*, will, when used with this collection, provide instructors of basic courses with an abundance of materials from which to choose, thus adding depth and interest to introductory geography. It is hoped that the inherent flexibility of the three volumes, as well as the coverage of the series as a whole, will allow the teacher to select articles consistent with his own emphasis and his own notions of how the course should be taught.

Deep appreciation is expressed to the authors and publishers of the articles included, and to colleagues and others who gave valuable suggestions and assistance.

F.E.D.

L.M.S.

CONTENTS

INTRODUCTION

One of the things distinguishing the geographer from other social scientists who are concerned with human activities and institutions on the surface of the earth is the former's recognition of the significance of the role of the physical characteristics of the earth in analyzing these activities and institutions and their patterns. This is not to imply a deterministic role for geography; rather, it suggests that a recognition and knowledge of the significant physical elements and patterns make possible a more complete understanding of human activities and their distribution.

As is well known, each of the physical elements of the earth constitutes an important area of study, a discipline and science in itself—ranging from astronomy, meteorology, and geology to the full spectrum of biological sciences, and including hydrology and oceanography as well. And recent achievements in manned space flight have opened new vistas, although one may question such concerns by geographers, considering the root words of their discipline—(*geo*, earth; *graphein*, to write).

In spite of the depth and breadth of these disciplines, and the obvious inability of even the most brilliant geographer to know and understand more than a fraction or fragment of any or all of them, as well as his own special field, a working knowledge of the fundamental principles underlying these fields is part of the intellectual equipment of the well-trained geographer.

Some professional geographers maintain their entire interest in the field of physical geography, which constitutes one of the major divisions of the discipline. Usually these specialists are interested primarily in one of the subdivisions of the field—they may be physical geographers with interest in weather (meteorology), or in climates (climatology), or in the distribution and character of land forms, or as biogeographers, in vegetation, soils, or animals ranging down to microorganisms. In most instances, the geographer tends to be somewhat less concerned with process and morphology than his counterpart in the allied field, and more concerned with their present character, distribution, and significance, but neither professional nor student geographer can ignore the processes of development that have brought about the character and patterns of the earth's surface, including significant subsurface and atmospheric conditions as well.

I. THE EARTH IN SPACE

Although frequently disregarded or overlooked, it is the unique place the earth has in space—especially in its relationship with the sun—that gives it the basic climatic conditions that make life as we know it on earth possible. The peculiar nature of the earth's origin is fundamental to comprehension of most of the conditions we find on and immediately within the earth's surface.

Because of a necessarily limited knowledge of the sequence of events in space billions of years ago, much of the thinking about the earth's origin must be theory based on evidence available on the surface or discernible through examination of other bodies and their movements in space. As technology and science have advanced, however—especially in the fields of astronomy, astrophysics, and geophysics—some theories have become far more tenable, whereas others are being discarded.

In spite of these great advances, life and the apparent infinity of time and space remain the greatest of mysteries to mankind. Our search for knowledge and understanding continues, whether at the most sophisticated level of space technology or through simple veneration of that single source of light and heat on the earth—the sun.

1. The Birth of Worlds
Raymond Arthur Lyttleton

Man's continual search to unravel the mysteries of life, the universe, and the earth is one of his strongest intellectual and philosophical drives. That we ever shall arrive at complete understanding of these complexities remains questionable, but the search continues. In this selection, Lyttleton, using the great advances of recent scientific exploration and theorizing, presents the best of contemporary thinking on this profound and important subject. Each additional scrap or fragment of information, however unrelated it may be initially, adds to the fund of human knowledge and to our understanding of the physical earth.

Source: *Saturday Evening Post*, CCXXIV, 50 (December 16, 1961), 54–57. The author, an English astronomer, mathematician, and physicist, is a Fellow of St. John's College, Cambridge.

Man's image of the world around him—his own earth, the neighboring planets and his life-giving star-sun, which together form the solar system —has changed radically during the last few decades. Modern scientific deduction, new observational techniques and actual space probes now suggest that our lonely enclave in space may not be the unique and accidental agglomeration we once thought, but a one-in-a-million concentration of energy and life that may be repeated endlessly throughout the universe.

The revealed facts of this greatest of mysteries—the clues of a 5,000,000,000-year-old Whatdunit, which forms a part of the science of cosmogony—are as yet by no means conclusive, but they do point to some strong and surprising probabilities concerning the beginnings of our world and the chances of similar systems existing elsewhere in the universe. To appreciate the implications of current thinking on these problems, we must first recognize the difficulties involved in any interpretation of cosmical events.

The cosmogonist is like a detective who arrives on the scene long after the event, when the clues have been largely obliterated. In the case of our solar system, gradual evolution may have brought about large changes, so that few of the existing features may be primitive. We simply do not know, for instance, whether the present, almost circular paths of the planets round the sun—and in nearly the same plane—have always characterized the system. Dynamical calculations, even with the help of modern computers, cannot be carried back far enough into the past to decide the question. Even if such calculations were possible, we would not be able to incorporate the unpredictable long-term effects of numerous other disturbances, such as collisions of the planets with asteroids and meteoroids, the drag of interplanetary gas and dust, and even the cumulative effect of distant passing stars. In view of all this, we can with safety assume little more than that the present size of the system and the masses of the planets really have not changed much since the beginning.

Another handicap to the detailed investigation of our solar system lies in the immense distances that separate the earth from the other planets. Jupiter at its nearest is about 400,000,000 miles away, and our knowledge of it must come from slight modifications of the sun's light as it is reflected by the outermost layers of the planet's deep atmosphere. This is also true for Saturn, at twice this distance, and for the still more distant Uranus and Neptune. Of the near planets, Venus is permanently covered in cloud. Only the tiny planets Mercury and Mars show solid surfaces, and Mercury is difficult to observe because of its proximity to the sun.

Why should we be interested in the distant cosmic past—in how it all began? Primarily because any theory that solved the genesial problem would have to account for all the features of the present solar system, and consequentially, any correct theory would assuredly disclose a lot more about the system than we have yet observed. There is the scientific challenge of the problem, arising from the belief that it must be possible to explain the existence of the solar system as a product of natural forces. That our system must have had an origin is beyond doubt, for we know the earth has a finite past of about 5,000,000,000 years, and that the sun, from the nature of its present composition, is probably less than 10,000,000,000 years old. A third important consideration is that some reliable theory of the origin of our system is necessary before we can begin to speculate seriously on whether other planetary systems —perhaps with their own life forms—may also exist.

Before considering the various theories concerning its origin, let us glance at some of the peculiarities of our solar system. They are important because they may have a bearing on the problem of its origin. Nearest the sun is the smallest planet, Mercury, which orbits in eighty-eight days—its year—and rotates on its axis in the same time, thus always presenting the same side to the sun. This sunny side remains at about 700 degrees Fahrenheit, hot enough to melt lead and too hot to permit a planetary atmosphere. Tidal action of the sun on the planet must have slowed the rotation of Mercury, which probably once spun much faster on its axis. The next planet, Venus, in some respects almost a twin of the earth, also turns slowly, taking at least two or three weeks for its "day." Venus's exact rotational speed is not yet known, for the planet's atmosphere is topped off by permanent cloud and no distinct surface markings can be seen. Here again, the braking force of tidal action has slowed the planet's spin; in the case of Venus, the sun's tidal pull may even have been supplemented by that of a one-time Venusian satellite— possibly Mercury—which has since escaped.

Skipping our earth, we come to Mars, the outermost of the four so-called terrestrial planets. Although it is only one-ninth the mass of the earth, the greater distance of Mars from the sun enables it to retain a tenuous atmosphere. The probable existence of traces of water vapor and, more doubtfully, oxygen in this atmosphere has suggested the possibility of life on Mars. Immediately beyond the orbit of Mars lies a belt of asteroids ranging in size from minor planets 500 miles in diameter down possibly to merest dust specks. Though myriads of these small solid fragments circle the sun in the same direction as the planets, their combined mass would not amount to 1/1000th that of the earth.

The main mass of the solar system resides in the four great outer planets, Jupiter, Saturn, Uranus and Neptune. Jupiter has one-one thousandth the mass of the sun, Saturn is about one-third the mass of Jupiter, and both Uranus and Neptune have about one-twentieth the giant planet's mass. Rapid rotation characterizes all of these four outer planets. Jupiter's tremendous rotational speed at its equator of 30,000 miles per hour—compared with the earth's 1000-mile-per-hour spin—

gives it a day of less than ten hours and perceptibly flattens the planet at the poles. This deformation is not surprising, for Jupiter is probably 90 per cent hydrogen—with perhaps a small central solid core—and is, on the average, but little denser than water.

Jupiter has twelve moons, the four largest having been discovered by Galileo with the first astronomical telescope. The largest of these Galilean moons is nearly half the diameter of the earth but is almost light enough to float in one of our oceans. Three of these Galilean moons chase each other around the planet at exactly gaited speeds, each of the second and third satellites proceeding at exactly half the angular velocity of its inner neighbor. An interesting consequence of this harmonic relationship—many others are found throughout the solar system—is that all three satellites can never be simultaneously eclipsed by the planet from the earth.

Saturn, at a distance of roughly 900,000,000 miles from the sun, is about one-quarter of the way out toward the known limits of the solar system. Somewhat smaller than Jupiter, but still ten times the diameter of the earth, Saturn has the lowest mean density of all the planets and must be mostly hydrogen—the lightest of all the elements. Saturn's famous ring lies exactly in the equatorial plane of the planet and is so extraordinarily thin that it disappears from view in even the largest telescopes when it presents itself edge on to us.

Some zones of this Saturnian ring, which may be only "one particle thick," are less bright than others—showing there are fewer particles present—and there is a clear division entirely devoid of particles, brought about indirectly by the action of Titan, the largest Saturnian satellite. Theoretical and observational lines of evidence prove that Saturn's ring is constituted of finely divided solid particles, each in separate orbital motion around the planet like a tiny moon—a fact to remember when we later discuss the possible origin of our system. Saturn has nine large-size satellites, or moons, one of which revolves around the planet with a retrograde or backward motion, suggesting a belated origin by capture. Saturn's temperature is some forty degrees colder than the visible surface of Jupiter, which ranges from 200 to 300 degrees below zero Fahrenheit.

Uranus, the next planet on the long journey out from the sun, is about four times the diameter of the earth and is some 1,783,000,000 miles from the sun. A barely perceptible point of light to the naked eye, Uranus appears as a little apple-green disc through the telescope. The rotation period of Uranus is about ten hours. The odd feature of this body is that its axis of rotation is tipped so far over that the planet is like a spinning top lying on its side, whereas the axes of the other planets stand more or less upright in relation to their plane of motion around the sun. Since Uranus takes some eighty-four years to make an orbit of the sun, each of its seasons lasts for twenty-one earth years, with the sun high above polar regions in alternate seasons. The planet's temperature in sunlight is 256 degrees below zero Fahrenheit.

Uranus, which was discovered in 1781, betrayed the presence of Neptune by straying from its calculated orbit. When the perturbations of all the known planets were taken into account, it was found that some unknown body must be influencing the Uranian course through space. Two youg mathematicians, U. J. J. Leverrier of France and John Couch Adams of England, tackled the puzzle mathematically, and as a result of their predictions, Neptune was pinpointed by the German astronomer John G. Galle in 1846.

About the size of Uranus, Neptune is another giant 1,000,000,000-mile stride farther from the sun, which it circles every 165 years. This long, slow journey will return Neptune to the place of its discovery during the year 2011. Neptune is probably a solid body surrounded by a vast envelope of gases which are frozen and compressed to extreme density below the observed planetary surface. One of Neptune's two satellites, Triton, is somewhat larger than our moon but surprisingly moves in a retrograde motion around the planet. This curious circumstance can be explained if it is supposed that the most distant of the planets, the tiny Pluto, was once also a satellite of Neptune; for it can be shown that if tidal force brought the paths of the two moons close enough, Pluto would be speeded up sufficiently to escape from the system and Triton would reverse its original course around the parent planet Neptune.

This possibility recently received strong confirmation by the discovery that Pluto has the long rotation period of six days, which would be just of the right order for a satellite always facing its primary, as our own moon always faces the earth. The same tidal action could have brought this about long before Pluto was expelled from the Neptunian system. Thereafter the spin would be unchanged, since the sun would be too distant to produce braking action on the new planet.

We know little about Pluto itself except for the fact that it is undoubtedly considerably smaller than the earth. The planet's strongly elliptical orbit, which crosses within that of Neptune, carries it around the sun once in every 247 years at a mean distance of 3,666,000,000 miles from the center of our system. From Pluto the sun would appear as an extremely brilliant star but without any perceptible disc. A flash of light, traveling at 700,000,000 miles per hour—the same speed that takes eight minutes to reach the earth from the sun—would take more than five hours to reach this last outpost of the solar system. From Pluto the same flash, traveling at the same speed, would have to travel about four and one-quarter *years* through the black void of space before it reached our system's nearest known neighbor, the star Alpha Centauri. No telescope yet conceived could detect whether even this star has attendant planets.

Though the mind and the imagination boggle at the distances with which we are here concerned, a useful analogy of the solar system itself can be envisaged through the rough model once described by Sir John Herschel, the nineteenth-century English astronomer:

Choose any well-leveled field. On it place a globe, two feet in diameter; this will represent the sun; Mercury will be represented by a grain of mustard seed, on the circumference of a circle 164 feet in diameter for its orbit; Venus a pea, on a circle 284 feet in diameter; the earth also a pea, on a circle 430 feet; Mars a rather large pinhead, on a circle of 654 feet; Jupiter a moderate-sized orange, in a circle nearly half a mile across; Saturn a small orange, on a circle of four fifths of a mile; Uranus a full-sized cherry, or small plum, upon the circumference of a circle more than a mile and a half across, and Neptune a good-sized plum on a circle about two miles and a half in diameter.

Pluto, on the same scale, would be represented by a pea or smaller object on an ellipse three and a quarter miles in length, with the globe that represents the sun one and a quarter miles from its perihelion, or nearest point of approach.

Though all the stars in our galaxy—and in the universe—are in motion relative to one another, the mutual distances involved obviously make close approaches by stars extremely rare. For this reason we may assume that for millions of years the motions of the planets have remained unaffected by any body outside the solar system. It would be wrong, however, to assume that this has always been so; indeed, some theories of the origin of the system have postulated direct outside stellar interference. Let us examine some of these theories.

The Nebular Hypothesis

In 1796 Laplace, the great French mathematical astronomer, put forward a verbal description of the origin of the planets suggesting that at one time the material of the system was spread out in a cool, rarefied disc-shaped nebula. This nebula, Laplace reasoned, would gradually contract and thereby rotate more quickly, leaving behind at its rim successive rings of material caught in the struggle between outward centrifugal force and the inward gravitational attraction of the rest of the nebula. Each ring then coalesced to form a planet. This process accounted for less than 1/500th of the total material; the remainder condensed into a central mass to form the primitive sun.

This attractive theory dominated scientific and philosophical thought for a century, but we now realize that it contradicts a number of dynamical and physical realities. We know, for instance, that if the nebula had rotated fast enough to loosen material at its edge, the remaining material would have far more rotational momentum than is now stored in the slowly rotating sun. It can also be proved that the material that formed the present sun, which is probably more than 90 per cent hydrogen, could not have supplied in sufficient abundance the heavy elements found in some of the planets.

The Catastrophic Theories

There are several of these, all based on the idea that some violent occurrence extracted the planetary material from the actual surface layers of the sun, or other star, where it is normally firmly held by a powerful gravitational field. The Tidal Theory postulated that another star swept by so close to the sun that it raised gigantic tides in the solar atmosphere. The outermost tips of the resulting tidal waves would become detached as small droplets—the newly born planets—and these would then be pulled sideways as they tended to follow the receding star, giving them an orbital motion round the sun, all in the same plane and in the same general direction. An objection to this process was that the droplet-planets would rotate at much the same twenty-five-day rate as the sun. Actually, as we have seen, the great planets have rotation periods measured in hours.

To answer this objection, a glancing collision between the sun and the passing star was next proposed. It was argued not only that the collision would augment the tidal forces to detach material from the sun, but also that two gaseous bodies sliding past each other at hundreds of miles per second would generate the whirling motion of turbulence needed within the material to account for the spins of the resulting planets.

The fatal flaw in both forms of the catastrophic theory is that the droplet-planets would not go into orbital motion around the sun. It can be mathematically proved that they would simply fall back to the surface and be reabsorbed when less than halfway round the sun. Calculations show that it would be impossible by such means to get a grain of sand to circle the sun even close to its surface—not to mention the mighty Jupiter with an orbit of some 500,000,000 miles.

A binary collision seemed to present a simple way out of this particular difficulty. Newton's laws require that the sun occupy the central position of the solar system because of its preponderant mass, and there is no justification for supposing that it *must* therefore have been the source of the planetary material. If the sun at one time had a *companion star*—double, or binary, stars are a common feature of our galaxy—moving round it at much the same distance as the great planets move, it can be shown that a grazing collision of the companion with a third incoming star could cause the companion to escape from the sun and disappear among the other stars. The satisfactory features of the collision theory could be taken over unchanged, and the problem of the system's great scale would be resolved.

The improbability of such a collision is not a valid objection to this type of hypothesis, though it would imply that systems formed in this manner are likely to be rare. There are, however, serious objections to the proposal. We now know, for instance, that unless the third star entered the binary system at prohibitively great speed it would not have the energy to remove enough material to form the planets. Also, the sun's companion would probably have consisted almost entirely of hydrogen, and this again presents the problem of forming planets of a lower proportional hydrogen content—that is, with far more of the heavier elements—than the sun. In sum, detailed analysis reveals that the binary collision theory is almost impossible to substantiate.

The Supernova Theory

One proposal to avoid the objections to the various collision theories was the suggestion that the second member of the binary had a much greater mass than its companion, the sun, and developed to the supernova stage, undergoing a violent explosion. When a star has burned all its hydrogen by nuclear processes, it may collapse with an enormous increase of internal temperature, which synthesizes the heavier elements very rapidly. The companion star's collapse would be accompanied by such an increased rotation rate that its material, now rich in the heavy elements required for planet formation, would be showered outward on a prodigious scale.

Modern observations of actual supernova explosions have shown that enough material to form several of our suns can be thrown off in such a cataclysm—though, as we have seen, a tiny wisp of the ejected material would, if captured by the sun, be sufficient to form all the present planets. The ejection of the material occurs at such immense speeds, hundreds of miles per second, that any lopsidedness of the explosion would produce the slight recoil speed needed to sever its weak gravitational bond with the sun. This, of course, obviates the necessity of introducing a third star, very accurately aimed, to remove the companion from the sun. It should be added that supernova explosions of stars are fairly commonplace and occur every few hundred years in our own galaxy.

One major problem posed by all the catastrophic theories is that material suddenly released from a star could not, because of its high temperature, immediately condense into small compact bodies such as planets. The now generally accepted conclusion is that the liberated material would expand to a gaseous nebula that would revolve around the sun as a consequence of the orbital motion originally possessed by the companion star. As this nebula cooled, it would flatten into a disc-shaped ring, resembling a gigantic Saturnian-ring system. Solidified particles would tend to arrange themselves in a plane within this ring, while material such as hydrogen, remaining in gaseous form, would float above and below the ring under pressure effects maintained by the temperature of the adjacent central sun.

The Modern Theories

Current hypotheses on the evolution of our system, while proposing various methods for the original accumulation of the material, seem all to agree that some sort of ring or disc of material around the sun is a necessary stage in the process of planet formation. The first step of planet growth would be a simple accumulation of solid material at the central plane of the disc. Low-speed collisions between particles, probably resembling snowflakes in texture, would produce larger particles; and these in turn would collide with others to get still larger, with a snowballing effect. This process would have to continue for tens of millions of years before any accumulation equaled even a small planetary mass. Sooner or later a few accumulations would have grown so large that the force of gravity would begin to take over and attract particles from a greater distance. The larger such accumulations grew, the more powerful this gravitational effect would be. Like large financial corporations, the larger primitive planets would dominate the scene and sweep the field locally, swallowing up the smaller concerns. A solid planet would cease to grow only when all the particles of the disc in its general neighborhood had been collected. The end of the first stage of the solar system's evolution must have been a few solid cores spaced out across the expanse of the original disc surrounding the sun.

The capabilities of these planetary nuclei to capture the hot hydrogen gas surrounding the disc would depend upon their distance from the sun and the strength of their gravitational forces. The earth itself, for instance, cannot presently retain hydrogen gas in its atmosphere and could scarcely have done so at any earlier stage when it was less massive. (It could, of course, have captured hydrogen combined with other elements such as oxygen, to the extent that these were present, since the compound—water—would be solid or liquid at our distance from the sun.) The same reasoning holds true for planets nearer the sun, and for Mars because of its small mass; so there is no difficulty in understanding why only small solid planets would form near the sun—their attractions are insufficient to control the thermal speeds that hydrogen atoms and molecules would have close to the sun.

Because the local temperatures maintained by the sun diminish with distance, even a small planet could retain hydrogen at Jupiter's position in the system. This means that the more distant planetary nuclei would be able to capture hydrogen from the disc. As this gas probably would constitute more than 90 per cent of the disc mass, large planets of low density would evolve. Thus we are led to picture the great planets as having small solid central cores surrounded by a deep shell consisting almost entirely of hydrogen, probably itself compressed to solid form at all but its outermost layers.

In the outer reaches of the system another effect must be considered. Near the edge of the disc, where the sun's attraction is far weaker, hydrogen would boil off into outer space even at the reduced temperature and be lost from the system altogether, so that the proportion of hydrogen to heavier materials would decrease as we go outward. It is significant that Uranus, despite its far smaller mass, has a density much greater than Saturn, and even greater than Jupiter, while Neptune is nearly twice as dense as Uranus, although little more massive.

In addition to the Supernova Theory, there have been a number of other recent proposals for the origin of the primitive dust and hydrogen disc around the sun. Vast tracts of interstellar dust and hydrogen gas, itself liberated by supernova explosions, already exist in interstellar space. The mechanism of capture of this material by the sun to form the requisite disc is being actively investigated. One possibility being considered is the capture of a planetary quantity of such material as a result of a three-body encounter of the sun with a second independent star, with a gas-dust cloud as the third participant. Such a meeting, in which the action of the independent star accounts for the required rotatory motion of the captured gas-dust cloud around the sun, demands such special conditions that planetary systems originating in this manner would be very rare indeed.

A more likely occurrence is that the sun itself may have captured the disc material solely by its own gravitational action while passing through a cloud at very low speed. Under such circumstances the sun could attract material from an immense distance—about 6,000,000,000,000 miles—and within such a range a typical interstellar cloud, despite its extreme rarity, would contain just about the mass of all the planets. Furthermore, the amount of rotational momentum that would be involved in such a capture is of just the right order to account for that of the planets. The chance of a star entering a cloud at the slow speed required for such a capture is extremely small, but in thousands of millions of years any particular star will pass through thousands of dust clouds, and sooner or later the requisite speed would occur. Estimates suggest that, of stars the sun's age, at least one in 1000 will have met these conditions and thereby have acquired a disc of material capable of developing into a planetary system.

Another possibility of a much more speculative nature is suggested by the process of star formation. If, as supposed, stars condense more or less rapidly within interstellar clouds, they will retain any rotational momentum the clouds possess. As the contraction proceeds, the resulting stars may spin very quickly, like a skater going into a spin. If our sun formed in this manner, it would have developed a rapid spin before it reached its present stable size. If the spin were rapid enough, centrifugal force might smoothly detach material from the protosun's equator and a disc would begin to form. Although this process would not start until the sun had shrunk to a size within the present orbits of the inner planets, a second mechanism—that of coupling with the sun's magnetic field—is seen as spreading the disc outward by transferring almost all of the sun's rotation to it, with the sun becoming a slowly rotating central star.

If this theory is sound, it would imply that most, if not all, slowly rotating stars possess planetary systems, which would mean the majority of stars in the heavens. In general, the same reasoning applies to the process of planet formation by the direct capture of interstellar material. In either case, there would be enormous numbers of planetary systems in existence—1 per cent of the stars in our galaxy would total 1,000,000,000, and there are thousands of millions of galaxies even within observational range.

Whatever the origin of the disc material, the various planets are the surviving successful accumulations within it. They would tend to move around the sun in circular paths, because this is how the material of the disc moved. The rotations of the planets and the formation of their satellites are also natural consequences of a revolving disc. For each part of the disc has its own circular motion round the sun, and this is such as to give the material forming the disc an intrinsic spin that cannot be destroyed. A planet formed from such material will necessarily have rotation about an axis of spin roughly perpendicular to the plane of the disc—as do almost all the solar planets. An explanation of the peculiar case of Uranus, whose axis lies almost in its orbital plane, could be that Uranus represents the coalescence of two large primitive planets; the final direction of rotation would then depend on just how they came together.

There is a further important consideration. A growing planet would gradually come to possess more rotation than it could store as a stable body, and eventually the planet would elongate and burst into two pieces. These pieces would be of different sizes, with one about ten times the mass of the other. The smaller piece would be thrown clear at a speed sufficient, if it happened at Jupiter's distance from the sun, to send it right out of the solar system. The larger piece would undergo a slight recoil and remain behind as a stable, slowly rotating body.

This very same process of disruption could also create satellites. The breakup of a planet produces a situation resembling the collision mechanism, but with the important difference that now the planet is highly elongated when it divides and the smaller piece is thrown off at high speed. Minute droplets will form in the stream of material drawn out between the separating main masses, and some of these would be set into orbital motion round the larger piece. When it is remembered, for example, that Jupiter's four large satellites total only about one-ten thousandth of the mass of the planet, it is plain that no more than a minute fraction of the total amount of material need be captured in this process. Thus the same forces that stabilize the rotation of a planet can produce satellites moving close to its surface.

It is even possible that in the same breakup that left Jupiter as the main survivor, the terrestrial planets themselves were liberated. Their combined mass is less than 1 per cent that of Jupiter, so they could have been the main small droplets, formed when the original giant planet divided. The fact that our moon closely resembles the four large Jovian satellites favors the idea, while the differing compositions of the four inner planets suggest that separation of material had time to take place somewhere before they finally formed as separate bodies.

As this brief survey of the various theories of the origin of our system suggests, current cosmogonical thinking is along lines vastly different from that of a few years ago. Whereas it had been thought earlier that planets could form only as a result of an excessively rare combination of events, and consequently that solar systems might be equally rare, the trend today is toward regarding them as fairly commonplace objects.

We know with certainty that there are an enormous number of stars available to play the role of a central sun. We know, too, that the conditions suitable for the development and maintenance of life on a planet depend on a special relationship between the planet and its star-sun—the type of star, the separation distance and the size of the planet are all involved. But there seems little doubt that here and there a planet-star relationship fulfilling all the necessary conditions will exist and that the evolutionary process could lead to the development of intelligent life from living matter.

It may be, on the other hand, that life and the universe have always existed together; certainly it needs the former for any appreciation of the latter. The solar system cannot go on forever; sooner or later the earth will become uninhabitable, for the sun will eventually, in one way or another, cease to shine and maintain conditions suitable to the system. It may become too faint or it may expand to become a red giant and successively swallow the planets. Continued observation of the universe would then require the existence of life elsewhere—unless we accept the view that the universe can exist independently of life, but this is a position that cannot be rationalized.

2. The Worship of the Sun

Lucia Harrison

All of us, whether we are willing to admit it or not, are to a greater or lesser extent sun worshippers. Some may worship inversely by virtually denying the existence of the sun and live their lives in the artificial light of our great cities. Others, going to the opposite extreme, are impelled to expose the maximum area of their bodies to the none-too-tender direct rays of the sun whenever the opportunity offers. Most of us, however, recognize the absolutely essential nature of sunshine, although we may not actually celebrate this by actual or implied worship. We must, of course, give the sun its due as the most important and, happily, consistent thing in our lives and the life of everything on the earth, because we recognize full well that without the sun the earth would be just an uninhabited cold cinder in space. In this selection, Lucia Harrison examines the variety of attitudes toward the sun displayed by humans past and present.

Characteristic of man, even in the primitive stages of civilization, is his craving to know the causes of the phenomena of Nature. In the childhood of his intellectual development, there was no awareness of the natural laws of the Universe. Conditions beyond his power to control were ascribed to deities possessing attributes similar, but superior, to his own. Many of the imaginative tales which we call myths evolved from man's speculations upon the causes of observed natural facts and his personification of the forces of Nature.

The Sun, most brilliant body in the sky, seemingly the essence of life, was a challenging mystery, both in its daily and in its seasonal ever-changing aspects. That primitive man should believe he could cause the Sun to shine or could delay its setting, by means of magic, was inevitable. As late as Biblical times Moses warned the Israelites (Deut. 4:19):

> Beware of looking up to the sky and then, as you see the whole host of heaven, the Sun and Moon and stars, letting yourself be allured to bend in worship to them.

The designation of the first day of the week as *Sunday* (fr. L. *sol,* sun; *dies,* day), the day on which religious worship is given precedence over

Source: Lucia Harrison, *Sun, Earth Time and Man* (Chicago: Rand-McNally, 1960), pp. 1–11. The author was formerly professor of geography at Western Michigan University.

secular activities by most Christian peoples, has its origin in a day dedicated by early peoples to Sun worship.

But what was the Sun? Bewailing the seeming futility of many human endeavors, Ecclesiastes lamented (1:5): "The rising Sun goes down, it hurries round, only to rise again." Why this ceaseless journey across the sky? Why the daily period of darkness? Was darkness a more powerful entity than the Sun and able to destroy its light? What gave the Sun rebirth? Did the gods create a new Sun? Why was darkness preceded by the deepening gray of twilight and followed by a gradually brightening light, heralding the Sun's reappearance in the east? How did the Sun make the transit from its place of setting to that of rising? Why was the Sun not equally high in the sky at midday throughout the year? Why did the Sun rise early and set late at one time of year and rise late and set early at another time? Why was there an unvarying succession of the seasons? Why was the Sun so dependable in its general behavior pattern, day after day, year after year? The solar drama of the battle between daylight and darkness, re-enacted each day throughout the year, with alternating seasonal periods of seeming victory for each of the combatants—this provides the motif for a considerable part of our heritage of mythology.

Phoebus (fr. Gr. *phoibos*, light) Apollo was a Greek divinity of radiance and light, possibly an importation from the north in prehistoric migrations. Gradually he assumed a complex personality. Not until the fifth century B.C. was Phoebus Apollo definitely identified with Helios, the Sun-god. To both were attributed brilliance and the power to produce and destroy life, to cause joy and grief, to bless with health or to harass with illness. They were differentiated in that Helios was the physical Sun, the fiery ball that daily rose, moved along a path, and set; Apollo was the benevolent god of light and warmth and, therefore, of growth and fruitfulness; a protector of man from evil and disease but possessing, also, the power to inflict harm, for even light may be baneful at times.

The early Greeks believed the Earth to be a flat, circular plate, divided into two parts by the waters of the Mediterranean and Black seas. Around this disk flowed River Ocean (*Oceanus*), from north to south on the eastern side, and from south to north on the western side, feeding the seas and the rivers from its waters. From eastern River Ocean rose the Dawn and the Sun; into western River Ocean sank the Sun and the Twilight; Darkness then descended upon the Earth. Among primitive peoples the belief was widespread that out of darkness comes the light, only to be extinguished again by the darkness. Nights are long and dreary in unlighted homes. It is natural that the passage of time should be measured by the period of darkness, unbroken by diversity of occupation and spent mainly in slumber. The importance attached to darkness survives in the term *fortnight*, a period of fourteen days counted by the passage of nights. Light and darkness lay beyond human control and therefore were associated with deities.

The Sun was represented in art in a diversity of ways—a ball of fire, a head with streaming golden hair, a spoked wheel. From the symbols of the hub of a wheel for the mass of the Sun and of steeds for his rays evolved the imagery of a chariot. The Sun as charioteer drove his flaming car, yoked to four horses, across the sky. The chief center of the worship of Helios was the island of Rhodes, granted to Helios by Zeus as his share of the world over which to exercise jurisdiction. Lest the chariot become worn and the horses weary after a year of toil, the Rhodians annually flung a chariot and four horses into the sea, into which the Sun-god disappeared at night, for his use in the coming year.

There were various explanations of the mystery of the Sun's nightly return from west to east. One theory was that a land of light connected west with east, whose inhabitants bathed and fed the Sun and his steeds, and where they rested until time to begin their journey again from the eastern horizon. Another belief held that during the night chariot and horses were borne in a golden boat along the northern edge of the Earth; others thought the transit was made in a golden bowl. The ancient Peruvians believed that the Sun-god was conveyed across the sky by the power of the Universal Spirit, entered a cave in the west, and traveled through a subterranean passage to the point where he emerged in the east. Anaximenes (*fl.* sixth century, B.C.) taught that the light of the Sun was cut off at night by a range of high mountains in the north.

The lack of adequate means of artificial illumination gave great importance to the morning twilight. The Homeric Eos (Dawn) was envisioned as a beautiful, rosy-fingered goddess near whom the Sun spent the hours of darkness. It was she who wakened him, and, rising from the eastern River Ocean, sped into the sky to announce his coming—a winged goddess with hair streaming behind. The beliefs of his time concerning the daily course of the Sun are embodied by Mimnermus (*fl.* 630 B.C.) in the poem *The Sun's Golden Bowl.*

> Toil is the Sun-god's portion, toil all the livelong day,
> Day in, day out, forever; there is no stop, no stay—
> So soon as Dawn leaves Ocean, and, rosy-fingered, speeds
> Upon her journey skyward—for him nor for his steeds.
> For when his course is ended, back through the dusky deep
> A hollow couch goes faring, wherein he lies asleep.
> A mighty bowl this couch is and lovely to behold,
> The gift of wise Hephaistos, who wrought it all in gold
> And furnished it with pinions. It darts across the seas,
> Swimming the crested waves from the far Hesperides
> Back to the ruddy Sun-folk, where steeds and car remain
> Till Morning's own dear daughter, the Dawn, comes up again.

The Sun then mounts his chariot, seeks that far western shore
And rushing, rushing onward, gives us the day once more.

The ancient Mexicans regarded the Sun as the source of all vital
force, *Ipalnemohuani*, "He by whom men live." Since he bestowed life
on the Earth, it was fitting that he should receive nourishment from it.
Hymns of praise were sung to the rising Sun and offerings were made
of food and drink. To ensure the annual return of the Sun's heat and
light and to maintain his strength for the ceaseless daily journeys, sacri-
fices were made of the bleeding hearts of men and beasts, the organ
most symbolical of life. Many an intertribal war was motivated by the
need for human victims.

A major puzzle in the solar phenomena was the absence of any devia-
tion in the diurnal and annual behavior of the Sun. The Sun's unswerv-
ing adherence to the performance of a task suggested servitude to a
higher power. Personal liberty would give freedom to roam the sky at
will. The myth of Sisyphus, King of Corinth, condemned, in the lower
world, to the task of rolling a huge stone up a hill, a labor never ended
for the stone ever rolled back again, may typify the slavish daily mounting of the Sun in the sky until, having attained its highest point, it
immediately begins its descent toward the horizon.

As primitive societies progressed from the pastoral into the agricultural stage of development, incentive for careful observation of the heavenly bodies came from the need for accurate foreknowledge of the
approach of seedtime and harvest, for a calendar by which to govern
seasonal agricultural activities. It was noted that vegetative processes
quickened when the lengthening hours of daylight began to approximate the hours of darkness; that the preparation of the soil for new
plantings and the pruning of the vines must precede this time; that the
maturing and harvesting of crops must be completed before the hours
of darkness exceeded those of daylight and twilight; that the delay of
fall ploughing until after the Sun had descended to its lowest noon
position would mean crops so stunted in height that they must be
garnered with a sickle; that the rising of the Pleiades signaled the time
for beginning the harvest of fall-sown crops and their setting the time
for ploughing. The Dyaks of the coastal plains in western Borneo plan
the time for sowing their rice fields with the date the Pleiades attain a
certain height above the horizon before daylight and when noon
shadows become a certain length—signs to them that the monsoon rains
will be favorable for the growth of the rice and will have ceased when
the grain is ripening. From the recurrence of the periods of alternating
long and short days and of increasing and diminishing warmth of the
Sun's rays arose the division of the year into *seasons* (fr. L. *satio*, a
sowing), or periods in which a certain temperature and a special type of
agricultural work might be expected to prevail.

In time a considerable body of factual knowledge concerning the behavior of the Sun was accumulated. When the interval between sunset and sunrise seemed about equal to that between sunrise and sunset, men may have noted that the place of sunrise or sunset was behind some particular hill, or tree, or dwelling; that thereafter the place of sunrise or sunset shifted steadily along the horizon for a time, then reversed the trend and gradually returned to the same relative position to the hill, or tree, or dwelling. They observed that a similar migration of the place of sunrise or sunset then occurred along the horizon on the opposite side of the object of reference, within approximately the same time interval. Additional truths discovered were: (1) The time requisite for the completion of one cycle is unvarying—perhaps the basis for the initial recognition of the *year* as a unit of time (fr. L. *annus*, annual, a periodical return). (2) The place of sunset is always the same distance and direction away from west that the place of sunrise is away from east. (3) There are the most hours of daylight when the arc of the Sun's path is longest and the noon Sun is highest in the sky. (4) There are the fewest hours of daylight when that arc is shortest and the noon Sun is lowest. (5) The hours of daylight equal the hours of twilight and darkness when the arc of the Sun's path lies midway between the positions of the longest and shortest paths. (6) The Sun is at its highest position for the day about halfway between the times of sunrise and sunset. (7) All midday points lie somewhere along an imaginary line in the sky from the overhead point of the observer, his *zenith*, down in either direction to the horizon, midway between the places of sunrise and sunset. To this line is given the name *sky meridian* (fr. L. *medius*, middle; *dies*, day), or the midday line.

There was no anxiety lest day not succeed night for that phenomenon recurred within a brief period of time. But before there was an understanding that natural conditions controlled the behavior of the Sun, the onset of the season of lowering noon Sun and the lessening duration of daylight aroused apprehension. Would the Sun-god behave as in previous years and, in time, reverse his path and bring a return of summer warmth and a rebirth of vegetation? For several days the Sun seemed to stand still at noon; any change in position from day to day on the sky meridian was imperceptible. We refer to this period as the *solstice* (fr. L. *sol*, sun; *sistere*, to stand), the *winter solstice* for peoples in the Northern Hemisphere. When it became apparent that the upward climb had begun and that the hours of daylight were lengthening, gladness reigned. Reference to such joy is made in Jeremiah 7:17-18:

Do you not see what they are doing in the towns of Judah and in the streets of Jerusalem? The children are gathering firewood, the fathers kindle the fire, and the women knead the dough, to make cakes for the Queen of Heaven.

The period of lowest noon Sun and shortest duration of daylight occurs in Peru at a time that corresponds with the month we designate June. The festival of the "diminished and growing Sun" was celebrated at this time by the ancient Peruvians. Following three days of fasting, they assembled in the cities at early dawn. They greeted the rising Sun with shouts of joy and with ceremonial rites. A fire was lighted on the altar in the Temple of the Sun by focusing the rays of the Sun reflected from a mirror; from this fire other fires were lighted in all the temples of the Sun in the city. These were not extinguished until the period of fasting preceding the next winter solstice.

Relationship of Church Festivals to Sun Worship

Festivals evolved from the worship of the Sun, timed to coincide with crucial incidents in its annual behavior. The dates assigned for the observance of some of the religious festivals of the Christian world are unrelated to the dates of the occurrence of the events they commemorate, the determination of which may not have been possible. The church found that pagans accepted Christianity more readily when the dates and some of the practices associated with their chief solar festivals were retained and other motives were substituted for the celebration, rather than by forbidding the idolatrous customs altogether.

Saturn was the Roman god of seed-sowing and the Saturnalia (December 17–24) was the general festival in his honor, celebrating the completion of autumn sowing in the Roman Campagna. It was a season of rejoicing over the cessation of the toil of the summer and autumn. Byzantine writers refer to a festival occurring at this time of year as the Brumalia (fr. L. *bruma*, shortest day of the year; *brumalis*, pertaining to the winter solstice). This, too, was a period of riotous merrymaking, marking the end of the period of shortening days, the birth of the new Sun, the beginning of the lengthening of the daylight hours. In the Julian Calendar, December 25 was dedicated to the festival of the Nativity of the Sun, because the subsequent increase in the duration of daylight and in the height of the Sun at noon signified a rebirth of its power.

The date of the birth of Christ is not recorded; astronomers and historians have used various methods to compute it. In Luke 2:1–5 we are told that

> In those days an edict was issued by Caesar Augustus for a census of the whole world. So everyone went to be registered, each at his own town; and as Joseph belonged to the house and family of David, he went . . . to David's town called Bethlehem, to be registered with Mary his wife.

The year of this census, 9–8 B.C., antedates that which has been accepted as the beginning of the Christian era, as does the flight of Joseph and Mary into Egypt with the infant Jesus to escape the slaughter of male babies decreed by Herod, whose own death is placed by historians in the year 4 B.C. Furthermore, astronomers have computed that the planets Mars, Saturn, and Jupiter came into close conjunction in the years 7–6 B.C. and may have seemed to merge into one object. Their brilliance may have suggested the story of "The Star of Bethlehem."

The early church did not celebrate the Nativity. In time Christians in Egypt chose January 6, and by the fourth century that date had been generally accepted by the eastern church. The fixation of the month and the day as December 25 was an attempt of the western church to give religious significance to the Roman pagan festivals celebrating the end of fall sowing and the period of shortening daylight, and the return of the Sun to steadily mounting daily paths. Some festivals were associated with Mitra, a solar deity, ultimately identical with the Persian Mithras, an earthborn hero who slew the divine bull from whose body were derived all the plants and animals beneficial to man. The Roman Emperor Auerlian (A.D. 212?–275) is credited with instituting the festival of *Dies natalis solis invicti* ("birthday of the unconquered Sun") about A.D. 273. Since about A.D. 400, the western church has observed December 25 as the Christian *Dies natalis*. The celebration in honor of the promise of a rebirth of the Sun's warmth and light was merged with one in honor of the hope of eternal life that came through the birth of Christ.

For several centuries after the introduction of Christianity into England, Roman Catholicism was the dominant form of worship and the Mass was an important part of the celebration of the Nativity. From "Christ's Mass" comes our word Christmas. The significance attached to words changes with the passage of time. The word "merry" is derived from an Anglo-Saxon term meaning blessed, pleasant, or peaceful. The gay greeting "Merry Christmas" formerly meant "The blessed Christ's Mass."

Although Sun worship ceased, in time, to be associated with the celebration, the gift-making, feasting, and jollity that characterized the heathen festivals have persisted. The profusion of lights in homes and on the streets and the lighting of the Christmas tree are symbolical of the fires built by the pagan worshippers to guide the Sun-god back to their land. A thanksgiving offering for his return, in the form of cakes of grain and fruit, laid on the altars by ancient Persians and Egyptians, is replaced today by a plum pudding. St. Nicholas, Bishop of Myra, in southwest Asia, about the fourth century A.D., dedicated his life to service for others. The assumed anniversary of his death, December 6, was long observed by secretly bestowing gifts upon children on St. Nicholas Eve. His name has survived but the gift-giving has been transferred to Christmas Day and is no longer restricted to children. Our decorative use of evergreens has its origin in their symbolism of the promise of eternal life to those who live in accordance with Christian precepts.

Reference to the Christmas season as "Yuletide" is an inheritance from the Druidical forms of worship that prevailed in Britain until the introduction of Christianity about A.D. 600. An archaic form of the word "yule" refers to the Sun and of "tide" to a period within which a festival occurs. The Festival of Yule occurred during December. It lasted for several days but focused on the winter solstice, for the subsequent lengthening of the daylight period, a victory of the Sun over Darkness, was an occasion for great rejoicing. The worship of trees and of anything growing upon them was a part of the Druidical religious system. The spark of fire produced by friction between pieces of oakwood was believed to reside in the mistletoe, and that plant became an object of veneration. Perhaps the practice of kindling great log fires in the homes and the outdoors arose from the belief that man could thus aid in the renewal of the heat of the Sun. The priests who brought Christianity to Britain permitted the inclusion of harmless Druidical customs in the celebration of the Nativity.

Another decisive moment in the ever-changing daily path of the Sun occurred when it had attained the highest noon position and the period of daylight was longest. It was a time for rejoicing in that light and warmth had brought some crops to maturity, and the good things that the Sun-god could bestow seemed to have reached a climax. But the joy was mixed with foreboding. Again the Sun would seem to attain the same noontime position for several days—a second solstitial period, the *summer solstice* in the Northern Hemisphere. Then the Sun would begin to follow a steadily lowering path across the sky and the hours of daylight would lessen. Perhaps the north European peasant custom of building great bonfires at this season was an expression of the hope that these would help the Sun to rekindle its diminishing flame. Locally, the custom persists today. Trundling a wheel encased in blazing straw down a hill may have symbolized the lowering path the Sun would begin to follow. But for many weeks after the solstice the Sun was still high at noon, the hours of daylight were long, and the summer warmth increased. A festival to welcome the season was also a joyous affair. A three-day festival at this time is still held in many Swedish towns and villages.

Attis was a Phrygian god of vegetation, beloved of the goddess Cybele, the deification of the Earth in its aspects of sustaining and reproducing wildlife. In their honor, rites and revelries were held in the spring, the great fertility festival. The cult spread to Greece and Rome. In the Julian Calendar, March 25 was the date on which the hours of daylight became equal to the interval from sunset to sunrise, the spring or *vernal equinox* (fr. L. *ver*, spring; *aequus*, equal; *nox*, night), a day of special significance. It was a day of rejoicing for it marked the resurrection of the god of vegetation, who had been sleeping during the cold of winter; it was proof of the stability of Nature and offered reassurance that the good things in her power to bestow would return.

The early church fathers were undecided about the date which should be designated the anniversary of the resurrection. Some wished to observe it on the Passover, on whatever day of the week that might fall; others preferred a Sunday. Some chose to place the observance on March 25 to make it coincide with festivities in honor of the pagan god of vegetation and be Christianity's reaffirmation of its belief in the victory of life over death. The date of our observance of Easter (*Eastre*, Anglo-Saxon goddess of spring) was fixed by the Council of Nicaea in the year A.D. 325. The councilors of the Christian churches then decreed that Easter should fall on the first Sunday after the first full Moon which occurs after March 21, the approximate date of the vernal equinox in the Northern Hemisphere. Relating the date of Easter to a phase of the Moon arose from the difficulties of travel on dark nights. Pilgrimages to holy places became a feature of the observance of Easter. The pilgrims journeyed on foot or by the crude means of transport of those times and they needed moonlight to find their way. Thus Easter became the wandering church festival; it may be celebrated as early as March 22 or as late as April 25.

Eggs and rabbits, symbols of fertility, were used in the ancient rites honoring the advent of the spring equinox; the wearing of new garments suggested the revival of vegetation. Featuring baby chicks and rabbits on Easter greeting cards, the donning of a new hat or suit—these are merely our perpetuations of pagan practices.

After the summer solstice, the duration of the daylight period steadily decreases. By our present calendar, it again equals the interval from sunset to sunrise on September 22 or 23. The rising and setting positions of the Sun are midway between the solstitial rising and setting ones. This is the *autumnal equinox* in the Northern Hemisphere. Most of us take no special heed of the occurrence, except, perhaps, to refer to it regretfully because the period of summer has come to a close. Soon after this equinox the ancient Egyptians held a festival called the "Nativity of the Sun's Walking Stick." The failing powers of the Sun suggested the need for a staff to sustain him. Supported by one, the king, as representative of the Sun, walked solemnly around the walls of a temple.

The ever changing noon position of the Sun in the sky; the ceaseless shifting in the place of sunrise and of sunset; the succession of daylight, twilight, and darkness, and their varying duration in the course of the year; the unfailing recurrence of the cycle of the seasons—these were natural phenomena which early peoples sought to explain. Worship of the Sun was their expression of dependence upon the mysteries of Sun-behavior. Much of the terminology we use today in describing natural phenomena is a heritage from the early thoughtful watchers of the sky.

Wherever people may live on the Earth, the apparent daily path of the Sun is an element in their natural environment that exercises a large influence upon their economic and cultural development. Few of us have the opportunity of dwelling in many widely separated parts of the Earth, thereby gaining first-hand knowledge of the conditions of daylight, twilight, and darkness experienced in other regions by those whose lives must be adjusted to them. Anyone, however, can acquire the ability to discover such information about any place on the Earth from its location in latitude and longitude, as portrayed on the globe or on a map of the region. . . .

II. WEATHER AND CLIMATE

Weather is probably the most consistent "front-page" news item in daily newspapers. This prominence indicates the significance of weather in the everyday life of people—even of people who have no daily newspaper. Weather, simply expressed, is the condition of the atmosphere at any given time and place; climate is the long-term average of weather—a generalization, therefore, of weather in an area. In his search for scientific truth concerning the earth, the geographer seeks to generalize about the surface of the earth and the associated atmosphere. Working from the details of collected data on weather in hundreds—even thousands— of places, it is possible to derive the generalizations called climates. Climate and weather are closely related but readily separable, and climatology is the science of these areal or spatial distributions of generalized weather.

Weather may have some influence on our behavior, as individuals, during short periods—from day to day or from hour to hour. It is climate, however, that often influences the larger patterns of mankind on the surface of the earth. Where rainfall and moderate or warm temperatures prevail, there usually are concentrations of population. In areas of no rainfall, where extremes of temperature—either hot or cold—exist, man is found only in limited numbers and in limited areas.

High-altitude flying and space research and remote-sensing vehicles are contributing greatly to our knowledge of a variety of weather phenomena. As recently as twenty-five years ago, some of these phenomena, such as the jet streams, were not even suspected of existing. Only recently has man been able to control the weather, but as yet these efforts have been effective in very limited areas only. They do point the way, however, toward a time when man may be able to do something more about the weather than merely talk about it.

3. The Human Body

David Blumenstock

Each of us is acutely aware of our individual mental reaction to the weather we experience—including such things as the "Blue Monday" character of a rainy day and the ebullient feeling of the bright sunshine, blue sky, and white

*clouds of a midlatitude June day. Yet most of us never really
have considered the exceedingly intimate relationship of
our bodies to the atmospheric environment in which we live.
In a very real sense, Blumenstock makes a strong case for
climatic, or at least meteorologic, determinism, as indicated
by the significant alterations in the body complex to
accommodate to or adjust for changes in local weather and
climate. He also indicates other responses made automatically
and unconsciously by man as a means of compensating
for weather and climatic conditions which make it possible
to live in many inhospitable areas.*

The human body is an efficient machine. The volume of the average
adult body is equivalent to only two and one-half cubic feet. Yet within
that space there is such an effective organization of structure and function that the body is capable of assimilating food, discarding waste
products, storing energy, maintaining constant temperature, growing,
thinking, warding off disease, and providing the means for reproduction.
These primary functions involve thousands of diverse regulatory processes that are closely related to one another and to the physical
environment of the body itself.

From minute to minute, year after year, the human body reacts and
adjusts to the air in which it is immersed so that its internal environment
will remain constant despite violent external changes. Sixteen times each
minute, it feeds on air—pulling it into the lungs, extracting oxygen from
it, and expelling the air with its carbon dioxide waste given off by the
blood cells as they pass through the lung capillaries.

Many of the effects of weather upon the body are indirect and difficult
to evaluate. Who can say with certainty what part the weather plays in
causing tropical neurasthenia—disorders of the nervous system that are
thought by some to be significantly high among peoples of the United
States and western Europe who move to the tropics? To what degree is
this ailment to be attributed to the heat, rain, and humidity of the
tropics; to what degree to diet, lack of exercise, mental strain induced
by foreign surroundings, and the daily tropical custom of sipping drinks
from work's end until bedtime?

Many of the effects of weather are direct, and of these a few can
readily be evaluated. Heat and cold evoke definite bodily responses,
and there are both high-temperature and low-temperature thresholds
beyond which even the most healthy body cannot continue to live. There
are also definite effects of sunlight and of low air densities, such as those
encountered on high mountains. Less well defined than these are the

SOURCE: David Blumenstock, *The Ocean of Air* (New Brunswick, N.J.: Rutgers
University Press, 1959), pp. 257–70. Copyright 1959 by Rutgers, The State University.

effects of various aspects of the weather upon disease, to be discussed later in this chapter.

Medical meteorology is a field in which there are far more questions than there are definite answers. It is necessary to distinguish carefully between proved relationships and merely probable or possible ones.

Heat and Cold

Fundamental to an understanding of the relationship between weather and the human body is the knowledge that has been gained by physiologists concerning heat regulation within the bodies of mammals, including man. Hundreds of millions of years ago, in the Mesozoic era, the reptiles were dominant among the larger animals of the land and air. In that time of mild climates, huge reptiles such as dinosaurs and brontosaurs abounded in the sparsely forested grasslands and along the edges of vast marshes choked with thick grasses and interlocking trees. For hundreds of millions of years these creatures ruled the lands. Then, toward the end of this Age of Reptiles, the mammals came into being.

At first the mammals were small animals and they still possessed many reptilian properties. But among the first nonreptilian characteristics that they gained, along with such changes as those in metabolic rate and the blood circulation system, was the ability to regulate somewhat the temperature of their bodies. Perhaps it was this ability that gave them a decided advantage over the reptiles; so that when over periods of hundreds of thousands of years the climate became more and more severe, with extremes of heat and cold over more and more of the world, it was the mammals with their self-heating and self-cooling systems that took over as dominant forms in wider and wider geographical areas, while the reptiles, at the mercy of the weather, died by the thousands each time an unusual cold or heat wave struck or fought the battle of self-extinction through overcrowding in the slowly contracting mild-climate regions of the world.

The heat-regulating system of many mammals has become more and more efficient over the millions of years since Mesozoic times. Though the environmental temperature may vary widely, these animals can maintain constant body temperature. The reptiles, now a rarity in contrast to their former abundance, remain incapable of body-temperature adjustment. A snake, trapped on a rapidly cooling rock as night comes on, will slowly pick its way toward warmer ground. It moves sluggishly because its metabolic rate is lowered in the cold. Its blood is at a temperature almost as low as the rock across which it crawls. Should the rock cool below the freezing point before it finds warmth, the snake will die—frozen to death because it cannot keep warm.

A price is paid by the mammals for their ability to regulate their body temperature. As Carlson and Johnson state:

. . . through the long ages of later mammalian . . . evolution the body tissues have become so adjusted to this fairly constant temperature that relatively minor fluctuations in temperature, under abnormal circumstances, are now injurious or fatal to cells, tissues, or the organism as a whole. Cold-blooded vertebrates tolerate temperatures well below 80° F. indefinitely, but mammalian tissues cannot long survive if the body temperature should temporarily fall to 80° F. or rise to 110° F. Needless to state, such temperatures would be reached only when serious defects in the temperature-regulating machinery develop.

The internal temperature of the human body is normally maintained at between 98° and 99°. The adult body, completely at rest, produces in seventy minutes about enough heat to bring one quart of ice water to a boil. In the body-heating process, the fuel is the food stored in the body as carbohydrates and fats; the fire is the oxidation of body tissues; and the pipes for heat distribution are the thousands of feet of blood vessels that comprise the arteries, arterioles, capillaries, and veins of the blood circulation system.

If an unclothed man stands motionless in a room where the air temperature is 82°, his body temperature will begin to fall slowly despite the constant production of body heat. The first body reaction to this lowering of temperature is vasoconstriction: the blood vessels near the surface of the skin contract to decrease the amount of heat lost from the skin to the air. The greatest constriction occurs at the extremities, in the fingertips and toes; the man literally gets cold feet. Still the body temperature continues to fall.

Now other mechanisms come into play. There is a change in muscle tone, and this increases the rate of heat production in the body. If the body temperature still continues to fall, shivering may set in, which changes further the muscle tone and speeds up the production of heat. In all of these processes the trigger mechanisms are messages that speed from cold-perceptive sensory nerve endings to the thalamus, in the forebrain, there to be relayed to the muscles of the skin and of the body interior. Through such rapid reactions the body temperature is brought back up before it has had a chance to slip more than a degree or so below normal.

The mechanisms just described are almost wholly automatic. Among them, shivering is the only one that can partly be controlled voluntarily, for it can often be inhibited at the will of the individual. There are in addition major actions that can be taken voluntarily to prevent the body temperature from falling. Exercise, the addition of clothing, or the ingestion of warm food or liquids all serve to raise the body temperature even though the air temperature is not raised.

Despite its efficiency, the heat-regulating system of the body is not able under extreme conditions to protect it against cold. The first parts of the body to suffer on a cold day are extremities such as fingertips, toes, ears, and nose. In its efforts to conserve heat and so to protect vital inner tissues, the body withholds heat from these outer regions through extreme vasoconstriction, which limits the amount of blood that reaches the extremities. The situation is the same as closing the door to an unused outer room in wintertime in order to hold more heat in the central part of the house. Actual freezing of skin tissue requires a skin temperature of 26°–30°. Because considerable heat is supplied to the skin even in areas of extreme vasoconstriction, unprotected extremities do not freeze until the air temperature is 24°, and then only when a strong wind is blowing. In still air, the temperature must fall to 12° to produce such freezing.

The soldiers who in the last war stood, lay, and tramped through the cold mud on Attu Island know what the combined effects of cold and water can be. When feet and socks and shoes are soaking wet and are embedded in cold mud, the water acts as a most effective conductor of heat. Heat is pulled outward from the foot more rapidly than the body supplies added heat. Blood vessels and even relatively hardy skin tissues suffer damage. Swelling occurs. Gangrene may set in, and in extreme instances amputation is necessary. There were over 25,000 soldiers in the Attu invasion. In one two-month period alone, 1,200 of these were hospitalized with cold injuries. Many underwent amputation of one or more toes or of entire feet as a result of freezing of tissues.

There is such a thing as moderate acclimatization to cold. If a person moves from a hot to a cold climate, his blood and plasma volume slowly decrease over several days, a process that necessarily accompanies increased vasoconstriction. The same effect is observed on a lesser scale when a cold wave hits during winter. On the first day of cold the public rest rooms are unusually busy because liquid is diverted from the blood to the kidneys and bladder due to decrease in blood volume. Another change produced by moving from hot to cold climates is in the level of the trigger mechanism for sweating. In a hot climate, sweating begins at a relatively low temperature to protect the body from excessive heat. In a cold climate, it does not begin until the temperature is distinctly higher, even though the individual may be working and so generating extra body heat.

Some investigators believe that there are changes in the metabolic rate with moves from one climate to another. It is possible also that thyroid activity increases in the cold. Certainly this is true for various animals whose reactions to cold have been intensively studied. The thyroid glands of pigeons are functionally enlarged during winter, then slowly decrease in size in late spring and early summer.

With the body at rest in the shade, the air motionless, the air temperature at about 91°, and the relative humidity at about 60 per cent, the skin feels neither warm nor cold. The body is in perfect balance with the surrounding air. It neither gains nor loses heat.

At higher temperatures, however, the body must call upon its heat-regulating mechanism to hold down body temperature. The first response to heat is vasodilation: the blood vessels of the skin dilate so that body heat will more readily be lost to the surrounding air. Then the two million sweat glands of the body come into play. The significance of sweating in holding down body temperature was demonstrated experimentally almost two centuries ago, although at that time the import of the experiment was not understood. Dr. Douglas H. K. Lee has succinctly described the experiments.

In 1775 Blagden reported to the Royal Society . . . upon experiments carried out by Fordyce in a heated room at 260° F. Men remained in this atmosphere fifteen minutes, without any noteworthy rise in body temperature, while a beefsteak was nicely cooked in thirteen minutes. These observers noted that water kept in a bucket did not boil, even though left in for some time. They failed, however, to draw the conclusion that man's failure to follow the beefsteak was of a kind with the failure of the water to boil; that evaporation provided the means of heat regulation.

Among the major studies that have been made of the heat-loss mechanisms of the body is one that was conducted in the California-Arizona desert in 1943–44, using United States troops as guinea pigs. The program permitted comparison of body behavior under a wide range of heat conditions. With the air temperature 130° and the sunlight scorching in the clear desert air, soldiers carrying full equipment marched at a stiff 3½ m.p.h. pace for hours on end, with few rest periods. For comparison, others lounged around in the shade. Soldiers dug foxholes, working furiously in the stifling heat. They lay relaxed in hammocks swung beneath canopies that shielded them from the sun. Soldiers drove across the desert in open jeeps. They lay motionless on the desert floor, unprotected from the heat and sun of early afternoon. Soldiers were deployed in dozens of different ways so as to study their reactions to heat under widely varying conditions of air temperature, sunlight, and wind while working, riding, running, marching, walking, sitting, and lying still; and under various conditions of food and water intake. And dozens of times each day, to learn how his body was reacting to the heat, each man was measured and tested.

From this thorough study of the effects of heat under desert conditions much was learned. At 100° F. on a bright day, a soldier sitting in the shade sweats water at the rate of one cup per hour; driving in an open car, he sweats three-fourths of a quart per hour; and walking at 3.4 m.p.h., one quart per hour. This enormous drain on body water—a drain that totals over two gallons on many days—must be made up by drinking water.

If a man fails to replace the water lost as sweat, his pulse rate increases, his rectal temperature rises, breathing is accelerated. In time, there is a tingling and numbness as his blood becomes thicker through water loss and the violently throbbing heart becomes less and less able to force the thick blood through the arteries and veins. He is seized with violent cramps and fits of vomiting. He moves with difficulty, as though half-paralyzed. Things seem confused, detached, far away. Visions appear. When the water loss exceeds 12 per cent of the body weight, and if the air temperature remains high, the deep body temperature suddenly becomes explosively high. If immediate relief is not at hand, the man is killed, cooked to death by his internal tissue heat.

In a hot environment there may be, through sweating, an excessive loss of body salt as well as of water. For the unacclimatized man, especially if he is performing manual labor, the daily salt loss may exceed the voluntary dietary salt intake. For an adult, the remedy is to take additional dosages of salt. Otherwise, with continued and accumulating salt deficiency, he will suffer heat exhaustion.

A person moving to a hot environment begins to adjust physiologically within ten days to two weeks. Complete acclimatization requires four to six months. Acclimatized individuals lose less salt through perspiration. They maintain a distinctly lower pulse rate when walking, running, or performing other exercise. However, they lose just as much water through sweating as do the nonacclimatized, and to make up the total loss they must deliberately drink more water than they crave.

The problem of adjustment to hot environments is especially significant today because there are large areas in the tropics, notably in South America and Africa, that are virtually unpopulated and that offer opportunities for settlement by peoples from the cooler, over-populated regions in Europe and in parts of the Americas. The available evidence supports the view of Dr. Lee that adjustment to tropical environments is largely a psychological matter. Except in rare instances, as when an individual has an abnormally low number of sweat glands or is abnormally obese, he can adjust to living happily and productively in any region of the tropics, provided his psychological outlook favors making the adjustment. If he considers his tropical sojourn to be a temporary assignment to a hell on earth, the prognosis for his doing well physiologically and mentally is not good.

If he has some strong motivation to adapt, as when he brings his family with him and settles down with the determined purpose to remain in the tropics, the prognosis for his success is excellent. The importance of motivation is illustrated by the experience of the naturalist Richard Spruce, who returned to England in far better health than when he had left, after having spent fourteen years in the Amazon Basin in an avid search for new flora and fauna.

In all environments, so far as comfort is concerned, social and psychological factors play a major role in influencing the effects of air temperature on the individual. The Londoner feels uncomfortable in the average United States home in winter. He can barely countenance the dry air, the temperature of 72°. The American is just as unhappy in a London house in winter, where the temperature is apt to be in the mid-sixties and the windows are kept open to admit damp, cool air whenever possible. A Buganda native from central Africa would be more comfortable in an American home in winter than in a British one; but he would wish that the air were moister, more like that of his homeland. These differences in defining comfort are mostly a matter of taste developed throughout the lifetime of the individual. To a much lesser degree they are a matter of physiological adjustment to the climates of the homeland. So far as the most careful experiments can show, they involve at most only slight physiological variations from one race to another.

Largely at the instigation of heating engineers, numerous studies have been made to determine preferred comfort conditions among persons of the United States. One out of two United States residents is perfectly comfortable in an indoor climate of 68°–83° with a relative humidity of 70 to 40 per cent in summer, the higher temperature tolerance existing only at the lower relative humidities. One out of two is comfortable in an indoor climate of 66°–78° with relative humidities of 70 to 40 per cent in winter. The more extreme the temperature, either toward cold or hot, the lower the relative humidity must be for the air temperature to remain comfortable. Wind also has an effect. Extreme temperatures are less tolerable in the wind than they are in still air.

Ellsworth Huntington, Clarence A. Mills, S. F. Markham, and scores of others have studied at length and in devious ways the effects of temperature on mental activity. Unfortunately, definite conclusions in this speculative field are almost impossible to come by. Yet it is equally impossible to discount entirely the effects of temperature on mental activity. To persons raised in areas such as the central or northeast United States, briskly cold weather does seem to be stimulating, while hot, muggy weather is debilitating and tends to inhibit both mental and physical activity. The changeability of the weather in these regions is thought by many inhabitants to be stimulating, while if such persons move to the rainy tropics they find the weather monotonously depressing. The effects of weather on mental activity require further study, which must include consideration of differences in cultural conditioning from one group of people to another.

Sunlight and Air Density

The direct effects of weather upon the human body are not confined to the effects of heat and cold. Sunshine and air density also have direct and important results. Ultraviolet light causes sunburn. It also converts certain fatlike substances in the skin to vitamin D. If the body is deprived of vitamin D, bones become deformed, teeth suffer decay, and bodily health in general is seriously impaired. Vitamin D is obtainable from egg yolk, fish oils, and many other foods as well as from the action of the sun. However, persons exposed to sunlight for appreciable periods of time each week can obtain thereby all the vitamin D required by the body.

There was a time when it was the vogue for fashionable physicians to consult the barometer in order to relate the diseases of their patients to the rise or fall in air pressure. Then it was commonly believed that air pressure had a marked influence on the course of such diseases as gout and consumption. Today the notion that day-to-day variations in air pressure have an influence on health or disease has been discarded. These variations are only sufficient to produce differences of 1 to 2 per cent in the pressure of the air upon the body; and since inward air pressure is balanced by pressure from the body interior outward, the body is always in balance in this respect so long as the individual does not rapidly change his altitude, as when he ascends in an airplane that is not pressurized.

High-altitude effects upon the human body are brought about by oxygen deficiency rather than by the lowering of air pressure. At Denver, one mile above sea level, there is 15 percent less oxygen in an average lungful of air than there is at New York or some other sea-level location. Most persons adjust automatically to this slight oxygen deficiency through inhaling more frequently and taking slightly deeper breath. At about 8,000 feet, where the oxygen deficiency is 22 per cent, there is a slowing down of the reaction time of individuals who have not become acclimatized to the altitude. This accounts for the practice of airplane pilots who, when flying a plane whose cabin is not pressurized, don an oxygen mask when the plane reaches 8,000 feet. Few individuals from low altitudes can even survive without an artificial source of oxygen at an altitude of 22,000 feet, where the oxygen supply is only half that at sea level.

The feat of the Mount Everest expedition of 1922 is unmatched. On this expedition, unlike the one that led to the successful assault of 1953, the climbers did not carry oxygen. Toward the end of their ascent, they were in air that was 60 per cent deficient in oxygen supply. Each exertion placed a strain upon their hearts and lungs. Each minute of painful climbing had to be compensated for by many minutes of rest. Mallory, Norton, and Somervell worked their way to 27,000 feet before finally being forced to retreat.

There are some inhabited tableland areas which rival in height the highest mountain peaks in the United States. In Bolivia, near Potosí, such a tableland throughout its extent lies above 13,000 feet. In Tibet there are contiguous areas, larger than the state of Texas, that are over 14,000 feet high. This Tibetan region is inhabited by natives who have lived there successfully decade after decade and century after century.

The region even includes inhabited areas that lie above 16,000 feet. But the highest permanently inhabited area known is in southern Peru, where for tens of centuries people have lived at an elevation of 17,400 feet, where the oxygen deficiency is 43 per cent.

More than any other man, Dr. Carlos Monge, director of the Institute of Andean Biology, has studied the effects of altitude upon permanent inhabitants of the highlands of the world. His chief laboratory has been Peru, which affords the greatest range of inhabited altitudes found anywhere in the world. Dr. Monge has studied old Spanish documents. He has conducted experiments with a wide variety of animals. He has studied, measured, and compared the attributes of highland man as contrasted with lowland man. And he has studied particularly the physiological effects induced by changes in habitation from lowlands to highlands and from high areas to low.

When cats, rabbits, goats, men, or other animals move from low to high elevations of 13,000 feet or more, their reproductive organs often are affected so that they become temporarily or even permanently sterile. When male cats were moved from lowland Peru to Morococha, 13,000 feet above sea level, their testicles became smaller and it became impossible to locate spermatozoa in their seminal fluid. Rabbits were similarly afflicted. Geese moved up the mountain produced no eggs. Sheep were temporarily affected at the relatively modest altitude of 9,300 feet.

The human picture is of particular interest. Shortly after the Spaniards arrived in Peru, they settled in Potosí, 13,000 feet above sea level. Young women were among the early settlers; yet for over five decades no Spanish woman at Potosí gave birth to a child that survived. When, in the fifty-third year, a child who survived was finally born, the event was so unusual that it became known as the Miracle of St. Nicholas of Tolentino. The Spaniards were keenly aware of the effects of altitude on reproduction and health; for when they moved their Peruvian capital from Jauja in the highlands to Lima in the lowlands, they wrote in the Act for Founding of Lima: ". . . neither there [Jauja] nor in its surroundings nor anywhere in the upland could pigs be raised, nor mares nor fowls because of the great cold and sterility of the land and because we have seen by experience among the many mares that have dropped colts their offspring usually die."

Yet high altitude does not inhibit reproduction among those whose forebears have long lived in the highlands. The Peruvian census of 1940 gives a birth rate of 164 per 1,000 women between the ages of fifteen and forty-five for persons dwelling above 13,000 feet, as contrasted with a rate of 144 per 1,000 on the coast. Physiologically, the highlanders are at least as capable of reproducing as are the lowlanders. The Incas at the time of the coming of the Spaniards had long since come to recognize the difference in physiological capabilities between the lowland and the highland Indians. They knew—and their conclusions have since been verified—that highlanders moving to the coast were almost immediately seized with respiratory diseases: pneumonia, bronchitis, pulmonary abscesses, tuberculosis, and related illnesses. They knew that lowlanders moved to the high Andes could not perform heavy labor, and suffered from stomach and lung afflictions.

It would seem that they knew also that marked changes in altitude in either direction tended to result in sterility, or at best in a high rate of childbirth deaths. Because of this knowledge, the Incas maintained special groups of slaves for work at high altitudes and other groups for work along the coast, and one of the punishments they sometimes invoked was to sentence a slave to an altitude zone that was foreign to him.

The studies of Dr. Monge and of a few others in the same field have raised some fundamental questions in the fields of physiology and genetics. How is it that a highland people can evolve with physiological characteristics so sharply at variance with those of most people of the world? Is this merely a matter of acclimatization? It would seem not. It would almost seem that here are peoples who are a special subspecies of the human race. As Dr. Monge states it: ". . . the Andean carries in his organism the hereditary soma which permits life at the great altitudes that mark certain large inhabited areas of South America."

Many authorities disagree with Monge's conclusions, but if he proves to be correct it will be necessary to explain how under present evolutionary theory a new subspecies of man could develop through mutation and selection in the relatively few thousand years that man has been in the Americas. Or perhaps the anthropologists will have to push back further the date of coming of man to the New World—a date that now stands at 20,000–60,000 B.C.

Weather and Disease

The lung and stomach ailments produced by changes in altitude and such other ailments as heat cramps, heat stroke, sunburn, frostbite, and snow blindness are all produced directly by weather or climate. Yet the effects of weather and climate in promoting health or inducing disease cannot be summed up merely in these direct terms. There are indirect effects of weather upon health which in the aggregate are of enormous significance. Some of these effects are clearly established and well understood; many are obscured to such an extent that they cannot be defined, even though the weather factor is clearly important.

Weather has a profound influence upon the incidence of disease where it limits the carriers of the disease or the disease organisms themselves. Dampness and warmth are absolute environmental requirements for the malarial mosquito, which breeds in swampy regions or in the stagnant waters along the edges of lakes or rivers. The mosquito is abroad only at night. Unless aided by wind, it can travel no more than twenty-two miles on a single night, so its radius of action is definitely limited. In areas where malarial mosquitoes exist, a small malaria-infested region may in a few days grow tenfold in size as warm weather pushes back the frontier beyond which the mosquito cannot thrive and as warm rains convert each low-lying hollow into a breeding place.

Hookworm is another disease that is limited sharply by weather. There are two worms that produce this disease in human beings. Each slightly under a half-inch in length and each penetrates the human skin as larvae, which are carried to the lungs in the blood stream, after which the worm casts off its old skin and makes its way to the stomach and intestines. Hookworm is endemic only in warm, damp regions because the larvae, which are hatched in the soil, cannot tolerate drought or low temperatures. In the United States, the disease is common only in the Southeast, the Gulf states, and eastern Texas. Occasionally, however, hookworm epidemics occur in other regions during spells of warm, rainy weather.

Most common diseases, whether or not the disease organism is directly affected by weather, are more common at some seasons than at others. Pulmonary diseases are most common in winter and least common in summer. Infantile paralysis is most common in summer, and its incidence declines sharply with the onset of cold autumn weather. Cholera and other types of dysentery are most common in warm, humid weather.

It is difficult to say just what part the weather plays in creating these seasonal variations in disease incidence. The common cold is an excellent example. Some doctors claim that even moderate exposure to wet or chill weather will often bring on a cold. Yet a few years ago a British physician, investigating this hypothesis, obtained negative results. While one group of men, women, boys and girls remained warm and dry, a second similarly composed group was exposed to damp and cold. Some members of this second group were required to stand unprotected in pelting rain for several hours, so that their shoes, socks, and other clothes became waterlogged. Others moved suddenly from the warmth of a well-heated room to the cold outdoors, where they walked up and down until thoroughly chilled. Two of the group were immersed in cold river waters and then remained exposed on the river bank for three hours. Nevertheless, the members of this second group did not catch colds with any greater frequency than did the members of the control group, which had been kept warm and dry. To conclude the experiments, the two groups were reversed. The results were the same.

Sinusitis, arthritis, and gout are other diseases whose course seems to be influenced by the weather. Yet there is no agreement as to what constitutes a favorable climate for sufferers from these afflictions. Some persons with sinusitis have fewer attacks in a moist climate than in a dry one; others have fewer attacks in a dry climate.

Probably individual differences are highly important in considering the effects of weather upon disease, just as there are marked individual differences in defining comfort in terms of weather. Perhaps psychosomatic considerations have some bearing on the problem.

Despite confusing and conflicting evidence, the conviction remains that weather is an important element in influencing the incidence and the course of most diseases. The body is a closely knit organism. All bodily functions, including the ability to ward off or subdue disease, are interrelated. It is inconceivable, therefore, that the physical environment to which the body must adjust in dozens of ways should have no influence upon the body's ability to ward off disease or to conquer disease once it has been contracted.

The challenge is to determine precisely how and to what degree the weather operates to aid or hinder the body in its attempts to remain free of disease. One promising line of inquiry regarding this problem would be to study further the effects upon the human organism of changes in the weather. Vital statistics show that the death rate rises every time there is a marked change in the weather. Careful examination of these statistics shows that the rise is due to increased deaths among persons who are already ill. Probably the change in weather, from cold to warm or wet to dry, places upon the body just that added strain which is required to tilt the balance in favor of death. It is possible that weather changes operate in the same manner to influence both susceptibility to disease and the course of a disease once it has been contracted.

4. The Ice off Iceland and the Climates During the Last 1200 Years, Approximately

I. I. Schell

Because of Iceland's location in the North Atlantic and because of the existence of records, however fragmentary, it has been possible to make some estimate of climatic change in this area. Although the particular study is confined to Iceland, its findings correlate fairly well with evidence of climatic change in other areas—particularly Britain, Ireland, and Western Europe—where other evidence has been collected and correlated. Although the evidence for climatic change in relatively recent times appears to be fairly conclusive, the amount and significance of changes remain in doubt.

We may think of climatic change in terms of great differences in temperature and precipitation, yet small, even tiny changes in atmospheric or water temperature averages, on the order of one or two degrees, may have profound influence on distribution of plant and animal life and human activities on the surface of the earth.

The collection of precise climatological records and information has greatly increased in the last 50 years. Yet we cannot be sure, on this very minimal time base, whether the changes of such a short period are sufficient to forecast or predict a warming or cooling trend; there is some evidence to support both positions. For the present, it would appear wise to recognize that in climates, as in other conditions and affairs on the surface of the earth, change is the normal order of events.

Introduction

The relative shortness of the instrumental meteorological and ocean-ographic records has long made felt the need for a geophysical element with a long record that would reflect the climates of the world in earlier centuries.

The long record of the ice off Iceland which extends in some detail back to the middle of the 18th century and in less detail to late in the 9th century, might be regarded as an index of the climates over wide areas, provided that a relationship between the ice conditions off Iceland and the detailed instrumental records of temperatures and other climatic elements from wide areas could be established.

In the following, the broad features of the ice conditions off Iceland were examined first in relation to the air temperatures from large areas in the northern hemisphere and several smaller areas in the south-ern hemisphere, next in relation to dates of freezing of lakes or duration of its ice cover, level of Lake Michigan and discharge of water in the Nile river, and finally in relation to the glaciation in widely different areas.

Representativeness of Ice Record

Before considering the relationship between the ice off Iceland and the instrumental weather and climate data, we wish to examine the ice record in terms of the other recorded climatic features in Iceland and adjacent areas during the same period of roughly 1,200 years or less, as a test of its representativeness.

For this purpose we have assembled in Table 1 mean values of ice

SOURCE: *Geografiska Annuler,* 43 (1961), 354–61. The author is with the Tufts University Meteorological Institute.

severity off Iceland by longer-time intervals based on determinations originally compiled by Thoroddssen (1884) and recently extended by Koch (1945) and Eythorsson (1952), along with information on the ice off south Greenland (Koch, 1945), glaciation in West Greenland (Weidick, 1959) and Iceland (Thorarinsson, 1943), and grain and cereal cultivation in Iceland (Thorarinsson, 1944). The results in Table 1 indicate a general correspondence between the long-term ice severity off Iceland and other climatic features in that area and in southern Greenland during the more than 1,000 years which this record covers, indicating the record to be representative of the broad features of the climate in that general area, and suggesting that Iceland and western and southern Greenland experienced a relatively mild climate during the first three centuries of the record (900 to 1,200 A.D.). This was followed by a deterioration around the beginning of the 13th century and by a further deterioration in the 17th century which persisted through most of the 19th. A marked amelioration, approaching in mildness that of some of the earlier periods, set in before the end of this century.

TABLE 1. Ice off Iceland and South Greenland, glaciation in West Greenland and Iceland, and cultivation of cereals and grain in Iceland ((865)–1950).

| | ICE OFF | | GLACIATION | | CEREAL AND GRAIN CULTIVATION |
	Iceland[1]	*South Greenland*	*West Greenland*	*Iceland*	*Iceland*
(865)– 900	0.1	—	—	Probably less	
901–1000	0.7	—	—	severe than at	
1001–1100	0.2	very occasional	relatively light	other time subsequently	All districts
1101–1200	0.0	generally	—	—	Ceased first in
1201–1300	7.8	moderate	—	—	north and east be-
1301–1400	6.0	to light	—	—	fore end of 12th
1401–1500	2.8	generally light	—	—	century, then altogether, near end
1501–1600	3.2	—	—	increase (2d half)	of 16th century
1601–1700	22.6		—		
1701–1800	25.3	generally severe	relatively severe	relatively severe	none
1801–1900	40.8				
1901–1950	8.6		decrease[2]	decrease[2]	Revived in 1920's

[1] Duration (in weeks) times extent along coasts.
[2] Beginning late in the 19th century.

Ice Severity and Temperatures

Since the more recent portion of the ice records runs concurrently with the instrumental meteorological record, we may compare the changes in the ice severity during the last 100 to 250 years covered by the instrumental record with the air temperatures from representative stations. It had been earlier shown that the fluctuations in the ice off Iceland are appreciably correlated with the decadal air temperatures of northern Europe and eastern North America in addition to Greenland and Iceland (Schell, 1952), as well as with the decadal and annual sea surface temperatures in the northern North Atlantic, and with the decadal values of precipitation and storm frequency in the northern North Atlantic and adjacent areas (Schell, 1956).

For this purpose, all available stations with carefully screened long temperature records were collected and their mean annual values averaged by 50-year periods. Table 2 shows the average values of temperature for the two most recent periods: 1851–1900 and 1901–1950 for some 30 stations in the northern hemisphere and five stations in the southern hemisphere that were taken from World Weather Records . . . and from individual publications. . . . In cases where the record did not cover a full 50-year period, the series was denoted by an asterisk*.

It appears that the sharp decrease in the ice severity from the second half of the preceding to the first half of the present century was accompanied by an increase in temperature at all stations, except at Adelaide, Australia (see Table 2), the increase in the northern hemisphere being most pronounced over Western Greenland (Jacobshavn, 1.5°C) and eastern Canada (Toronto, 1.1°C). Next in magnitude were the increases over the northern United States (St. Paul, Blue Hill, New Haven, Washington, D.C.), with a range in temperature between 0.9°C and 0.7°C, and the increases at Iceland (Stykkisholm), northern Europe (Archangel, Oslo, Stockholm, Copenhagen, Helsinki, Leningrad, Moscow, Sverdlovsk, Vardo) and western Siberia (Barnaul), with a range between 0.9°S and 0.6°C, except as noted below. The increases at northern points with a strong maritime influence (Bergen, Edinburgh, Central England) were less, ranging between 0.4°C and 0.2°C. Smaller increases were also registered at the continental stations situated in

---

The question of the effect on the temperature due to city upbuilding is not a simple one. Thus, the average increase in the mean temperature during the period 1916–1940 at the rapidly expanding city of Djakarta was 0.44°C as compared with 0.67°C at the nearby mountain station Pangerango at an altitude of 3023 m. Earlier it had been shown by Kincer (1933) from a comparison of the records from Baltimore, Md., and Philadelphia, Pa., with those from the nearby rural Easton, Md., and Chester, Pa., respectively, that the long-term increase in temperature at the rural stations was the same as at the city stations. On the other hand, Lysgaard in comparing the Copenhagen record with that of a nearby rural station found the increase in temperature for the years 1861–1936 at Copenhagen to have been greater by 0.15°C. Similarly, at the rapidly growing industrial cities of Japan the upbuilding effect may have been bigger. From the fact that the increase in the temperature in the 100-year period, 1851–1950, at rural Blue Hill, just outside of Boston, was 0.7°C (see Table 2) we may conclude that the increase at "nearby" New Haven during the same period was probably also 0.7°C rather than 0.8°C as given here (Table 2).

TABLE 2. Severity of ice on Iceland and mean annual temperature in Greenland, Iceland, North America, Europe, and Western Siberia by 50-year intervals (1851–1900 and 1901–1950).

	ICELAND	GREENLAND	ICELAND				NORTH AMERICA						EUROPE	
	Ice off Severity¹	Jacobshavn °C	Stykkisholm °C	Toronto °C	St. Paul °C	Boston (Blue Hill) °C	New Haven °C	Philadelphia °C	Washington °C	St. Louis °C	San Diego °C	Vardo °C	Bergen °C
1851–1900	44.4	−5.8	3.8	6.9	6.3	7.5	9.5	12.1	12.6	13.1	16.3*	0.7	7.1
1901–1950	8.6	−4.3	4.7	8.0	7.2	8.2	10.3	12.9	13.3	13.6	16.4	1.3	7.5
Difference	−35.8	1.5	0.9	1.1	0.9	0.7	0.8	0.8	0.7	0.5	0.1	0.6	0.4

EUROPE (Continued)

	Copenhagen °C	Oslo °C	Stockholm °C	Helsinki °C	Archangel °C	Leningrad °C	Moscow °C	Sverdlovsk °C	Prague °C	Vienna °C	Kiev °C
1851–1900	7.5	5.5	5.6	4.0	0.0	3.8	3.9	0.7	9.1	9.1	6.9
1901–1950	8.2	6.3	6.2	4.8	0.9	4.5	4.7	1.3	9.5	9.4	7.1
Difference	0.7	0.8	0.6	0.8	0.9	0.7	0.8	0.6	0.4	0.3	0.2

EUROPE (Concluded)

	Edinburgh °C	Central England °C
1851–1900	8.4	9.1
1901–1950	8.7	9.4
Difference	0.3	0.3

			EUROPE (Concluded)				WESTERN SIBERIA		AFRICA	AUSTRALIA		SO. AMERICA	
	Bucharest °C	Sibiu °C	Rome °C	Geneva °C	Athens °C	Tbilisi °C	Barnaul °C	Capetown °C	Adelaide °C	Sydney °C	Buenos Aires °C	Santiago °C
1851–1900	10.6*	8.5	15.3	9.6	17.8*	12.6	0.6*	16.8*	17.2*	17.2*	16.1	13.4*
1901–1950	10.9	8.9*	15.7	10.0	18.0	12.7	1.2	17.2	17.1	17.5	16.5	13.9
Difference	0.3	0.4	0.4	0.4	0.2	0.1	0.6	0.4	−0.1	0.3	0.4	0.5

¹ Duration (in weeks) times extent along coasts.   * Based on somewhat less than 50 years of record.

TABLE 3. Severity of ice off Iceland and mean annual temperatures by 50-year periods (1701–1950).

	Iceland Ice off Severity[1]	Central England °C	Edin- burgh °C	Copen- hagen °C	Stock- holm °C	Geneva °C	Prague °C	Vienna °C	New Haven °C
1701–1750	18.2	9.2	—	—	—	—	—	—	—
1751–1800	32.3	9.1	—	—	—	9.8*	—	—	—
1801–1850	37.2	9.1	8.2	7.5	5.6	9.5	9.6	9.4	9.4
1851–1900	44.4	9.1	8.4	7.5	5.6	9.6	9.1	9.1	9.5
1901–1950	8.6	9.4	8.7	8.2	6.3	10.0	9.5	9.4	10.3

[1] Duration (in weeks) times extent along coasts.
* Based on somewhat less than 50 years of record.

lower latitudes, the increase ranging from 0.5°C at St. Louis to values between 0.4°C and 0.2°C at Prague, Vienna, Rome, Bucharest, Sibiu (also in Rumania), Kiev, Geneva, and Athens. Least of all was the increase of 0.1°C at Tbilisi, south of the Caucasian mountain range, and at San Diego, California, also 0.1°C, the increase in temperature on the whole decreasing southward. . . .

Table 3, in which both the record of ice severity and temperatures are extended farther into the past, shows that the highest temperatures as judged by the record from Central England were experienced in the 50-year periods: 1701–1750 and 1901–1950, during which the ice off Iceland was in each instance quite light (Table 3). This table further shows a difference in the temperature changes from one 50-year to another 50-year period between the two or more continental stations at Prague and Vienna and the stations with a maritime influence (Central England, Edinburgh, Copenhagen, Stockholm and Geneva in Europe, and New Haven on the east coast of North America). Thus for Prague and Vienna, lying close together, the temperatures during the 50-year period 1801–1850 were about as high as during the recent 50-year period 1901–1950, which is marked by an ice severity of 8.6 units as compared with 37.2 units in the former; at all the other stations the temperatures were lower in the first-named period. This suggests that the ice off Iceland, when considered over relatively short 50-year intervals, may be an index of climate changes of areas with a maritime influence only although a greater representation of continental stations in the middle latitudes would be needed to substantiate this limitation.

Ice Severity and Freezing Dates of Lakes, Lake Level, and River Discharges

Introduction

For additional information about the ice off Iceland as an index of climate change, we may turn to the records of dates of freezing of lakes or duration of ice cover, discharge of water from rivers and lakes, lake and sea level, it being understood that periods of severe ice off Iceland would be associated with earlier freezing dates, increased precipitation, and increased discharge of waters, or higher lake levels in areas under the influence of an equatorward advancing storm track and also in equatorial latitudes that are closer approached by a subtropical high (see below). Similarly, periods of little ice would be associated with later freezing dates, decreased precipitation, lower lake levels, and lowered discharge of water from lakes and rivers in areas from which the storm track is retreating poleward, as well as in equatorial latitudes from which the subtropical highs have shifted away.

Freezing Dates of Lakes

1. Lake Suwa. The earliest record of freezing dates of a lake appears to be that of Lake Suwa, near Tokyo, which goes back to the winter 1443–1444. However, the record for a large part of its length (1682–1923) is very sparse. Also, this lake is quite small, some 14.6 km² in area and 7.6 m at its deepest point, raising the question about its effectiveness as a climate indicator.

2. Lake Champlain and Lake Kallavesi. In North America the record of the rather large and quite deep Lake Champlain goes back to the winter of 1815–1816. The average date of its freezing during the 50-year period, 1851–1900, was January 30 as compared with February 10, or 11 days later, its freezing date during the second 50-year period, 1901–1950. Similarly, the average number of days Lake Kallavesi in Finland was covered with ice each winter during the period of 1851–1900 was 179, as compared with 160 days, or 19 days less, in the 1901–1950 period; the later freezing date of Lake Champlain and shorter duration of the ice season of Lake Kallavesi agreeing with the lesser ice severity off Iceland and higher mean annual temperatures at New Haven, Conn., and Helsinki, in the vicinity of each of these lakes, respectively (see Table 4).

TABLE 4. Severity of ice off Iceland and average freezing dates of Lake Champlain and duration of ice cover on Lake Kallavesi, and mean annual temperatures at New Haven and Helsinki (1850/1851–1949/1950).

	Iceland Ice off Severity[1]	Freezing Date Lake Champlain	Temperature New Haven	Temperature Helsinki	Ice-cover Duration Lake Kallavesi
1850/1851–1899/1900	44.4	Jan. 30	9.5°C	4.0°C	179 days
1900/1901–1949/1950	8.6	Feb. 10	10.3°C	4.8°C	160 days
Difference	−35.8	11 days	0.8°C	0.8°C	−19 days

Duration (in weeks) times extent along coasts.

Lake Level and River Discharge

Although a number of lakes and rivers have had their level or discharge recorded for many years, few can claim a continuous and relatively homogeneous record.

TABLE 5. Ice off Iceland and (A) annual values of level of Lake Michigan and rainfall and temperature at Toronto (1860–1950) and (B) Nile total discharge (1871–1950).

	A					B	
	Iceland Ice off Severity[1]	Lake Michigan Level 500' +	Toronto: Rainfall in.	Temp. °F		Iceland Ice off Severity[1]	Nile discharge m³ × 10⁷
1860–1900	46.4	81.3	32.1	44.6	1871–1900	42.3	1,078.3
1901–1950	8.6	79.8	31.2	46.3	1901–1950	8.6	832.1
Difference	−37.8	−1.5	−0.9	1.7	Difference	−33.7	−246.2

[1] Duration (in weeks) times extent along coasts.

Lake Michigan appears to be of special interest, since its watershed, taken together with that of Lake Huron, with which it is connected, spreads over a considerable area. Similarly, the fluctuations in the level of the Nile River, which are largely determined by the rainfall over the Ethiopian highlands, which in turn is dependent on the moist winds off the Indian Ocean and the proximity of the Indian Ocean High to the coast of Africa, reflect conditions over a wide area.

1. Lake Michigan. The record of this lake begins with the year 1860. This provides a continuous history of 91 years (counting to 1950) of fluctuations of its level. Table 5 shows that its level has appreciably decreased from the 1860–1900 period with severe ice off Iceland, to the following 1901–1950 period with little ice off Iceland. This is corroborated by a decrease in rainfall and increase in temperature at Toronto in the same period, the decreased rainfall and increased temperature (Table 5) reflecting a northward retreat of the mean storm track, whose normal position is somewhat to the north of this lake.

2. Nile flood. The modern record of the Nile Flood begins with the year 1871. The annual values of the total discharge of water at Aswan show an average of 1078.3 × 10⁷ cubic meter month for the period 1871–1900, a period of relatively severe ice conditions off Iceland, as compared with a value of only 832.1 × 10⁷ cubic meter month in the following 1901–1950 period, a period with very little ice off Iceland. (Table 5.) The lower values of the discharge in the more recent period suggest a shift of the Indian Ocean High away from Africa.

Precipitation

In accordance with the pattern of shifts in the high-latitude storm track and subtropical high referred to above, we would expect diminished precipitation also in other areas reflecting a northward displacement of the middle latitude high pressure belt during the period 1901–1950 with little ice off Iceland and, similarly, increased precipitation in the higher latitudes over which the storminess zone was retreating or became better developed. This is apparent from the results in Table 6 showing a de-

TABLE 6. Ice off Iceland and annual values of precipitation at Charleston, Boston, Toronto, Milan, deBilt, Edinburgh, Uppsala, Haparanda, Helsinki, Stykkisholm during the 50-year periods 1851–1900 and 1901–1950 and their differences (precipitation) in % of the 1851–1900 period.

	ICE OFF ICELAND	PRECIPITATION (mm)			
	Severity[1]	*Charleston*	*Boston*	*Toronto*	*Milan*
1851–1900*	44.4	1 303	1 151	815	1 015
1901–1950	8.6	1 097	978	792	956
Difference	−35.8	−16%	−15%	−3%	−6%

		PRECIPITATION (mm) (*Concluded*)				
	deBilt	*Edin-burgh*	*Uppsala*	*Hapar-anda*	*Hels-inki*	*Stykkis-holm*
1851–1900*	711	672	540	463	609	657
1901–1950	765	678	550	544	663	727
Difference	7%	1%	2%	18%	9%	11%

* Haparanda 1861–1900; Stykkisholm 1857–1900.
[1] Duration (in weeks) times extent along coasts.

crease in the precipitation at Charleston, Boston, Toronto, and Milan, in the middle latitudes and a corresponding increase in the precipitation at Stykkisholm, deBilt, Uppsala, Edinburgh, Haparanda, and Helsinki, in the higher latitudes. Diminished precipitation during roughly the same period (1901–1950), apparently resulting from a shift away from the equator of the subtropical highs and hence weaker trades and reduced advective evaporation and precipitation, occurred also at many other stations in the lower latitudes, as shown earlier from extensive studies made by Kraus.

Larger Time-Interval Relationships

It had been suggested earlier on the basis of palaeo-climatological evidence and more recently also from a consideration of the instrumental rainfall record in tropical regions that the longer the duration of a fluctuation, the greater the area similarly affected. From this we may assume that over intervals of the order of several hundred years or longer, the limitations with respect to continental stations in the middle latitudes (see above), if real, would not hold and that a period of longer duration with little ice off Iceland would be one with higher temperatures, not only in Iceland, southern Greenland, east coast of North America, northern Europe, and western Siberia, but also over large neighboring areas. The temperature rise over the Greenland Ice cap would be considerably smaller and would be smaller still over the Antarctic ice cap on the same principle that a large ice field during a "brief" period of warming would remain intact, while the same mass, consisting of smaller ice fields and individual ice flows, would melt rapidly. Hence, we might expect that the 300-year period from 900 to 1,200, with an average ice severity of 0.3 units off Iceland (Table 1), was considerably milder in the higher latitudes, and to a lesser extent in the lower, than the 300-year period 1601–1900, with an average ice severity of 29.6 units; and also milder than the 400-year period, 1200–1600, in between with an average ice severity of 4.7 units.

A comparison of the ice severity off Iceland with the pattern of glaciation in extensive areas in both hemispheres covering the period of the sea ice record either in part or as a whole shows that the glaciation during the period 1600 to 1900, approximately, was more severe in Iceland, Norway, and Sweden than the period 900–1200, approximately, the period in between being one of transition. Similarly, indirect evidence from Greenland covering the period from the time of settlement to about 1300 and actual observations made from about 1700 to the present indicate the 18th and 19th centuries to have been more severe than the early period. Similarly, the evidence from Iceland, albeit sparse, for the early centuries indicates that the period 900 to 1200 was less severe than the period 1600 to 1900. Again, the last three centuries in southeastern Alaska have been preceded by a period of less severe glaciation, possibly as long as several thousand years. Also, the glaciation in southern South America the past three centuries, which culminated in a peak around 1880, appears to have been more severe than at any other time during the present millenium. The later occurrence of the maximum glaciation in southern South America, as compared with the maximum in southeastern Alaska, suggests the influence of the large ice cover of Antarctica, which would retard a general amelioration in that area.

The principle of spatial coherence referred to above requires elaboration. While it calls for an ever larger spatial similarity in the temperature anomaly as the duration of the climatic change increases, the precipitation pattern associated with such a change would be more complicated.

Keeping in mind the character of the atmospheric circulation systems, which consist essentially of a belt of relatively low pressure in the equatorial latitudes, a belt of high pressure in the middle latitudes, another belt of low pressure in the high latitudes, and another belt of high pressure about the pole or a circumpolar high, we would expect in response to a slight increase of solar heat a somewhat intensified equator-to-pole temperature gradient and an increased meridional circulation and, hence, higher temperatures in areas with a greater penetration of warm air from the tropics and lower temperatures in areas with more frequent polar outbreaks. If, however, the increased solar output persists, then a warming would result everywhere, with the biggest temperature increase in the high latitudes because of the poleward convergence of the increased heat flux due to the poleward decrease in area. This rise in temperature would be associated with a gradual, poleward expansion of the middle latitude high pressure belt and shift from the tropics, and also with a similar poleward retreat of the high-latitudes low pressure belt and mean storm track associated with it, and a shrinking of the circumpolar high, as a result.

The precipitation would then decrease in the high latitudes encroached upon by the middle-latitude high pressure belt, but increase in the higher latitudes over which the storm track would be retreating—the latitudes that were formerly occupied by the fringes of the circumpolar high—so that the character of the precipitation anomaly, unlike that of temperature, will be of different sign in different areas depending on the circulation system which dominates the particular area.

Thus, we would expect the interval 900 to 1200, with no ice off Iceland, except for very brief periods, to have been a period of diminished precipitation, lower lake level, lower lake and river discharge, and lesser storminess in the middle and higher latitudes of the northern hemisphere, and of increased precipitation over the high latitudes over which the storm track is still retreating. The precipitation at first would also be greater over the outer zone of the Antarctic ice cap where the massive edge of the ice cap serves as a virtually standing line of discontinuity, with the warmer and moister air associated with the poleward expanded high pressure belt being denuded of its moisture as it is forced over the high barrier.

Similarly, the interval 1200 to 1600, with relatively severe ice conditions off Iceland, would be expected to be a period of heavier precipitation, except in the high latitudes in the northern hemisphere that would now be behind the southward advancing storm track, and also over the outer reaches of the Antarctic ice cap, now less subject to an inflow of warm and moist air from the south as the middle-latitude high pressure belt is shifted northward. Again, the period 1600 to 1900, with severe ice off Iceland, would be expected to have been a period of still heavier precipitation except as noted above, with the characteristics previously outlined being more accentuated than in the preceding period.

Thus, the number of major floods on the coasts of Britain for the period 1000–1450 varied from 7 in the first 200 years to 19 in the last 250 years, when the ice severity off Iceland showed a substantial increase (see Table 1). Similarly, the frequency of severe winters in western Europe, that would also reflect the mean position of the storm track and polar front, appears to have been greater in the 1600–1900 period than in the preceding 1200–1600 period with less ice off Iceland. It also appears from a study comparing the fluctuations in the ice in the Greenland and Barents Seas with the decadal precipitation that the relationship outlined above holds for additional areas.

Summary

Limited evidence was available to show that the ice off Iceland, when considered by longer time intervals, is a measure of the climate of Iceland, Greenland, Europe, North and South America, and probably also other large areas.

Longer time intervals with little ice off Iceland appear to be associated with higher temperatures and, on the whole, less precipitation and lower lake level and river discharge; and intervals with much ice are associated with lower temperatures and, on the whole, more precipitation and higher lake level and river discharge. Thus, the period 900–1200, with very little ice off Iceland, was considerably milder and probably also drier on the whole than the 1600–1900 interval, with severe ice off Iceland, and the interval 1200–1600, in between, was less severe on the whole than the following 30-year period.

5. The Jet Stream Is the Villain

Frank J. Taylor

Our knowledge of weather conditions is continually growing, and frequently new information displaces long-established "traditional knowledge" and concepts concerning these conditions. For the last 100 years a somewhat simplistic notion of atmospheric circulation was accepted, but it is slowly being modified. The existence of jet streams has been known for some twenty years, and as our knowledge of them increases, so also does recognition of their important role in weather making. Correlations now show that the results of shifts in the tracks of jet streams influence the movement of the "intertropical front," which in turn has marked effects on the development of monsoon winds and rain.

The following two selections examine one of the important correlations between jet streams and those violent storms known as tornados. The first also considers the development and character of jet streams themselves.

The phone jingled in the office of Don C. House, Supervising Forecaster of the SELS (Severe Local Storm) Forecast Center in Kansas City Mo. On the long-distance line was a New York reporter who had an assignment to do an eye-witness story on tornadoes. "When can you guarantee me some tornadoes out there?" he asked.

"Wait a minute," said House, shuffling his weather maps. "I can't guarantee them, but if you'll be here tomorrow I think we'll have some for you."

Catching a plane, the newsman arrived in Kansas City just in time. A series of storms swirled up in the predicted area. The SELS forecasters even pinpointed one of them in advance so accurately that the reporter was on hand when the twister spiraled into the sky.

The astonished visitor wanted to know how House could tell in advance where and when the tornadoes would be born. For although the area within 500 miles of Kansas City is the tornado incubator of the country—last year it gave birth to 900 of them—the average life of a tornado is only 10 minutes. Pinpointing them in advance calls for some meteorological wizardry.

House spread out a sequence of weather maps. Across each of them was a wide, black band, which had shifted south as each new chart was drawn, at 12-hour intervals. The dark, curving line across the country indicated the meanderings of the polar jet stream, a swift, high-altitude torrent of wind that whips eastward around the Northern Hemisphere between the 30th and 50th parallels.

This polar jet stream is the villain to blame for much of the country's disaster weather. In the six years since they established the SELS Forecast Center in Kansas City, Don House and his team of advanced weather experts have learned much about the affinity of the polar jet stream for severe storms—tornadoes, hailstorms, cloudbursts. Whenever the polar jet veers south at the same time that moist, low-level tropical air masses are moving north from the Gulf of Mexico, the tornado spotters can expect trouble on the weather front.

A dramatic example occurred last spring. On May 19, the polar jet stream whipped in from the Pacific about halfway between San Francisco and Los Angeles, was tracked over Phoenix, Denver, Sioux City, after which it blew across the Great Lakes, New England and out into the Atlantic, causing no weather disturbance. But by May 20, at 9 a.m., it had detoured south and was checked over Alburquerque and Ama-

Source: *Popular Mechanics,* April, 1958. Reprinted with the permission of *Popular Mechanics.* All rights reserved. The author is a writer residing in California.

rillo, after which it veered north. That afternoon, another shift brought it over Kansas City and St. Louis at an altitude of 30,000 feet, just as a mass of moist tropical air moved north up the Mississippi Valley. Recognizing the makings of catastrophic weather, the SELS Forescast Center alerted the threatened area over a network of radio stations.

During the late afternoon and evening, 50 tornadoes kicked up in Kansas and Oklahoma. In three days, there were 160 tornadoes in the area, accompanied by cloudbursts over the Kansas City environs. What happened, according to House, was that the atmosphere over the area was thrown off balance by the polar jet's shift. It took about five days of severe weather to restore equilibrium in the skies, just as it takes several days for the waters to recede after a river goes on a rampage during a flood.

The polar jet stream was to blame for the Kansas weather binge mainly because it triggered the cloudbursts that followed the tornadoes. Unlike low-level air mass movements, the big wind aloft carries little moisture. But often it does whip along cirrus banners of powdery ice particles which see the clouds below. This kicks off a chain reaction of precipitation, such as the one that deluged Kansas, Missouri and Oklahoma in May and one earlier that had drenched Texas last April, ending a five-year drought.

Airmen have known about the mighty wind upstairs since late in World War II, when B-29 bombers based in the Marianas encountered it is over Japan. Often it blew so hard that bomber crews bucking it found themselves pinned motionless in the sky. To cope with it, they were obliged to overfly Japan at low levels, climb into the jet stream, make their bomb runs flying eastward, then ride the tailwind home. Pan American World Airways pilots have been riding the big wind eastward across the Pacific during the winter months for the past five years.

After the war the airlines, the Air Force and the Navy assigned teams of meteorologists to research the fantastic river of wind and find out how to put it to work. They soon concluded that planes could safely ride the jet stream nonstop from Tokyo to Honolulu, bypassing the refueling station on Wake Island entirely. At first, pilots were reluctant to try it, but in November 1952 Pan American's Capt. Logan D. Scott clipped seven hours off the Tokyo-Honolulu schedule and made the 3908-mile trip in 11 hours, 30 minutes. Since then Pan Am pilots have made hundreds of Tokyo–Honolulu nonstop flights during the winter months, November to March, when the polar jet stream shifts southward to the Japan-Hawaii track across the Pacific. The record flight was made by Capt. John H. Kelly, who brought a Stratocruiser with a full load into Honolulu 9 hours, 18 minutes out of Tokyo. On that single flight, Pilot Kelly saved his company $3000 in fuel and airplane time.

According to Kelly, "Inside the jet stream there's no weather at all.

There are no clouds. You do not sense the extra speed. It is smooth flying unless you drift too close to the north edge, where there is sharp turbulence."

Kelly and other pilots have discovered a trick for staying in the invisible, meandering jet stream. The center of the great wind river is 10 to 15 degrees warmer than its northern edge. By keeping an eye on the thermometer recording the temperature outside the plane (usually around 30 degrees below zero C.) they can hold a course in midstream. And garner the maximum free ride, because the big wind's velocity is greatest at its center.

Though the jet stream was discovered and first put to work by airmen, it now looms even more important in the daily lives of the millions on the ground who are affected by the great wind's deviations from normal. Thus, tracking its willy-nilly meanderings from day to day and season to season has become a routine operation for a U.S. Weather Bureau-Air Force-Navy task force. Every day, for example, an Air Force weather-reconnaissance plane, jammed with instruments, takes off from Honolulu, flies north halfway to Alaska, then returns via a dogleg that makes a 3700-mile overseas triangle. On two legs of the triangle, the flying weathermen usually pick up "the global wind band," as the Air Force calls it. If the Honolulu-based airmen don't find the big wind, another daily weather plane out of Fairbanks, Alaska, picks it up. A third triangle over the Pacific is flown out of Sacramento, Calif. The Navy operates weather planes out of Guam. The Air Force scouts the sky from Okinawa and Japan.

Planes Drop Dropsondes

The weather planes release ingenious expendable mechanisms known as dropsondes, which are attached to small parachutes. As they float slowly down to the sea, tiny transmitters in the dropsondes report temperature, barometric pressure and humidity. On the weather planes, outside thermometers and wind indicators tell the airmen when they have cut across the jet stream. This and other weather information is relayed immediately to land stations which feed the facts into a vast international network.

"Each reconnaissance flight is like having 20 weather stations in the Pacific," explained Dean Parry, the Weather Bureau's jet-stream expert in Honolulu. "There's nothing more perishable than the weather, so in a matter of minutes the information is in the mainland forecast centers.

Mistaken for Flying Saucers

On the continent the detecting is taken over by 100 U.S. Weather Bureau stations, each of which releases similar reporting mechanisms known as radiosondes, two to four times daily. The featherweight radio-sondes are carried aloft by helium-inflated balloons—often mistaken for flying saucers as they glisten in the sky. As they rise, the radiosonde transmitters beam back a steady stream of reports on atmospheric pressure, humidity and temperature. In addition, the radiosondes, tracked by radio direction-finding equipment, reveal the wind direction and velocity at all levels up to around 60,000 feet, where the balloons explode. Other radiosondes are sent up and tracked by ships at sea. Meteorologists in Japan, Canada and European countries are checking, too. Even Soviet Russia and Red China broadcast limited reports. Tracking the polar jet stream has become a global operation.

Four Rivers of Wind?

The concept of a single invisible global river of wind has changed to a possible four in the Northern Hemisphere. Another stream has been identified in the Southern Hemisphere, and meteorologists think there may be more. Some meteorologists consider the name "jet stream"—which was coined by the late Dr. C. G. A. Rossby, meteorologist from the University of Chicago—an unfortunate choice, because "it's neither a jet, nor a stream, but a meandering global band of wind, often a hundred miles wide and two to five miles deep."

Over the Northern Hemisphere, the southernmost of these rivers of wind is the subtropical jet stream, usually 40,000 to 45,000 feet aloft, which whips over Texas and the Carolinas at such lofty altitude that it apparently has little effect on surface weather. The arctic jet, in the far north, cuts across northern Alaska and Canada, at lower altitude, around 25,000 feet. The most recently discoved "planetary wind band," dubbed the polar night jet, flows around the earth 80,000 feet above the Arctic Circle.

The stream which wanders across the temperature latitudes in which live close to a billion Americans, Europeans and Orientals boasts the full name of polar front jet; it meanders above the ever-changing weather front where the cold polar fronts from the arctic meet the warm air masses from the equator. A curious habit is that of splitting unexpectedly into two or more rivers of wind, with vast islands of comparatively still air in between. A few hundred or few thousand miles beyond these forks, the branches may merge again, for this temperamental stream shifts not only north and south, but up and down in elevation. Generally it flows between the 30,000- and 40,000-foot levels. But now and then it suddenly drops, as it did over northern California late in December of 1955, to 10,000 feet, accompanying cloudbursts that inundated several communities, among them Yuba City, which spent Christmas under water.

Big Winds Blow Fast

The big wind has been clocked blowing 200 miles per hour 40,000 feet above Philadelphia when the surface winds were but breezes. It was once tagged above Spokane blowing a 480-mile gale when the ground winds were gentle zephyrs blowing west. High-flying airmen have reported that above the furious global wind band the atmosphere is almost still.

The jet stream's affinity for forest fires has been revealed by Dr. Vincent Schaefer, General Electric's weather wizard, who traced 21 major "blow-up wildfires" which devastated 365,000 acres of timber in 1955 to the proximity of the big wind. Meteorologist Jerome Namias, of the Extended Forecast Section of the U.S. Weather Bureau cites convincing evidence that the destructive hurricanes of recent years—Ione, Diane, Hazel, Carol and others—swung inland over the Atlantic Coast states because the polar jet stream had shifted its course north and west instead of heading out to sea in the vicinity of the Carolinas.

What Makes Them Blow?

What makes these violent rivers of air swirl around the earth is good for a debate any time two or more meteorologists get together. There is agreement on this much: the jet streams are cradled in the sky layers where the heavier lower atmosphere, known as the troposphere, meets the lighter, thinner upper atmosphere, the stratosphere. This layer slopes from about 60,000 feet above the equator to around 30,000 feet above the poles. Along the northern edge of the polar jet stream, there is usually an invisible atmospheric cliff in the troposphere falling off one or two miles like the land cliffs of the Grand Canyon. Dr. Namias and P. F. Clapp of the U.S. Weather Bureau advanced another explanation, namely that "the jet stream is due to the confluence of vast streams of [warm] equatorial air and [cold] polar air at great heights. When these warm and cold masses are brought side by side, the resulting pressure differences set up a strong circulation which may develop the strength of a jet." SELS Forecaster Don House says that the jet stream is "the result of kinetic energy, the transformation of energy of position to energy of motion."

Whatever their cause, the jet streams play havoc with the weather unexpectedly. But, as forecaster House says, "By watching the jet stream, with good analysis, we can pick out the three or four danger spots across the country where trouble might occur, in time to warn people and save life. Four years ago, our chances of spotting tornadoes before they occurred were 20 in 100. Now they have improved to 65 in

100. Severe storms may not always occur when and where we forecast them, but at least we know we should be on the alert."

6. The Twister
Walter Sullivan

Palm Sunday, 1965, will be long remembered in the Middle West as Tornado Sunday. That day more than thirty-five tornadoes were spotted and tracked and nearly 250 persons were killed. Because of the relatively small size of an individual tornado coupled with its frightfully destructive effects in limited areas, our detailed knowledge of tornado formation and structure remains quite limited. Tornado Sunday is described here in the words of those who experienced one of the "twisters." Current efforts at forecasting and warning are also discussed. It is important to note the massive quantities of violent energy released by small storms such as these, relative to the power now created by man in nuclear weapons.

Since midday, radio and television announcers had reported a danger of tornadoes in various Midwest areas. Along Route 32, east of Shannondale, Ind., heavy rain had been falling on the fields of corn stubble, but the family of Wayne Rose felt snug in his spacious farmhouse. The great trees on both sides of the driveway swished and groaned in the wind.

Toward evening it became very dark. Farmer Rose stepped out and found the air oppressively warm and humid. Suddenly he noticed that the wind had died. "It was as quiet as a morgue," he said later. "Then I heard an express train—no, 10 express trains—and there it came, not an upright funnel, but lying almost on its side as it snaked across the fields.

Devastation

"I shoved the family into the Buick, but it outran us." For a few moments there was a chaos of noise and bombardment. Then it was over. House barn, silos, outbuildings all were gone. A heavy washing machine, torn from its plumbing in the heart of the house, had been dropped in

SOURCE: *The New York Times*, April 18, 1965, p. 12E. © 1965 by The New York Times Company. Reprinted by permission. The author is science writer for *The New York Times*.

the middle of a debris-strewn field. Distant barbed wire fences had caught fugitive bedding, clothes and children's toys. Left upright were only the driveway trees, each a nightmare of twisted trunks and stripped branches.

From other houses along Route 32 came groans and screams, but the Rose family was lucky. Their car, batered and dripping mud, had saved them. Only a few homes along the road had storm cellars, for tornadoes are not common that far north, "but you can bet everyone around here is going to build one now," Mr. Rose said.

In Settled Areas

Over and over, last Sunday, deadly funnels dropped from the black sky, devastating a patch of Chicago suburb, an Indiana trailer park, a community near Toledo, Ohio. Close to 2,500 were injured and at least 237 killed. Not since 1925 had a series of tornadoes taken such a toll. The casualties were high in part because the storms swept heavily settled sections instead of the more sparsely inhabited region, centered on Oklahoma, where tornadoes are common and the residents better prepared to take shelter. Most important of all: there is at present no effective way to warn those in the immediate path of a tornado. The best that can be done is to announce that the occurrence of such storms is likely in a certain area.

In fact, little is known about what initiates the wild vortex of a tornado. A hurricane is a spiralling wind system hundreds of miles wide, and it can be explored by aircraft and ground observations. A tornado is so compact, violent and short-lived that it defies analysis. Its lifetime may be measured in minutes, even though the squall line of which it is the child endures many hours, marching across the land and spawning a succession of tornadoes.

While there were reports of 37 tornadoes last Sunday, the number has little meaning. A single funnel may drop repeatedly to the ground, or it may cut a swath close to 100 miles in length.

Tornadoes seem to have some points of similarity with the whirlpools that appear along the front where two moving bodies of water meet one another.

Why Tornadoes?

The encounter that produces a tornado-breeding squall line is typically between moist, warm air from the Gulf of Mexico and cold air that has crossed the Rockies, from the West, and been drained of moisture. In such an encounter the cold air, like a wedge moves in under the warm air, which rises. The warm air then cools and this squeezes out its moisture in heavy rain.

The energy originally required to evaporate the rain reappears as latent heat when the raindrops form and this further warms the humid air, making for greater turbulence, more upward motion and more rain —a sort of wet chain reaction.

This effect is typical of cold fronts the world over, but there is something unusual about these phenomena when they occur over the Midwest in spring. Tornadoes are then a peculiar feature of this region. They occur nowhere else in the world with such frequency, although they have been reported from as placid places as the British Isles.

Dr. Edwin Kessler, head of the Weather Bureau's storm laboratory at Norman, Okla., has suggested that in spring the Gulf air may be cool enough to hug the ground as it moves inland. In that season the strong winter westerlies of the upper air, whose core is known as the jet stream, still retain considerable strength. Finally, the smooth terrain offers little resistance to the surface winds.

Tremendous Energy

These factors conspire to produce violence, be it in thunderstorms, hail or tornadoes. The latent heat released when the rain begins to pour down is enormous. A two-inch downpour on a region measuring 10 by 10 miles, according to Dr. Kessler, releases energy equivalent to 350 atomic bombs of the Hiroshima variety. Only about one per cent of this goes into air motion, but that is still a great deal.

Last week Dr. Kessler and five other Weather Bureau specialists toured the disaster area in two small planes trying to find ways to improve the warning system. The group was headed by Paul H. Kutschenreuter, deputy director of national meteorological services.

No Signals

A spot check of communities in the stricken area by this writer indicated that few, if any, have special whistle signals or other warnings to announce the approach of a tornado.

The eastward advance of the squall line from the Mississippi Valley was monitored almost to the East Coast minute by minute by giant Weather Bureau radar stations. There are more than 30 of these from coast to coast, each with a range of about 250 miles. Their observations are compiled and plotted on a map of the country at RADU—the Radar Analysis and Detection Unit at the weather station in Kansas City. Every hour or two RADU transmits facsimiles of this map to some 200 weather stations throughout the country.

Also in Kansas City is SELS, the Severe Local Storm Center, which examines the reports and issues warnings.

The chief difficulty is that a radar operator can only rarely identify a tornado from the pattern on his scope. The squall line stands out sharply because of its heavy rains, hail and dense clouds. Once in a while there is, within it, a suggestion of spiral structure—a hook-like form that is the earmark of a tornado—but tornadoes are often indistinguishable from heavy thunderstorms.

At the Oklahoma laboratory efforts are being made to develop radar systems that will overcome this weakness. One exploits the so-called Doppler effect. If a musical note is echoed off a stationary wall, the pitch of the echo is identical to that of the outgoing sound. However, if the wall were moving toward the source, each reflected sound wave would be shortened by this motion and hence the pitch of the echo would be raised. If the wall were receding, the pitch would be lowered. The extent of the change in pitch could be used to assess the speed of this motion.

Doppler radar works on the same principle. It is hoped that it will be able to detect the violent motions of dust, raindrops and debris within a torando vortex—movements that probably reach many hundreds of miles an hour.

Another line of research seeks to devise a system for computer analysis of radar data, plotting target densities from the echo strength with an accuracy that cannot be displayed on an ordinary radar scope. Some believe the ultimate solution will be to combine these various tools into an automated system that will spot incipient tornadoes, several at a time, and warn each community in their probable paths.

7. How to Live Through a Hurricane
Philip Wylie

The tropical hurricane, or typhoon, as it is called in the Far East, is one of the most violent and destructive forms of weather. Far greater in extent than the tornado, which originates over land, the hurricane develops great power over sea areas and may then move across land areas, causing widespread damage. Florida is well within the hurricane zone, but these storms have ravaged eastern coastal areas as far north as New England. So great is their violence that they must be experienced to be believed. Wylie, a well-known writer of short stories and critical essays, resides in Miami, and by virtue of having lived through a number of hurricanes is well equipped to relate the measures necessary for self-preservation in a hurricane—certainly weather at its worst.

The sky was blue innocence, the air as washed and warm as on any tropic day, and the sun made the landscape glow. It was the morning after another hurricane. I came downstairs and began the usual inventory.

Our rooms would have been very dark—because of the cypress shutters over the windows and glass doors—but we had left one deeply recessed opening unbarred. Light came grayly from there; the outdoors, seen through it, was as brilliant as the color picture on the screen of a dim theater.

I flipped a switch. No light. I'd expected none. The telephone, lifted from its cradle, emitted no hum. It had gone out at eleven the evening before. In the kitchen I turned a tap unhopefully, but this time our city water flowed. I let the hot tap run, since the tanks would still be warm, filled a kettle and set it on the miniature stove beside the inert coils of the electric range. I struck a watch, but its damp had smeared, so I snapped a cigarette lighter and set afire the can of solidified alcohol.

The louvers on the kitchen door opened with effort. The door itself resisted until I pushed hard enough to crack branches, of which there was a drifted heap in the carport where our two automobiles were jammed deliberately against each other and a concrete wall. The cars were polka-dotted with thousands of poinciana leaflets and stood hub-deep in debris. But no glass was broken and they seemed all right.

No morning paper on the steps. A glance down the curving driveway gave one possible explanation: it was blocked by limbs from our live-oak trees, limbs thigh-thick, heaped as high as the top of a big truck. The lawn lay invisible beneath vegetation, with pans, tins, pots, flower containers and other objects here and there—objects less careful neighbors or people somewhere had failed to take indoors. I walked toward the green barricade in the drive. Lo and behold, the newspaper lay there, after all! The boy had come as close to our house as he could and tossed it over the heap. Its headline read:

DAMAGE MAY REACH 30 MILLIONS

To the left was the poinsettia bed, a hundred feet long, hewn in hard rock by the gardener and myself, filled by wheelbarrow with special dirt and planted with choice cuttings which this year were expected to pro-

Source: *Saturday Evening Post*, December 30, 1950. Copyright 1950 by Philip Wylie. Reprinted by permission of Harold Ober Associates. The author, a novelist, essayist, and short-story writer, has written *Generation of Vipers*, *Opus 21*, and *Night Unto Night*, among other works.

duce a wall of scarlet. Two great oak branches and a tree now lay upon the bed, poinsettias crushed beneath. The foot-thick trunk of the tree was splintered; it had been tossed by last night's wind from a nearby woods onto our floral border.

I walked around the high brick wall that masks the clothes-drying yard. A huge solanum vine, still in flower when the red-and-black hurricane-warning flags were hoisted, lay prostrate in the yard, and not a blossom left. Where the parasol-wide leaves of the taro had tented a corner of the house, was a green wreck. The pads of the tropical water lilies in the pool I'd spent months digging and cementing were turned up and tattered like flounces on the dress of a drowned girl. Rain that fell inches in minutes had brimmed the little pond; leaves, twigs and branches filled it.

The oak at its base was probably done for. Two branches of seven remained; the rest stood stiffly in the sunshine, like the shot-off fingers of a cupped hand. Beyond, in the acres of our land that are pine and palmetto, the blasted stumps of a few trees showed; but most still stood. And the house itself was unscathed.

I went back into the murky kitchen, slapping at mosquitoes, perspiring a little from the October sun and the dampness of the green-smelling morning. The kettle was hot now. I put a heaping spoonful of powdered coffee in a cup, added sugar and then cream from the still-cold but slowly defrosting refrigerator, poured the hot water, drank coffee and opened up the morning paper.

Mrs. Wylie came downstairs. Ricky, we call her. She looked at me for a moment and smiled. "How did we do?"

"Dandy," I said. "Just dandy!"

On the morning of the day before, a friend, knowing that we rarely listened to the radio, had phoned early. She had been a little bit leering: "You should have stayed north longer! That hurricane fumbling around Jamaica is headed this way now! It's the ninth or tenth spotted this year, and I hope it misses, like the others!"

We were busy. We had other plans. But the same thing was true of all the half million people that morning in South Florida: the business went undone and the plans were canceled. Ricky, like tens of thousands of other housewives, has a routine for such occasions, and I, like as many husbands, have my set chores.

We tested our radio, but it didn't work. So that got priority on the list. We were warned at nine o'clock. By noon we'd had new batteries put in the radio, so it would work without its regular power supply.

Our gardener, luckily on hand, by noon had spread the solid board hurricane shutters on the lawn and commenced to carry them to the proper windows. Galvanized wing nuts and washers, brass screws and heavy bolts in glass jars marked "Hurricane" had been brought down

from shelves. Both cars had been filled with gasoline, for there is no
way to tell, when a hurricane is hours distant, how bad it will be, and
therefore how many days may pass with the power off and gasoline
pumps not functioning. The extension ladder was leaning against the
house. The stepladders had been carried outdoors.

Ricky had shopped. The two-gallon kerosene can was full, for lamps.
The can for "white" gasoline also was full, for the lantern. Extra batteries to fit sundry electric lamps and flashlights were on hand. She had
stocked a fresh supply of candles, a dozen cans of solidified alcohol,
powdered coffee, enough tinned staples to keep us fed without heat
or ice for two weeks, if need be. People with freezer units can sometimes get dry ice to carry their produce over a period without electric
power, but we have no unit. So she cooked the meat on hand. It would
keep longer that way.

We have a spaniel named Popcorn; there was a three-weeks supply of
canned food for him. Ricky had also bought a half-dozen bug bombs,
against the good possibility that our screens might be damaged beyond
easy and early repair, so that to sleep in any comfort we would have to
seal up and spray a bedroom.

She'd set out raincoats and heavy boots and old towels in case of leaks
just as I'd set out an ax in case of blockaded doors and fire extinguishers
because of the lamps and the approaching wind.

Play by Play of Approaching Storm

Every two hours on the half hour, our radio stopped playing dance
music or reporting world affairs or discussing the merits of advertised
goods, and we—the half million of us—were transferred to the Weather
Bureau. There, a calm but urgent voice made its reports, which are
called advisories and were repeated at half-hour intervals by the regular
announcers on all stations—stations which, in a few more hours, largely
would fall silent as their tall steel towers crashed in a roaring night.

The storm, the voice would say, is at such-and-such latitude and longitude. Then it would translate: so many miles south and east of Miami
and coming north and west at ten or eleven miles an hour. Or standing
still for a while over some empty, tempestuous stretch of the sea. "Plane
scouting the storm report wind velocities near the center at upward of
a hundred miles an hour. This is a small but dangerous hurricane, and
all safety measures and other preparations should be rushed!"

After the Weather Bureau, would come the voice of an announcer for
the Red Cross. He would tell the listeners—sure of an excellent audience
—what schools and other public buildings had been designated as shelters. Anybody who felt unsafe would be welcome—men, women and
children, bearing their own food and water and flashlights, if they had
them, but no pets. Pets were to be left behind with supplies of food and

water. And expectant mothers were to be taken to Jackson Memorial Hospital; the storm might be so furious that the stork could get through, but not the doctor.

People in trailers, people in rickety houses, people living near the sea and frightened by the expectation of rising tides, packed up their families in family cars or took busses to the shelters—which were opened at two in the afternoon. Some other people, listening, but oversanguine, decided to ride it out where they were. Of those, some were subsequently regretful, and at least three lost their lives.

Toward one o'clock we decided to eat lunch downtown. The commercial buildings were already boarded up. But it seemed to us that Miami's pre-hurricane overture of hammers pounding wasn't loud enough in the residential sections. Perhaps the storms had called "wolf" and missed Miami too often that year. Or perhaps that word "small" sounded more cogent to many householders than the familiar word "dangerous." Most people with homes, at any rate, weren't doing much. But the boat owners were taking precautions. The city's many drawbridges went up and down as yachts, fishing cruisers, houseboats, sailboats and even outboards paraded up the rivers and canals to anchorages between high banks.

The restaurant was battened down, electric-lighted and full of people. Some seemed excited, but others looked tired and grim. Perhaps they'd been in hurricanes before and doubtless they'd boarded up for nothing several times that year. Near our table sat a group of badge-wearing delegates, members of one of the three conventions in town at the time.

A man among them proclaimed in a facetious shout, "If this hurricane misses, I'm going to ask the Chamber of Commerce for my money back! Always did want to see what happened in one!"

"If it hits," Ricky said to me quietly, "he may get his money's worth." After all, we'd been through five.

Eating lunch in a restaurant saved our food supplies and saved energy and time. If the storm speeded up, time might become valuable. We drove home, part of the way in a hard shower that threw thunder across the green landscape and gave way to blue sky again in a few blocks. The storm, said the Weather Bureau, was stalling as of noon. Building up in force, they said.

Now the gardener and I began to fasten on the shutters. Each was lifted, fixed over threaded bolts in the window frame, pressed tight and secured by washers and wing nuts. One by one, upstairs and down, most of the windows of our house were thus darkened. Then the doors. Inside it became hot and gloomy. Outside the shower was repeated, the sky turned blue again and the wind picked up. The big garbage cans went into the shed where the shutters had been stored. The wheelbarrow and sawhorses were put in the concrete-block compost bin, on top of the heap, but below the walls. We brought in the gardenia and the potted plants. Porch furniture was stowed in bedrooms. With a garden hose I set a siphon going to lower our lily pond, knowing the rains might otherwise wash out its population of tropical fish.

Our grapefruit and papayas were too green to bother picking. We had no avocados. With a pole-handled tree trimmer, I cut off various fronds and branches which, in a tempest, might be expected to bat against eaves or the power lines leading to our house. I forgot to cut back the nine-foot tulip tree, and in the morning what was left was less than two feet high. And I thought of wrapping up the big, double yellow hibiscus at the corner of my workroom. But I didn't, and that was gone next day. I checked the hand pump on our well, and it was working; we'd have water—potable water—unless the concrete pump house blew away, and the pump with it.

Indoors, Ricky and our maid, Hester, had taken up rugs and hung away clothes, filled all the flint lighters, finished the cooking, locked or left open interior doors according to a plan, and set the hurricane gear at strategic points. Hester was dismissed early, and she joined the home-going throngs. School had been let out everywhere at noon and the yellow busses had already taken the children home. We were set now, and this was the time for the phone calls and the visits.

Other people, also finished with their precautions, came to see if they could help us. We got into a car and drove over to find out if our friends needed helpers. Some did.

Soon after our return, the contractor who had built our house the year before stopped by to see if we were snug, and decided my preparations needed reinforcements. He and I went back up on the ladders and the broad, flat roofs. Afterward he had a cup of coffee. More people phoned. We phoned to a few more, and the wind began to hiss in the treetops. It grew dark. Ricky cooked supper and we ate and then washed the dishes.

At eight-thirty the radio said South Florida was surely in for it. The Red Cross gave staccato lists of aid stations and shelters. People had been told everything they could be told. The wind downtown in Miami, in the next couple of hours, rose to hurricane force, which is seventy-five miles and above.

At five minutes of eleven our lights went out, after dying and coming on again a few times. We know the moment because the electric clocks stopped then, and the hands stayed there afterward. We had been phoning periodically to relay the advisories to a family whose radio had stopped working in the afternoon. The husband lay abed with a high fever, and one of the children, in trying to light a candle with a damp match, got a blazing coal in her eye. A doctor made it to their house through the rising tumult and found the child painfully, but not seriously injured. We phoned the ten-thirty bulletin to them, and none after that, as our line went dumb at about the same time our lights went out.

Outdoors it poured. As long as the power lasted, we kept our flood-lights on, so we could watch the trees surge and glitter in the horizontal rain, catch sight of vague objects hurtling across the wet night and bounding anonymously on the lawn, and see our shrubs bend low, wave, twist and dig funnels in the earth at their bases. A steady wind steadily rose, giving the landscape just such an appearance and producing just such sound effects as the movies of hurricanes do. Over that wind, however, came the gusts, audible in the distance, screaming as they plowed troughs in the woods around us. The cinema is too feeble to reproduce such sounds as those. It was possible to go out on lee porches, but it was difficult to hear even shouts at any distance.

When our lights went, everybody's did near us; the comforting glow of other houses disappeared. It was replaced by flashes far and near—pink and blue and white lights—as transformers burned out and hot wires shorted on the ground or amidst the hurtling tree stems. Then utter darkness, filled with unspeakable din. The radio, now on batteries, stopped and we turned to another station. A tower had gone down, the new announcer said. His station had switched to a non-directional beam to cover for stations temporarily out of commission.

"Look at the barometer!" Ricky cried.

The eye could see it move. Down and down. Twenty-five hundredths in as many seconds. Our ears popped and hurt. Wind rushed from the house through the doors and windows we had left open for the purpose of keeping pressure equalized.

The radio talked fast now. Downtown in the main streets, it said, metal shutters were being ripped off many of the big stores. Their great plate-glass windows were bursting into the streets as the outdoor pressure dropped. All firemen and police near a certain address were urged to hurry to it: a woman and two children were trapped there in an unroofed home. People were desperately ordered to stay off the streets. Casualties from the exploding windows were mounting where the fool-hardy lingered in some supposedly protected spot to watch. More radio towers were falling. More roofs were lifting everywhere. Walls were collapsing. Huge electric signs were falling or dangling and grinding in the wind. The sea was up around thousands of houses. The sand it carried had made streets impassable where fallen trees had not already done so. *Cabañas* along the ocean front, torn up by the seas and the wind, were blowing around the beach.

Our house was now a dot in a pitch-black world. The lamps guttered. A tongue of water slid under a door and spread out on the white terrazzo floor. Ricky threw some of the old towels over the little inundation and wrung them into a pan and left them at the wet crack. The noise was a tremendous roar overridden by the squealing gusts and punc-tuated by rare cracking sounds as trees broke. Most such noises, how-ever, though loud in themselves, were lost in the general bellow.

Now the direction of the hurricane changed and our front porch became a protected place. We went out there. The screens still held, but we could see in the lightning and the beam of a big flashlight that our pines, slim and sixty or seventy feet tall, were bent low. The palms blew all one way, like the loose hair of a woman in a fast-driven roadster. The gusts had become appalling. Though the Weather Bureau had recorded nothing over a hundred and six miles an hour, I told Ricky I'd eat everything hurled into our yard if the gusts weren't hitting a hundred and a quarter by that time. They were . . . and in some places maybe a hundred and fifty, the bureau said later. We went back indoors, soon—a little afraid a branch or board might ride the pandemonium onto the porch.

The hurricane had reached its peak, but we had no way to tell. Our house, like all properly built houses in that area, was set on foundations of steel and of concrete poured in trenches in the underlying limestone. Ferroconcrete beams at the corners were tied by steel rods into similar heavy beams under the eaves; steel bands attached each separate member of the roof to the beams. Our rafters were double.

Ricky and I were far from terrified, but it would be untrue to say we were without apprehension. I've been worse scared by a California quake and in a burning building in Dakota, in a Canadian forest fire, in the 1913 Ohio flood and during a tornado in that same state. I've been more alarmed in a storm at sea. But hurricanes are tricky. Sometimes they contain tornadoes of their own which no construction can withstand. Occasionally a freak, twisting gust wreaks some particular havoc. And this was a strong storm. News of the falling steel towers—that had stood through other blows—and of the unroofing of many houses made that plain. As we felt the majestic mallet blows of the wind, we couldn't help glancing up where the rafters met the beams, to see if a crack showed there or if water was dribbling in.

Our exile, like that of all the rest in private homes, was absolute. For an hour, or possibly six or eight hours, we would be alone. The streets and roads were impassable. Communications were nil, except for radio and radio hams. A person might be able to flounder through the frantic night for aid; a person might fail in such an attempt. Any injury, acute sickness or disaster to our house would be our problem to deal with, probably without aid for hours. We sat on the divan and smoked limp cigarettes. Popcorn, our white cocker spaniel, stayed close in spite of the heat, shook, and eyed us with worry. We thought and spoke about the sleazy houses built for veterans in some of the outlying real-estate developments, and we spoke about the ramshackle sprawl of "colored town," where our Hester had lived until recently.

Morning was to see 20,000 houses, mostly the shabby or badly built ones, hit, unroofed or wrecked. Three dead and nearly a hundred hurt, and a miracle the total was so low. But that night the myriad disasters

—bits and pieces of which the radio continued to report—were used by us and by hundreds of thousands like us as indices of personal hazard. Would we be next? And how long would we have to endure passively the effort of the elements to tear our house apart?

The October hurricane proved the old adage about the want of the nail for which the shoe was lost. The littlest violation of the building codes, the most minor skimping of material—nails too far apart or too small, mortar too poor or too sparingly used, a roofing felt lighter than the prescribed kind, flashing of too thin a gauge let in a finger of the tempest, and the hand and brawny arm thrust in behind. A tile rattled and flipped into the night; the tiles above it were plowed loose. Metal began to vibrate and then tore; the material beneath ballooned, ripped, raced into oblivion, and the roof after it, and then, sometimes, the walls buckled. In days to come, Miami would learn new lore concerning building against hurricanes and learn, shamefacedly, that among its capable builders there were a few cheats. Some people lost everything because a contractor had saved himself as little as ten dollars on a home.

"The barometer!" Ricky exclaimed again, after an hour or so. It was rising!

The terribleness of the gusts diminished; the general tumult lost energy. In another hour we had such a wind as might blow on any night of a gale, and soon only a stiff breeze. A neighbor—a man who said he liked to cook, but had no opportunity except before hurricanes—had brought us half of a cake. We ate most of that and drank a bottle of milk, which would sour if we did not use it. We were able to realize how tired we were. It was three A.M.

I let Popcorn out by a porch door and followed him a few feet through the rain. Not far. Overhead, branches still hung dangerously amongst the treetops; now and then we heard one let go and crash to earth. Somewhere nearby the wires were down, and of these some carried 13,000 volts; they might be alive still. There was another possible hazard in walking in the dark through fallen brush. It rains so hard in hurricanes that the effect is like that of a flash flood. When the adjacent lowlands are flooded, rattlesnakes sometimes scurry to such high ground as ours. The breed is *adamanteus*, the biggest of the diamondbacks, and we've found him on our lawn, bird hunting, even on pleasant days. I whistled Popcorn back presently, and let the damage census go till we'd had some sleep and until the light came.

The next morning, when we'd finished our coffee and made another tour of the premises, we toilsomely began the third part of every hurricane's routine.

While Ricky mopped up the mud tracks through the house, I chopped apart the limbs on the drive and manhandled them to one side. Then I tried starting both cars; neither was damped out. We drove over to see how the family with the sick father and the hurt child had fared.

At the corner we saw the daughter of another neighbor playing in an uprooted and overturned mountain of trees which till then had stood for perhaps a century.

Our friends were safe and we went back, driving past houses with tile roofs like half-scaled fish, under leaning power poles, around roped-off areas where live wires lay, zigzagging through hastily cleared paths in the streets and noticing that not just the brittle trees, but even the mahoganies were riven. Heavy-husked coconuts lay everywhere like a giant's green marbles. Snapped palm and pine trunks stood conspicuously. Stone walls were notched where trees had fallen on them, and sidewalks were sundered where roots had lifted them. People in hundreds were oudoors, doing things or merely looking.

Already city trucks were collecting and carting off the mess. Portable cranes were straightening trees. On power poles among the snaggled spider webs of wire, umbrellas were lashed to shield from the hot autumn sun linemen who had begun to work as soon as the wind commenced to drop. Men were setting up concrete lampposts and moving up replacements for metal posts broken by the flung trees. A boy was staring morosely at the ruin of his convertible, and we saw a householder examining a car that had been rolled onto his crotons. Bulldozers shoved boughs and fronds about. Here a roof was gone, yonder a small building had become a pile of cement blocks, and in the distance the stump of a chimney showed.

Our shutters had to be set out to dry in such a way as not to warp. I began unbolting them. I next cleared the poinsettia bed, chopping up the large fallen tree to movable sizes. Since our house was dry inside, Ricky went to help people who had wet rugs, sodden draperies, soaked beds, bedraggled linen, drenched and often ruined clothes; people whose windows had broken because they hadn't bothered to put up shutters or whose windows and shutters had failed to keep out horizontal, pressurized streams of water that spurted even through keyholes and drowned whatever was in the rooms.

At lunchtime we knocked off and, since the restaurants were open, we met in one. From a human-relations standpoint, it is too bad hurricanes aren't universal and frequent. The restaurant was crowded, strangers doubled up at tables, everybody talked amiably to everybody else— talked a little excitedly and trustingly. Shared peril and subsequent release make all men brothers, briefly.

We worked all that day. Hester didn't show up and we worried about her. That night we bathed in the last of the warm water and read by kerosene lamps till we were sleepy.

In the morning Hester returned. Her house had suffered only a broken window, but her daughter and six grandchildren had escaped from theirs after the roof came off, but before the walls fell in. These seven, with all possessions lost, had moved in with Hester. "A bad storm," Hester said sorrowfully. "This one was just too bad."

By late afternoon of the second day, all the shutters were down again and the house was airy. The limbs and debris I'd piled up ran for fifty feet along the drive in a heap higher than my head, but you couldn't see the grass for the leaves, still, and there were acres I hadn't even investigated carefully. Our floors were spick-and-span, the lamps were full for another evening, spoiled food had been buried, because it breeds maggots swiftly in this climate, and I was raking oak leaves out of the lily pond—so their acidity wouldn't kill the fish—when Ricky came bursting from the house. "The light's on!" she shouted.

It seemed a great victory. We felt, for once, not the classic American impatience with utilities, but great pride in a company and in the men who could make swift sense out of the copper shambles the power lines had been. We wanted to thank somebody, but there wasn't a phone. Light also meant that our stove would work again and our bath water would heat, our fans would turn and we'd have ice and could store fresh food again. Two days! It might have been two weeks.

The following morning I trimmed back the beat-up shrubbery and straightened up those bushes, especially hibiscuses, which might reroot and live. I cut down the taro. Ricky put out food for her birds— cardinals and jays, quail and two kinds of doves, woodpeckers, towhees and flickers—which were extra hungry because their natural food had largely blown away. A plague of mosquitoes descended. But the big event that day was the ringing of our phone and the announcement by a technician that it would from then on be pretty constantly usable.

We—and 40,000-odd other people—went to the Orange Bowl that evening and watched the University of Miami defeat Boston University. During the first half, it is true, we were all a shade uneasy, owing to another phenomenon common in the hurricane latitudes: a new storm had been discovered in the gulf. It was headed toward us. Perhaps we'd have it all to do, go through and undo again. That had happened to Ricky and me twice before. But during the game the public-address system announced the blow was going to miss Miami—word that got quite a hand. Eventually that storm petered out, doing no damage.

A week after the hurricane, most of the streets were clear. Most of the tipped-over trees had been set upright and most of the ruined ones had been chopped up and carted off. Nearly everybody had lights and phones again. The open roofs were nearly all at least temporarily repaired enough to ward off the rains of the rainy season. The glass shortage was over and the stores were getting back their windows. Here and there, scraps of evidence remained: a boat aground, a plane demolished, a leaning tree, a cat's cradle of overhead wires, a missing cupola, a hotel with a wrecked sign. But our poinsettias were already coming up from the roots, the yellow hibiscus was growing anew, and the rapid vegetation of the tropics would soon obscure the wounds.

Long before the winter tourists arrived the landscape was normal—normal for a land where orchids bloom on trees. The tourists now look in vain for proof of what his us in October. Only a few thousand people out of half a million remember the mid-October storm of 1950 as anything particular. The rest blur it with other, lesser or more violent recollections. But always, inland people and people who live up north, curious about our different way of life on the tropical big toe of Florida, will cap their inquires with the question: "——and what about hurricanes?"

Well——

8. Sirocco in the Levant

Tage Sivall

Many local weather phenomena have properties and effects peculiar to a limited area. Among these is the sirocco, a thoroughly dry wind blowing north from the African and middle Eastern deserts. Although not violent as are the hurricane and tornado, nevertheless the sirocco, because of its dessicating character, causes great devastation to crops and discomfort to people as it passes. Winds, especially, seem to be given local names that may or may not suggest their peculiar character: The sirocco is also known as the khamsin; *others are* mistral, foehn, chinook, *and in our own West, "they call the wind Maria." Effects similar to those Sivall describes resulting from the sirocco have been fashioned by the English author Norman Douglas into a fascinating novel,* South Wind, *showing the impact of the debilitating sirocco on a group of humans living on a Mediterranean resort island.*

General Survey

During the greater part of the year, settled and what is commonly called fair weather predominates in the Levant, however it should not be inferred from this, that the weather may also be regarded as agreeable. Its influence upon the mental and physical well-being contains a series of subjective factors, as constitution, acclimatization etc., varying from

SOURCE: *Geografiska Annaler*, 39 (1957), 114–42. The author is with the Swedish Meteorological and Hydrological Institute.

case to case, but only temperature, humidity and wind are directly measurable and of decisive importance. By means of these three factors, the so-called cooling factor $C\omega$, in millicalories/cm²/sec., can be estimated by the following empiric formula:

$$C\omega = (0,21 + 0,17\,v^{0,62})\,(98 - t^1);$$

in which v = wind speed and t^1 = temperature of wet-bulb thermometer. The feeling of well-being is determined by the quantity of heat emitted by the body per unit of time and this in turn depends on the extent of physical activity and on the cooling factor. If the latter is below a certain amount, the body is overheated, and this will soon lead to heat-stroke. Normally this limit is at $C\omega = 1$ at rest, and $C\omega = 7$ at hard work. By $C\omega = 20$ however most people will feel a certain discomfort, which according to their varied ways of reacting is usually characterized as suffocating or oppressive. $C\omega$ has been estimated for some places within the area. Too great an importance should not be attached to the absolute values, even though all places except Jerusalem are situated on the coast and accordingly show relatively small diurnal variations, above all as regards temperature and humidity. The wind conditions, too, are very stable and it may thus be regarded as allowable to include an estimation of the average wind speed in the formula. Nevertheless, the main interest of these estimations is because they are used to compare the different stations within the same climatic region.

	Jan.	Febr.	March	April	May	June	July	Aug.	Sept.	Oct.	Nov.	Dec.
Tripoli	26	26	24	22	18	15	13	14	15	17	21	25
Beirut	26	23	22	21	17	14	11	12	13	15	20	22
Haifa	28	30	25	21	14	11	10	9	11	12	22	27
Jerusalem	27	28	25	19	20	18	17	16	15	16	20	24
Gaza	22	22	20	18	18	14	11	7	11	14	17	20
El Arish	33	34	30	26	21	18	15	13	14	16	23	29
Alexandria	45	50	40	37	28	27	26	23	21	18	22	27

If $C\omega = 20$ is thus accepted as the lower limit in dividing the climate as being more or less agreeable, the coastal regions of Israel are the least favoured. Northward along the coast of Lebanon as well as southward along the Egyptian coast the climate improves gradually. The border district between Israel and Egypt is particularly remarkable, as the difference between Gaza and El Arish for instance is considerable in spite of the short distance. Generally speaking, the months from May up to and including October are the least agreeable climatically, however in Gaza this period extends over March—December. In the Egyptian stations a displacement of the least agreeable period towards the latter part of the year can be noticed; and in Alexandria October is the worst.

It has been impossible to take into consideration in this survey the

mentally depressing factor of the monotony of the weather in summer-
time. These conditions too have in time a reducing effect on vitality and
capacity.

Local Winds

Contrary to summer, the transitional seasons present phenomena as
interesting from a meteorological point of view as they are dreaded by
the inhabitants in the districts concerned. The very character of the
Mediterranean, an immense inland sea enclosed by land masses of highly
varying structure, indicates that it could become the scene of the most
extreme weather changes. The winds connected with these disturbances
are quite often devastating and have penetrated so deep into the con-
sciousness of the inhabitants that they have been given different names
in varied parts of the Mediterranean.

Of the winds prevailing during the cold season, the cold northerly
"Mistral" in the Gulf of Genova and the similarly cold "Bora" in the
Adriatic Sea are best known. They both imply invasion of extremely
cold air in the otherwise warm Mediterranean, and often attain the
force of a strong gale.

The desert winds of the common name "Sirocco," blowing over the
Mediterranean from Sahara and the desert regions in the Arabian
Peninsula, are equally well known. The sirocco implies a radical and
often fatal interference with various branches of commercial and
industrial life. Its consequences to agriculture can thus be disastrous, as
the sparse vegetation withers or is choked by the great quantities of sand
and dust generally carried along by these desert winds. To navigation
and air traffic the sirocco causes great obstacles through the gusty gale
and the reduced visibility. Banks of sand are often driven together on
the runways making all air traffic impossible. From a medical point of
view, the sirocco is of some interest too. Above all the nose, throat and
eyes are subject to great strains which often result in infections.
Statistical investigations at the American Hospital in Beirut do however
also show that the number of different fever diseases and above all
neuroses reaches a marked maximum during days when the sirocco is
blowing. It has been possible to prove a concentration of the occurrence
of these diseases towards the final phase of the sirocco.

In his book "Wind in the Sahara" R. V. C. Brodley gives a dramatic
description of the sirocco south of the Atlas Mountains:

I woke at dawn with a feeling that my hair was about being singed off my
head. The sheep, camels and donkeys crowded together, their heads dropping
and their hind quarters to the wind, which came in suffocating gusts. A pall
of yellow dust obliterated everything. As it got light the heat increased. My
throat felt parched and my eyes smarted. It was like standing in front of a
furnace in a glassworks. The wind no longer came in gusts. It came in a

steady, roaring current . . . . When on the third evening the wind lulled and ceased as suddenly as it had begun, I saw that there was not a green straw left. It was like a prairie fire had passed by. The air was still clouded with dust and it was several days before we saw the blue of the sky.

This account from the interior of the Sahara has a remarkable resemblance to the one given from the desert region immediately east of the Sinai Peninsula in "Seven Pillars of Wisdom" by T. E. Lawrence:

It was a panting wind with a touch of the heat from a smelting-furnace, a heat sometimes felt in Egypt, when a "chamsin" is approaching. As the hours passed by and the sun climbed higher up in the sky, it grew stronger and more saturated with dust from the Nefudh, the vast sandy desert in northern Arabia lying over there, quite close to us but invisible in the haze. At noon there was a gale blowing, so dry that our shrunk lips broke and the skin of our faces cracked, whereas our eyelids, covered with grains of sand, seemed to draw back laying bare our shying eyes . . . . As we came farther into the desert and the hours passed by, the wind grew stronger and its heat more frightful. Every resemblance to a friendly duel had vanished. The mere movements of my camel were sufficient to increase the irritating effect of the suffocating waves, the dryness of which destroyed my skin and made my throat so sore that for the next three days I could only eat but little of our doughy bread.

Common to these descriptions of the sirocco in two different desert regions is on one hand the high temperatures together with the low humidity, and on the other hand the great wind speed and the reduced visibility caused by the whirling sand and dust. However, these characteristics will change rather considerably as soon as the sirocco has left it region of origin. No doubt it absorbs great quantities of moisture as it sweeps over the adjacent seas. When the wind reaches the countries around the northern part of the Mediterranean it is therefore still warm but at the same time moist.

In the Red Sea the conditions are about the same. Thus, the distribution of the annual precipitation in the coastal region of Eritrea turns out to be quite different from that in the inland. Asmara, situated in the tableland, receives a precipitation amounting to 548 mm per year from the damp southwest monsoon, the months of July and August being the most rainy. From Asmara, situated at an altitude of about 1,800 m, the land slopes steeply towards the coast, where the southwest monsoon consequently appears as a relatively dry foehn current. The seaport Massaua therefore receives very little precipitation from the southwest monsoon, the rainfall being distributed during the months when the northeast trade wind is blowing. This wind, although extremely dry in its region of origin over the Arabian Peninsula, is capable of absorbing so much moisture during its fairly short passage over the Red Sea that the annual precipitation in Massaua amounts to 188 mm, most of the rain falling in December and January.

The Levantine sirocco, which is to be the object of a more detailed description in the passages to follow, is as a rule warm and highly polluted by sand and dust. As we shall see later, the humidity may vary within very wide limits. The sirocco originating in the Arabian Peninsula and reaching the Levant as a southerly current should be very dry. On the other hand, the sirocco rising in Libya and Egypt and reaching the Levant from a southwesterly direction has to pass the area of the Mediterranean enclosed by Egypt, Cyprus and the Levant, and consequently becomes relatively damp. The wind speed is generally quite high and the duration of these winds varies from one or two hours to a day. The swiftness with which it rises and decreases is another of its characteristics. In less than an hour the wind can increase from absolute calm to 25–30 knots and sometimes even more.

Sirocco

The statements as to the frequency of sirocco in the eastern Mediterranean vary considerably as there is no clear and unambiguous definition of it. For example Zistler, basing his statement on a five year series, fixes their average at 41 per year, distributed among the following months:

Jan.	Febr.	March	April	May	June	July	Aug.	Sept.	Oct.	Nov.	Dec.
4	6	7	8	6	1	0	1	1	2	3	2

But, on the other hand, if we place confidence in the opinion of the characteristics of the sirocco generally accepted by the inhabitants in the areas concerned, we would have to reduce the number considerably, as far as the Levant is concerned. The characteristics the inhabitants ascribe to the sirocco are in some cases clear from the names given to it in different regions, and this should of course be a basis for a somewhat more scientific definition of it, provided the name does not directly contradict well-known facts. The common designation of "sirocco" can be derived from the Arabian word "shorq" or "sharkia," which means "east." "Sirocco" can thus be translated as "eastwind," which implies its pre-frontal character. This statement is of a very old date, for already in the Book of Jonah of the Old Testament the following lines will be found: "And it came to pass, when the sun did arise, that God prepared a vehement east wind, and the sun beat upon the head of Jonah, that he fainted. . . ."

Meteorological informations of a similar kind are to be found in other passages of the Bible as well. In Libya and Cyrenaika, on the other hand, they speak about "ghibli." This word can be derived from "Ghibla," which is the name given to the building in Mecca where the Black Stone —Ka'baa—is located. The direction towards this place from Libya and Cyrenaika is close to southerly or southeasterly, and the nearest meaning of "ghibli" in a free translation would then be "wind from Mecca", i.e., south- or southeastwind. Its pre-frontal character is thus made clear in this case as well. In the interior of Sahara and the Sudan, the inhabitants speak of "haboob." The proper sense of this word being "lift," it would refer to the consequence that the sand is whirled up rather than to the wind itself. In Syria and Saudi Arabia we find the designation "somoom," which implies something unwholesome or poisonous and is thus connected with the medical effects of this phenomenon. With some imagination we may perhaps also describe the orange tinge of the polluted air as "poisonous." Also "shlouch" is to be heard in the Levant, the word simply being the Arabian for a "hot wind." "Chamsin," finally, is the common designation in Egypt. Bearing in mind that "chamsin" is the Arabian for the number fifty, we shall perhaps find it difficult to discover in this word any characteristics of this weather phenomenon. The designation seems to come from an old Egyptian weather maxim stating that this weather type is most frequent during the fifty days following "Shemel Nessim," i.e., the Coptic Easter, which falls one day later than the Catholic.

The reduced visibility and the quality of the hydrometeors must be pointed out as the most important conservative characteristics. On the other hand, the values of temperature and humidity are as a rule significative only in the areas of origin, whereas outside these areas they may vary within very wide limits. This can also be applied to the wind speed, which, judging by experience, would amount to at least 25 knots in the areas or origin, or else the sand would not whirl up to such an extent that it causes an obvious reduction of the visibility. Based on this fact, Zistler's statistics can possibly be applied to the desert regions, but not to the Levant. Zistler speaks of a so-called "cold sirocco" blowing in winter. As the coastal regions of North Africa are comparatively cold by then, the southerly current in front of a depression is bound to be rather cold, at least in the beginning. But further southward the temperature rises fairly quickly, and provided the depression moves slowly enough, these warm air masses must gradually be drawn into the cyclonic circulation, thereby causing a striking rise of temperature in the coastal region. As the depressions move comparatively swiftly in winter, there is as a rule no rise of temperature. As for North Africa, however, the term "cold sirocco" is correct, as the significative reduction of the visibility, which is caused by sand and dust, generally occurs if the wind is strong enough. On the other hand the term cannot be applied to the Levant. The Mediterranean is warm in winter in comparison with the cold sirocco, which is consequently rapidly labilized at sea. The hydrometeors are thus washed away by the showers and the visibility improves considerably. In spite of the fact that the depressions are most active in winter, the sirocco is very rare in the Levant during this season. Only later in spring does the sirocco begin to assert itself, and a marked maximum of both its occurrence and intensity can be noticed during March and April. In autumn there is a secondary maximum during October and November. However, this distribution is opposed to the frequency of depressions, which is more active in autumn than in spring. Consequently there should be several other factors contributing to the maximum occurrence in the spring, and so it is quite natural that we should direct our attention southward to the intertropical convergence zone and its oscillations.

This zone, which on the whole follows the culmination of the sun, the phase being displaced four to six weeks only, extends during December and January exclusively in the southern hemisphere. In February it begins to advance towards the north, crosses the geographical equator in March or April, and has normally reached its northernmost limit in June. Generally speaking it then extends from Lake Tchad in the west via Khartoum to Port Sudan on the Red Sea coast. From there it turns off in a southeasterly direction along the Eritrean Mountains to the Gulf of Aden, where it deflects eastward. The pressure distribution under these conditions is characterized by a relatively deep low with its center somewhere about Port Sudan, from where a trough stretches towards Lake Tchad in the southwest, and towards a flat low over the southern part of Arabia. The currents under these conditions have been studied by El-Fandy in connection with the sirocco in Egypt. From the regions south of the equator—probably from both the Indian Ocean and the South Atlantic—moist air masses are transported toward the geographical equator, where the current turns eastward and reaches the intertropical convergence zone as the southwest monsoon. But the greater part of the moisture is delivered in the Ethiopian tableland and in the southern Sudan as orographic precipitation, whereby the monsoon further northwards gets the character of a warm and dry foehn current. East of the low at Port Sudan a southeasterly current predominates, which turning northward becomes the northeast trade wind. Over northern Egypt there is another zone of convergence, where the southeasterly current meets the colder Mediterranean air. Now and then there is under these conditions a certain increase of the intensity of the southwest monsoon, and this as a consequence causes the low at Port Sudan to oscillate northward. Thus the southeasterly current too pushes northward toward the colder Mediterranean air over the Nile delta.

9. Climate Made to Order

H. E. Landsberg

*Without question, the old saw attributed to Mark Twain,
"Everybody talks about the weather, but nobody does anything
about it," is becoming less true every day. As knowledge of
the atmosphere increases, so also does our ability to control
or at least influence local weather conditions. As a matter
of fact, the building you are living in constitutes an area of
made-to-order climate, limited to be sure, but nevertheless
ordered. Many of the things Landsberg suggests may lie
well in the future, but such developments sometimes take
place rapidly. The ability to alter weather and climate at
will over large areas of the earth's surface is bound to
have profound effects on all patterns of human activity on
the earth and may have significant geopolitical consequences
as well.*

Could a dam across the Bering Strait change the earth's climate? What
would we do if climatic changes engineered by scientists didn't work
out the way the scientists thought they would? Have atomic bombs
changed the weather? These questions are no longer mere matters for
idle speculation. Now that man has moved, over millennia, from his
tropical habitat to all parts of the globe, it would be a good thing if the
entire global climate could be made comfortable and pleasant.

We have engineered ourselves into some quite unpleasant places.
Clothing, housing, and heating have helped us to survive the rigors of
winter in the far north and far south. Air conditioning, open architec-
ture, and irrigation have made possible survival and agriculture in areas
whose temperatures would be very uncomfortable, and even lethal, in
many places. Transportation improvements have made it possible to dis-
tribute in quantity fuel and food to locales which cannot supply their
own. Transportation improvements have also made it possible to ship
out from these areas the raw materials, manufactured goods, or agricultural products which have made settlement in these unfriendly
places desirable.

But, although we can warm ourselves before oil staves in snug
quonsets in Antarctica, or sit in comfort in a cool air-conditioned room
in the desert, we are still tied to natural conditions for many resources.

SOURCE: *Bulletin of the Atomic Scientists* (November, 1961), 370–74. Copyright
1961 by the Educational Foundation for Nuclear Science, Inc., and reprinted with
their permission. The author is Director, Office of Climatology, U.S. Weather
Bureau.

Trees are restricted to suitable climates; so are all our crop plants. Livestock depends on local food sources, since it is rarely profitable to ship feed for long distances. Fishery has climatic controls in fresh water, in ocean bays, on the open seas. The vagaries of wind and weather control the production of all these resources. And, as yet, we cannot air-condition a whole desert, nor can we heat the soil of a frozen continent. Storms lash towns and cities, sink boats, and delay transportation, and we are far from being able to control or even to predict the destruction that may be wreaked.

The restless spirit of inquiry has been chafing under these conditions for some time. Could we not become completely independent of the climate? It seems as if climate control is a rather unequal struggle, because we are trying to pit our puny terrestrial energies against the tremendous stellar energies of the sun. On the average, 2.8×10^{18} calories per minute arrive from this source. By reflection, scattering, and absorption of this heat within the atmosphere and at the earth's surface, the general circulation of the atmosphere is set into motion. Large wind systems, the trades, the monsoons, the westerlies, are created at the surface. Aloft the meandering swift currents of the jet streams transport enormous masses of air in an unending stream around the globe. These currents are never steady; they are always turbulent. Eddies, from small whirls to enormous storm systems, change potential to kinetic energy, which is dissipated in friction. Within this system of motion is another complex system of tranformations of energy, the evaporation of water and transformation back again to water or ice. A rough estimate shows that this water cycle involves an annual energy transaction of 3×10^{22} calories. What can we pit against the solar energy, the energy of storms, the vapor transformations? Even nuclear energies now at our disposal dwindle into insignificance. A measly local thunderstorm transforms more energy than a half dozen 20-kiloton nuclear bomb explosions. And there are 10^4 thunderstorms per day on earth.

In spite of the huge energies involved in climate, many people think man already has changed the earth's climate. Since prehistoric times, every weather catastrophe—flood or drought, hurricane frequency or a change in its tracks, tornado incidence or torrential downpours—has been blamed on human interference. In prescientific times, the "interference" was sometimes considered to be action displeasing to the gods. During the Civil War, and even during World War I, the cannonades were supposed to be the culprits. Lately, nuclear explosions have been blamed for moving hurricanes into populated areas on the east coast of the U.S., despite the fact that they had been occurring there long before the atomic age, and have occurred there since the test moratorium went into effect. None of these imputed relations can stand up to objective calculations and statistical tests.

Circular Row of Dominos

Despite the huge energies involved in climate and weather processes, many ideas have been advanced for producing climatic changes. Some of them are disarmingly simple, and appear to have a scientific basis. Others disregard the magnitudes of energies, and are unlikely to work. Ideas for climatic change fall mainly into two areas: interference with the heat balance (transport of heat), or interference with the water balance of the atmosphere. It appears easiest to change the surface albedo (reflectivity) to cause changes in the heat balance. If there is greater reflection of radiation, there will be a general cooling; if less, general heating. Increasing the absorption of radiation has been advocated for changing the global climate. If the ice and snowfields (especially the poles) could be made to reflect less sunlight back into space, there would be general heating; ice would melt, and areas now exposed to the cold polar blasts would be warmed.

But how could we darken the whole Antarctic continent? Any new snowfall would provide a reflecting surface, and in any case, the cost of putting the poles to bed under a huge blanket would probably be prohibitive. The effects of polar windstorms would have to be taken into account also, which would mean that the "blanket" would have to be pegged down in some way. These difficulties are among the reasons why such a scheme for climate change would be impractical. Another reason is that the rise in ocean level (from the melting ice) would flood low-lying coastal areas. The problem of meltwater remains unsolved for variants of the "blanket" scheme, one of which calls for maintenance of a cloud cover over glaciated areas during the polar night to reduce outgoing radiation. No one yet has come forth with a practical scheme for maintaining such a cloud, even if it could be produced initially by suitable nuclei or vaporization of seawater (possibly by nuclear energy). Another plan for general heating is a space mirror which would focus more solar energy on various points on earth.

The Gibraltar and Bering Dams

To come down to earth, a dam across the Bering Strait has been advocated. Such a dam is supposed to assure ocean circulation in the Artic basin of warmer Atlantic waters which would melt the sea ice. While this could help ocean traffic between Alaska and Siberia, there are both meteorological and oceanographic reasons why it probably would not work. The warmer but saltier water from the Atlantic would be heavier than the cold water of the Arctic Ocean, which would have its mineral content diluted by water from melted ice, and hence would form a lower layer and contribute very little to melting of ice. Even if the winter temperature were raised in the Arctic, the outgoing radiation during the Arctic night, which increases with the fourth power of the temperature, would quickly cause return to lower values. Calculations show that the net effect of the Bering Strait dam would be only a fraction of a degree centigrade.

Another enormous engineering program is a Gibraltar dam. This would raise the water level in the Mediterranean Sea, and desalted water might then be pumped from the Mediterranean into the Sahara region for a huge irrigation project. This scheme would produce a regional, rather than global, climatic change, but if it proved successful, similar attempts might be instituted to water all the world's desert regions—at least those near enough an ocean to make the idea practicable. Irrigation of the fertile, unused soil of the Sahara region would unquestionably be useful, so the success of such desert irrigation plans depends on economic feasibility and technological limitations, such as those limiting a large salt-to-fresh water conversion program.

Have we already produced, unwittingly, global climatic changes? It has been argued that we have, by pouring carbon dioxide from combustion processes into the atmosphere on a large scale. The effect, if it is such, is a possible slight overall warming, of perhaps a fraction of a degree centigrade, and even this is in dispute. If there is such an effect, it is certainly uncontrolled, and hence no model for action. The possible effect of increasing the percentage of atmospheric carbon dioxide on plant and animal life is also uncertain.

When we are changing the climate of the whole world, a mistake could be disastrous. Even if the total effects had been calculated, there might be local effects that would create many economic, political, and social problems. Variations in the general circulation that might make the weather better in one area would probably make it worse in others, even if large-scale climatic changes should be proved feasible.

However, it is possible that the consequences of interfering with normal atmospheric circulation could be estimated by computers handling mathematical models. Equations that show atmospheric motion as resulting from simple assumptions about energy gains and losses have been worked out. We can play a theoretical game with these assumptions, predicting what changes in the flow pattern would result from changes in the initial assumptions, or from interference with the natural course of events. These theoretical manipulations should provide a model that would show the probable consequences of any proposed scheme of change. This theoretical approach, while not yet perfected, is quite feasible, and certainly much cheaper than possibly futile small-scale experiments.

Weather Control

While sweeping global climate changes appear to be some distance in the future, on a smaller scale there are both more possible ways of making changes and better chances of success. Included among what might be termed large small-scale changes are those dealing with weather control. These embrace instantaneous manifestations of the atmosphere rather than the more or less permanent condition of the air environment termed climate. At critical stages in the development of circulation patterns, interference might have a good effect.

Examples of such interference have included dissipating incipient hurricanes (one group advocates doing this by exploding hydrogen bombs!) or deflecting their courses. Advocates of this mainly think of cloud seeding to sway the thermodynamic balance by interfering with the condensation-evaporation-precipitation process of the storm, and possibly by releasing the latent heat at human command, rather than at the rate ordained by nature. The mathematical model approach should precede experiment, since the processes are too complicated to permit judgment of their feasibility.

Also on a regional scale, it has been proposed to feed the southwest monsoon of the summer season in West Africa with additional moisture. This is certainly one of the most intriguing schemes because it is meteorologically sound. The moisture added to the air might be precipitated and evaporated several times over the whole region, and could beneficially affect the semiarid savannah regions. But its success depends critically on the availability of cheap energy to evaporate the water.

More localized weather control schemes include dissipation of hail by cloud seeding, and elimination of lightning in areas where it causes forest fires. Experiments for both of these are being done, but there are no definitive results. In contrast, the dissipation of supercooled water fogs and stratus clouds by dry ice seeding has been highly successful.

Cloud seeding to increase local rainfall has been experimented with for two decades. It is generally conceded that much earlier effort was wasted because adequate statistical controls were lacking. Although the mechanisms of seeding have been backed up by laboratory results and by theory, the quantitative aspects are still in doubt. It is true that under favorable conditions of updraft we can wring some additional rain from clouds in the vicinity, if there are any clouds there. But there are widely differing opinions on how much this increase actually is. Nor is it certain whether this is a net increase in rainfall or whether it robs some area downwind. More knowledge of the microphysics of cloud particles is likely to lead to more predictable results. Cloud seeding seems to be a most hopeful area for further research. It would certainly be important to be able to control where rain falls, even if we cannot control the total amount. In areas with limited rainfall, if clouds could be made to dump their rain over the fields and settled areas, instead of passing these by and raining on barren areas, this would make cloud seeding economically worthwhile. The energy needed to seed a cloud is relatively small—just that required to get an airplane with seeding material above the cloud layer. But there are some limitations. There must be an adequate moisture supply and suitable vertical air motion. Where mountains or convection supplied the necessary updraft, cloud seeding might in the foreseeable future be reduced to an engineering routine.

Atmospheric resonance effects, to produce large changes with small energy expenditure, have also been advocated. Resonance effects require that the phenomena to be affected have characteristic periods over large-scale fluctuations. There are some climatic oscillations which have short periods and seem to be inertial, but stimulation of these would scarcely produce climatic effects. There may be oscillations with longer periods for which the atmosphere shows a preference but does not always follow. One of these seems to be an intermittent seven-day rhythm found in meteorological data such as rainfall reports. Reinforcing such a rhythm could be valuable, assuring rain-free weekends and rainy Wednesdays to replenish water supplies. Interference with periodic rhythms, though not inconceivable, is still very much a matter of speculation, especially since it has not even been certainly established that there *are* such rhythms.

Local Changes

The story is quite different when it comes to small-scale conditions. Here we deal with problems of mesoclimate or microclimate. These spot conditions have been modified in various ways, and the process of modification is well understood. Climate in cities has been changed on a sizable smale. This is not deliberate and certainly not an improvement generally. The worst aspect of urbanization and industrialization is the change in composition of local atmosphere, as noxious substances have been added to it. These changes have decreased solar radiation and increased fog. There are ways out of the smog and fog, most of them regulatory or engineering. Among the latter are electrification of all traffic and the installation of smoke sewers.

Among other notable city climate changes are a slight increase in precipitation and a notable increase in night temperatures. The former is probably in part a result of the pollutants. There are changes in the electric field and the humidity, and a reduction of wind speed. In the megalopolis of the future these effects are likely to be multiplied. Adequate ventilation is a serious problem, especially where stagnant air conditions are common. Open construction and green spaces are helpful but probably not sufficient for coping with the progress of urbanization.

In the rural areas fairly noticeable local climatic changes can be brought about by windbreaks. Their interference at the lowest layer of the atmosphere increases the terrain roughness and reduces low-level wind speed. It decreases snow accumulations on lee slopes and, in general, reduces evaporation of moisture from the soil. Where ample water is available, redistribution either by canals, or pipes and sprinklers can cause beneficial microclimatic changes. Temperatures can be reduced because of increased evaporation, and moisture can be supplied when and where needed. Artificial lakes can be helpful as reservoirs and equalizers of water supplies from wet to dry seasons. On a small scale, they also modify temperatures and humidities in their environments, usually helping to level temperature extremes. Monomolecular films of cetyl alcohol or similar substances can reduce water evaporation losses from lakes and reservoirs. Where strong winds disrupt the films frequently, their cost may be fairly substantial.

Microclimatic changes as results of deforestation and reforestation can be quite noticeable. In either case a rather radical change in surface is involved. By and large deforestation leads to a wide swing of temperatures, faster runoff, increase in evaporation, lower humidity, and higher wind speeds. Reforestation on the other hand reduces temperature extremes, retards runoff, increases humidity, and reduces wind speeds. There is some tenuous evidence for increase in rainfall after extended reforestation, but this is not uncontested.

Make Your Own Climate

There is a long list of microclimatic remedies to improve the conditions of the spot climate in gardens, orchards, vineyards, on farms, and around houses. Best known are the many devices which attempt to forestall frost damage. These include artificial fog to cut down outgoing radiation; direct heating by fires, steam pipes, or buried cables; wind machines to mix upper warm and lower cold air; and using fine spray on fruit to take advantage of the heat of fusion. Soil moisture can be conserved and changes in soil temperature effected by suitable covers and mulches. Polystyrene covers have permitted quite radical changes in protection of valuable crops. Highly reflective aluminum foil can keep soil temperatures in sunny climates low and will also reflect more light to plants, thus aiding the photosynthetic process. Even simply changing the slope of the land by appropriate tilling can have good effects in areas with low solar incidence. In other areas appropriate shading by trees or thin netting may help some crops.

Aside from mechanical devices, literally dozens of procedures are available to change the microclimate in a house. Suitably placed hedges, shade trees, and ponds can help to mitigate extreme conditions. Proper orientation, paints, roof pitch, and window size can create more comfortable conditions indoors. Mechanical devices do the rest. Well-planned houses and towns can make the most of favorable aspects of local climate and mitigate those considered unfavorable.

Intelligent pooling of climatological knowledge with engineering practices will help to modify local climates. On a scale from a few square miles to 10^3 or even 10^4 square miles climatic modifications are feasible (hopefully) with energies within our reach. The ratio of cost to benefit will govern the practicality of such changes. We will be able to calculate the effects of suggested changes on a large scale by mathematical procedures. Since the earth has about 2×10^8 square miles of surface, all of them participating in the stupendous energy exchanges that take place in the atmosphere, there are no immediate prospects for interference on a large scale in climatic conditions. Even an area the size of the United States (3.6×10^6 square miles) is still far beyond the order of magnitude for which an effect of any duration can be foreseen. Because of the enormous areas and energies involved, the restoring forces are also tremendous and would quickly return conditions to the *status quo ante* even if present conditions could be upset for a brief period.

III. LANDFORMS

Despite his increasing capability of traveling and, indeed, living in the air and in space as well as under the sea, man remains essentially a land animal. Yet the land surface of the earth amounts to slightly less than 30 per cent of its total, and the differentiation of this into continents and islands, and into surface configuration as well, constitutes another great area of study in the field of physical geography. The arrangement of these land features and their relationship to the underlying geologic structure is often called geomorphology or physiography (the latter is the older term). Entailed in a study of landforms is their description, classification, and genesis. Such study of landforms is important to the real differentiation of the world—a major objective of geographic study.

Current and past changes of the earth's surface demonstrate that its nature is dynamic. Internal processes such as frequent volcanic eruptions and earthquakes affect the surface of the earth; surface inequalities resulting from these processes are constantly being acted upon by the external gradational forces of weathering and erosion. The sum total of all these surface-shaping processes is not the same in any two regions of the world; hence the tremendous variety of landforms.

As in the case of his colleague studying the atmosphere, the physical geographer has attempted effectively, along with his geologist colleagues, to bring scientific order to what may appear superficially random and chaotic distributions of land and landforms, large and small. Nevertheless, there is a sense of order and pattern in landforms, whether in the processes of their development or their distribution on the surface of the earth. This "logic of the landscape" is particularly well exemplified in the selections following, which consider a wide variety of landform types, processes, and effects. Many of them offer evidence, based on field work, of some of the conceptual materials usually presented in textbooks. In nearly all of these articles, the role or even the presence of man on the earth is not a matter of primary consideration. Yet it is perfectly evident throughout this section that landforms, whatever their scale and distribution, are important to man in carrying on his varied activities.

10. The Origin of Continents

Marshall Kay

The origin of the greatest of land masses, the continents, remains still a subject of widespread controversy among scientists. It would be well to recognize that, despite our great knowledge of many things about the earth, we can be positive about very little concerning the subsurface character of the earth—conditions obtaining only a very few miles down from where we are now sitting. Professor Kay has gathered and synthesized present knowledge concerning the great differences between the origin of the continental land masses that stand above the sea and that of the sea floors. The evidence of the rocks, he theorizes, shows that the great land masses grew by cycles in which chains of volcanoes rose from the sea and sediment washed into their flanks.

The continents and the ocean basins are distinctly different aspects of the earth's crust. Not only do the continents stand higher, but they are made of different material. The difference can be summed up roughly in two chemical terms: sialic and simatic. The continents are composed chiefly of sialic (for silica-alumina) rock, which is especially rich in silica and comparatively light in weight and color; the ocean basins are mainly simatic (silica-magnesium) rock, which is denser and darker. Because granite is the chief sialic rock and basalt the chief simatic one, the continents are most commonly described as granitic and the ocean basins as basaltic.

For decades it has been realized that any attempt to explain the origin of the continents and the oceans must account for this fundamental difference in the respective portions of the earth crust. Many hypotheses have been erected on theories as to how the earth itself was formed. Those who supposed that the earth grew by the coming together of small, cold bodies (planetesimals) reasoned that the difference between the oceanic and continental parts of the crust was due to chemical evolution: the areas covered with water developed differently from those exposed to the atmosphere. The much larger school who believe that the earth was originally a molten mass have suggested a great variety of other explanations. Many have argued that the cooling earth was once crusted over its whole surface with a thin layer of granitic

SOURCE: *Scientific American*, September, 1955, pp. 2–6. Reprinted with permission. Copyright © 1955 by Scientific American, Inc. All rights reserved. Available separately at twenty cents as offprint No. 816 from W. H. Freeman Company, 660 Market Street, San Francisco, California. The author is professor of geology at Columbia University.

material, and that this layer was later parted in places to expose the basalt underneath—either by gradual drifts of the granitic material which piled it in continents, or by catastrophic events, such as a great oscillation that tore a chunk out of the earth and threw it into space as the moon, leaving the hole that is now the Pacific Ocean. Others have proposed that the entire earth was originally basaltic, and that the separation of ingredients to form the differentiated oceanic and continental areas was started by deformations of the earth's outer layers. Still others have suggested that the granitic rocks crystallized and floated to the top as the molten earth cooled.

Many of these hypotheses have collapsed in the face of new information about the crust and the interior of the earth obtained during the past decade. The question as to how the continents and oceans were formed is approached by geologists from the opposite direction: instead of starting with speculations about the beginning of the earth and projecting hypotheses from those speculations, they start from the known facts about the present earth and work backward to reconstruct its unknown history. What we know about the continents and oceans gives us a number of clues for deducing their past.

Our firsthand information about the inside of the earth of course is still scanty: it is limited to studies of surface rocks, to soundings and samples of the ocean bottoms and to borings some four miles down into the earth's crust in mines and wells. But in recent years explorers of the interior have probed the earth deeply and intensively with revealing instruments. Foremost among them is the seismograph. Tracing the travel of waves from earthquakes and artificial explosions through the earth, timing their speed and plotting their paths, it has been possible to obtain a kind of X-ray picture of the earth's layered body. And this picture has been confirmed and filled in to some extent by gravity measurements which define areas and belts of differing density.

About three fourths of our planet is covered by ocean waters, but not all of that is actually oceanic basin, for the continents have broad shelves extending far out under a wash of shallow sea. The deep ocean basins— two miles or more below water level—account for about half of the earth's solid surface. These are the areas of the earth's crust that show a sharp contrast to the continents.

The conventional division between the crust and the "interior" of the earth is a boundary known as the Mohorovicic discontinuity—a transition zone between crystalline, basaltic rock and denser, noncrystalline rock beneath. This boundary is not level: it is lower under the continents than under the oceans. In other words, the continents not only stand higher but also plunge deeper into the dense sublayer. It is as if the crust of the earth consists of relatively light but thick continental blocks and thinner but denser oceanic blocks, both of which float on the substratum of the interior. As measured by the seismic yardstick, the continental blocks are some 30 miles thick and the oceanic basins only about six or eight miles thick. The continental blocks are not granitic all the way down: at their base they have a layer of basalt, like the rock of the ocean basins.

Now to this general picture there are certain exceptions which look extremely significant. Some areas of the earth crust are neither strictly continental nor strictly oceanic—they seem to combine a little of both! These areas are the island archipelagoes: the islands of Japan; the chain consisting of the Philippines, the East Indies and New Guinea; nearer home, the West Indies. The principal islands in such chains have a dominantly continental character: their rock is chiefly granitic and the crust goes deeper than in the ocean basins. Yet each chain also includes parts which are dominantly oceanic; that is, they are underlain by a thin layer of basaltic rock (covered with sediments) and the crust is comparatively shallow. Gravity readings show long, sinuous bands of gravity deficiency, usually along the submarine troughs associated with the island chains. Seismic studies indicate that the island rock does not pass beneath the troughs. Apparently the gravity deficiency is due to the thinness of the crust under the trenches rather than to any downfold of granitic rock.

The island archipelagoes, then, are something intermediate between ocean basins and continents. Are they, perhaps, embryo continents in the process of growing up to become larger continents or additions to continents in the future? The question sends us back to examine the rocks of continents with a fresh eye and a hypothesis to investigate. Let us consider the North American continent. What light does the distribution of its various rocks throw on how the continent may have been formed?

The surface of a continent has two general classes of rocks (if we disregard the volcanic rocks, formed from lavas erupted onto the surface here and there). The first great class is the sedimentary rocks—the hardened remnants of sediments laid down by ancient rivers and seas. These are the sandstones, limestones, shales, marls and clays that cover much of our continent. In the central plains they lie in flat layers under the surface soil; in the mountain regions the layers may be tilted, warped, folded and broken, but the rock still has the same character and is unmistakably identified as sediment by the fossil remains of sea animals. These are the rocks that the prospector's drill probes in search of oil and gas. Along the Atlantic Coast the sedimentary rock is only a few thousand feet thick, but at the Gulf Coast in Texas and Louisiana it is piled to a depth of as much as eight to 10 miles.

If we peeled off the sedimentary layers, we would find below, mantling the whole continent, the second great class of rocks. This class includes two types: (1) the "plutonic" or "igneous" rocks, notably granite, and (2) the "metamorphic" rocks—schists, gneisses, quartzites, slates. The metamorphic rocks evidently are sedimentary rocks and lavas altered by heat and pressure. Just how the granites and other igneous rocks are formed is still a matter of debate; there is strong new evidence that they crystallize from molten magma deep in the crust. . . . In any case, the metamorphic and igneous rocks are generally found together. And wherever we may go on the continents, if we drill deep enough, we will find these rocks forming a "basement" beneath the sedimentary cover.

There are three large areas of North America where the granites and metamorphic rocks are not buried but form the surface of the continent. The first is a broad, circular region around Hudson Bay in Canada, extending east to the coast of Labrador and south into Minnesota, Wisconsin and New York, where the granitic and metamorphic basement disappears under layers of sedimentary rock and slopes down gradually to its greatest depth at the Gulf Coast. The second belt lies along the Atlantic Coast from central Newfoundland to the Piedmont. The third is on the Pacific Coast from southern Alaska to the tip of Lower California.

This picture is somewhat simplified: parts of the Pacific Coast are covered by sedimentary rocks, and platforms of granite and metamorphic rocks appear in other, smaller, areas of the continent besides the three large ones mentioned. But if we concentrate our attention on these three great areas, we discover some significant relations which bear on the origin of continents.

In the belts along the Atlantic and Pacific Coast, we can read in these rocks the record of a long series of moutain-building events, marked by the sinking of deep troughs in the crust and the rise of lands nearby. The troughs were deep enough to catch and pile up miles of sediments and volcanic rock, poured in from adjoining volcanoes. The sediments contain pebbles which must have been washed into them by streams eroding rather rugged lands. And they were invaded by granitic rocks and fluids which transformed them into metamorphic rocks. Moreover, some of the rocks along both the Pacific and Atlantic Coast have intrusions of very basic rocks (unusually poor in silica) which must have come from considerable depth—peridotites and serpentines, including such rocks as the verd antique marble found in Vermont.

Several lines of evidence indicate that these belts of metamorphosed sediments and volcanic rocks with intrusions are the descendants of belts like the present island chains. (Indeed, the Pacific Coast belt still has an island arc—the Aleutians—extending from its northern end!) So we may deduce that the North American continent has grown on its western and eastern sides by the addition of what were once separate island archipelagoes. The period of upheaval and deformation that formed these additions to the continent seems to have ended, though there is still some unrest along the Pacific Coast. Dating events by the fossils and the radioactivity of rocks, it is judged that the time of principal activity along the Atlantic Coast ended about 200 million years ago, and along the Pacific Coast, perhaps 100 million years ago.

Let us return to the great shield of igneous and metamorphic rocks that covers central Canada. It, too, has granite and granitelike rocks which invaded and altered sediments and lavas. Hence, by analogy, it likewise should once have been an island belt margining the continent. But the rocks are now in the midst of the continent—in fact, as we have seen, the whole continent basement is made of such rocks. How, then, did the continent begin? Did it start as a single small island and grow by addition of island belts? We might be able to answer that question if we had dates for all the intrusive rocks of the continent, so that we could tell whether the central ones are oldest and surrounded by successively younger belts. There do seem to be belts of progressively younger intrusions around the central part of the Canadian shield. But on the other hand there are dated rocks that seem pretty old in far-flung parts of the continent—such as Colorado and Texas. So probably it is not as simple as one might like it to be. A working hypothesis is that the continent has grown from volcanic island belts which were formerly separated by subsiding, sediment-collecting troughs.

It seems that in the beginning all was ocean, from which the continents began to rise as small lands. Perhaps stresses upon the surface of the original whole-ocean earth caused it to buckle, producing troughs, ridges, folds and fissures. The more volatile or acidic or silicic constituents of the fluid rock beneath the surface may have concentrated in the original uplifts. Weathering by the oxygen-rich atmosphere may then have segregated the more acid material of these ridges in sediments. The silicic sediments, deposited along the edges of the raised lands, would have formed the first sialic areas on the earth.

The big question—how the continents became sialic—is full of difficulties and uncertainties. Seemingly the great long-term troughs in the crust of the earth, where thick deposits of sediments and volcanic rocks collect, are in some manner invaded by the underlying magma. Either the rising masses of fluid magma displace these rocks and themselves crystallize as granite, or their fluids and gases transform the existing deposits into granitelike rock. The popular hypothesis for the past decade has been that the furrows plunge so deeply into the substratum that the temperatures and pressures are sufficient to fuse the rocks and force fluids into them from below. Yet an invasion of this kind can hardly account directly for the production of sialic rock, since the substratum seems extremely dense and low in silica. Perhaps the process is roundabout: first sedimentary rocks, made more silicic than the original rocks by weathering, are laid in the troughs; then they are deeply buried, become fluid and eventually emerge as igneous magma which we no longer recognize as the original sedimentary and volcanic rock.

Any convincing hypothesis of the origin of the continents and oceans must be consistent with a reasonable theory concerning the origin of the earth itself. Geologists can be judges only of the end of this beginning—the time when the earth began to inscribe a permanent history in rock. The theories of the origin of the earth have been principally the inventions of astrophysicists, celestial mechanics and physical chemists, for the problems lie in those fields. The geologist is concerned only that the result be an earth which conforms to what can be deduced from the earliest known rocks.

Our knowledge of the earth has expanded tremendously in the past decade. Some old hypotheses have had to be abandoned; intriguing new ones are taking their place and will be tested in the next decade by geologists, geochemists and geophysicists all over the world.

11. Single Land Mass?
U. S. Geologists Reexamine Continental Drift Theory
Christian Science Monitor

The amount of land and water on the earth's surface, the nature of the surface of continents and ocean basins, and the world position of the continents and the oceans are fundamental to an understanding of the world and the nature and distribution of its major landforms. Geologists generally agree that the continental surfaces are composed of lighter rock than the heavier oceanic basins. The loss of the moon from the Pacific Basin probably accounts for heavier materials being found there than in the other ocean basins. Geologists also usually accept the theory that the earth's interior is a molten, plastic, or viscous mass. The continental-drift theory has been proposed to explain the present position of land masses. This much-discussed theory postulates a world island that fractured into continental blocks; these blocks "drifted" on underlying plastic material to their present positions, owing, perhaps, to the force of earth rotation or to their attempts to achieve better balance on the earth's surface. This theory may explain the hemispheric land area differences, the present location of continents, and the shapes of continents and ocean basins. It has been largely discounted by United

States geologists but recent evidence summarized in this
article adds new support to the theory.

Startling changes are being considered in the outlook of American geology toward current theories explaining how continents got their form and structure.

Earth scientists are polishing up their best arguments on the hypothesis that existing continents were once a single land mass until unknown forces set them adrift some 180,000,000 years ago.

Several generations of school children now are familiar with the exercise of fitting continental cutouts together so the nose of South America nestles into the Gulf of Guinea; North America swings over to match up with Europe; and Australia, New Zealand, and Antarctica fit in at the south in the Indian Ocean.

Much Research Done

This was the supercontinent of Gondwana, or Gondwanaland, insofar as many overseas geomorphologists are concerned. But the geography seldom led much farther on this side of the Atlantic where geologists Schuchert, Bailey Willis, and J. W. Gregory gave the "continental drift" theory short shrift.

Lecturing before various groups of researchers of the American Association of Petroleum Geologists in 1951 and 1952, Dr. Lester C. King, University of Natal geologist from Durban, South Africa, noted "a new spirit of impartial inquiry and broad outlook" in his United States audiences. As a result, the AAPG, which now is finding room in its Journal for up-to-the-minute reports on South American geology, especially in Peru and Venezuela, is also running a series on "The Necessity for Continental Drift," by Dr. King.

Because a great deal of research has been done on this subject since World War II, and there is need for much more, Dr. King says he feels the time is peculiarly opportune for re-examining basic evidence.

While following the works of Taylor, Baker, Wegener, du Toit, Robert, Leonardos, Fermor and Windhausen in the main, Dr. King reassembles the continents a bit differently than his predecessors.

Based on the present distribution of late Paleozoic and Triassic land formations, including glacial deposits and coals, Dr. King swings Antarctica much farther north into the Indian Ocean than others have done and visualizes Australia as having executed a counterclockwise turning movement of about 90 degrees while drifting eastward following continental dissolution.

SOURCE: *Christian Science Monitor*, December 3, 1953, p. 3. Reprinted by permission from *The Christian Science Monitor*. Copyright 1953 by The Christian Science Publishing Society. All rights reserved.

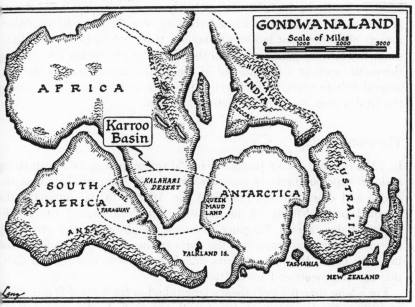

FIGURE 1: Some natural scientists theorize that "existing continents were once single land mass until unknown forces set them adrift some 180,000,000 years ago." This map, based on restoration by Lester C. King, South African geologist, shows how the coastlines might be fitted together to substantiate that view. This supercontinent was called Gondwana or Gondwanaland.

He traces Africa's Great Karroo basin from a western beginning in Brazil, Paraguay, and Uruguay, across a sizable area of South Africa to Queen Maud Land in Antarctica.

Land Beyond Continents

Both driftists and nondriftists agree that at some time in the past there must have been land beyond the boundaries of the present continents. But it is in the manner of deriving these lands that the cleavage of opinion has come about. Some geologists backcast a time when deep ocean floors were elevated as land masses. Driftists say the movement was not vertical but horizontal. They point out that the continents are built of light material that cannot sink and disappear in the ocean depths; that all the evidence from earthquake measurements of the constitution of the oceanic floors indicates (in the main) only heavy magmatic material.

The lighter (sialic) continents thus float above the heavier material (sima) of the oceanic floors, just as a raft floats on water. Like rafts the continents are seen capable of drifting horizontally.

Historically, Francis Bacon discussed "continental drift" as early as

1620. F. B. Taylor in 1908 was probably the first geologist to attempt
to outline the problem in an orderly way. For 30 years he published
reports of studies that led him to believe that back in Cretaceous time
some 180,000,000 years ago when the age of giant reptiles was ending
the earth captured a satellite out of space (the moon) and for the next
several million years, he said, giant tides rose and fell on earth, causing
the land masses to be pulled hither and yon.

Theories Tested

In 1911 Howard Baker presented his "displacement globe" postulating
a single supercontinent or pangaea which split from Alaska across the
Arctic and down the full length of the Atlantic to the Antarctic, the
unequal parts drifting off in opposite directions toward the Pacific
region. Later, Alfred Wegener, German geophysicist, put prevailing
theories to test and assembled the parts in the working hypothesis that
bears his name. He quoted astronomical observations to support a claim
that the continents still are drifting.

For a long time the drift theory languished in the United States. Then
in 1948 at the University of Cincinnati, Dr. K. E. Caster reopened the
question following four years of geological work in South America
where he traveled thousands of miles gathering data under auspices of
the United States Department and the Guggenheim Foundation.

"None of my findings in South America definitely proves or disproves
the drift hypothesis," he says, "but they are significant enough to war
rant additional field studies in South Africa, India, and Australia to
make necessary comparisons."

Patterns Correlated

It was the late Alexander L. du Toit, another noted South African
geologist, presenting a mass of detailed data published by the Carnegie
Institution of Washington in 1927, who showed Africa to be "the key
to the whole problem," the heart of ancient Gondwanaland.

Dr. du Toit stressed fossil relationships that indicated a widespread
similarity of flora and fauna in the days before separation, increasing
diversity since. Ten years later he presented a more finished work, "Our
Wandering Continents."

He worked out beautiful correlations of fracture patterns as shown b
the location and direction of sea deeps and rift valleys. He found foss
evidence and living species of plants and animals native to the Falkland
Islands, South America, and South Africa, but known nowhere else in
the world.

Following his own work in South America, Dr. Caster revised d

Toit's work as it was published, translating this into Portuguese for the benefit of Brazilian geologists studying these problems.

In the current AAPG Bulletin, Dr. King calls attention to the manner in which the Great Karroo basin is cut off at both the east and west coasts of South Africa, asserting that this is evidence that widespread land areas formerly extended in those directions.

"Useful Hypothesis"

"The conditions of accumulation of the Karroo beds resembled those of the existing Kalahari basin" he says, "about which extend broad plains and uplands from which was supplied the detritus that accumulated in the basin.

"But the Karroo basin was on a vastly greater scale: the basin stretches beyond the borders of Africa to an unknown distance on both east and west; and the marginal lands beyond that, which supplied the sediment (maximum thickness of terrestrial sediments approaching 20,000 feet) must have been of continental dimensions."

Dr. King expresses amazement that "so useful an hypothesis should have been allowed to fall into neglect or provoke such violent opposition in other quarters." The arguments advanced by some opponents, he says, that similar fossil species and similar geologic sequences in sundered regions such as South America and South Africa are "merely fortuitous," amounts "to a negation of the scientific method. It denies the attempt to classify like data and to generalize from them. . . .

"The conception of drift harmonizes completely with what is known of the physical condition of the earth's crust: high-standing lighter continents, deeper, heavier oceanic sectors, isostacy (general equilibrium in the earth's crust) involving horizontal transfer of material at depth, the existence of at least one level of no strain."

Corroborative Evidence

The hypothesis of drift is not to be proved by idle armchair theorizing, but by hard work in the field, he concludes. Physicists and chemists insist that if an experiment is to be accepted it must be repeatable.

Therefore, "in the rocks that can be seen, sectioned, measured, hammered, and compared, individually and in sequence, structurally and in age, by anyone who cares, lies the geologist's repeatable experiment."

Also appearing in the same issue of the Bulletin is corroborative evidence offered by D. L. Niddrie of the University of Manchester, England, who recently visited the Falkland Islands and made comparisons between the rocks and fossils of South Africa, Uruguay, and the Islands.

He had been stationed previously as a Naval Meteorological Officer at Simonstown Naval Base (Cape Province), and later had access to geological museum collections in Montevideo. Gondwana and pre-Gondwana rocks and fossils were studied and many of the conclusions of Dr. du Toit were verified. For convenience he summarizes the rock types and sequences in tabular form.

12. Linear Topography in the Southwestern Palouse, Washington-Oregon

Peirce F. Lewis

In this study—which, incidentally, won a $1,000 prize for scholarly papers given by the Association of American Geographers—Professor Lewis undertakes to explain a peculiar pattern of hills and valleys found in a part of the Columbia River basin. He raises questions of the origin of the materials forming the hills: Is the unique linear arrangement of these landforms the result of wind or of stream action? If the answer to this can be found, does it explain the present topography? Finally, if explanations are devised, are they consistent with field work results discovered in similar areas of other parts of the world? In short, this is an outstanding example of the geographer—a scientist—at work.

The Palouse region of the Columbia Basin is an area of rolling loessial hills which differs conspicuously from the mountains and basaltic scablands which surround it. Within the Palouse, however, there are major topographic differences. The northeastern part is an area of stream-dissected topography in a mature stage of erosional development, and the drainage pattern is characteristically dendritic. In the southwest, by contrast, topography is markedly aligned, with a system of linear hills and valleys trending approximately N. 30° E. with great regularity (Fig. 1). The purpose of this paper is to explain the origin of the linear topography, and to provide reasons for its geographic distribution.

The area of aligned topography totals about two thousand square miles and comprises almost half of the Palouse. Boundaries of the area are usually indistinct, especially to the northeast where the pattern of parallel ridges and valleys grades into the dendritic pattern which

SOURCE: *Annals of the Association of American Geographers*, L, 2 (June, 1960), 98–111. The author is professor of geography, The Pennsylvania State University.

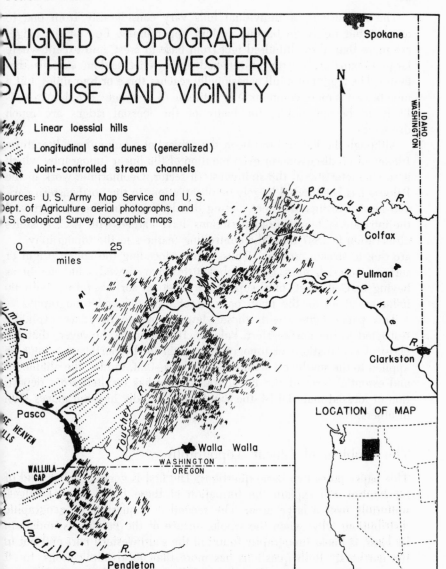

ALIGNED TOPOGRAPHY
IN THE SOUTHWESTERN
PALOUSE AND VICINITY

Linear loessial hills

Longitudinal sand dunes (generalized)

Joint-controlled stream channels

Sources: U. S. Army Map Service and U. S.
Dept. of Agriculture aerial photographs, and
U.S. Geological Survey topographic maps

0   25
        miles

Spokane

N

IDAHO
WASHINGTON

Palouse R.

Colfax

Pullman

Snake R.

Clarkston

LOCATION OF MAP

Pasco

HORSE HEAVEN HILLS

Touchet R.

WALLULA GAP

Walla Walla

WASHINGTON
OREGON

Umatilla R.

Pendleton

FIGURE 1: Aligned topography in the southwestern Palouse and vicinity.

characterizes the remainder of the Palouse. The area is fragmented by
large stream valleys and scabland channels, but lineation is a dominant
feature of the landscape throughout large tracts, with the trend of
alignment maintaining a constant and uniform direction. Taken as a
whole, the linear area of the southwestern Palouse forms a discrete and
unmistakable topographic entity, despite its discontinuity and vaguely
defined boundaries.

The dimensions of individual hills vary considerably from one to another but rarely go beyond certain upper limits. Few of the ridges are more than three hundred feet from base to crest, and except where large streams are deeply entrenched, local relief seldom exceeds that figure. The length of a hill occasionally reaches three or four miles, but a mile or two is more common. Any estimate of "average" size, however, is likely to be unreliable, for many of the loessial ridges are much dissected.

Although the Palouse has been the subject of a voluminous literature, I know of no discussion or even mention of the linear topography which is so characteristic of the southwestern sector. Geomorphic work in the Palouse has been based largely on observations in the northeastern part, and most investigators there, noting the dendritic drainage pattern and the intricate system of graded streams, have agreed with I. C. Russell's observation in 1897 that "the controlling features in the topography . . . are due to stream erosion." Thus, while conceding the eolian origin of surface *material*, most geomorphologists have viewed wind action as having had, at most, only superficial effect on surface *forms*, with no influence at all on the main patterns of drainage and topography.

This paper agrees with these views, provided they are explicitly restricted to the northeastern Palouse. It will argue, however, that the classical explanations of topographic origin in the northeast cannot be applied to the southwest with its linear hills—that, in fact, the alignment and essential form of the linear topography has resulted from deposition of loessial material by the wind, more rapidly in some places than in others.

The Problem of Linear Topography

This paper poses two basic questions. The first is genetic: what kind of mechanism will explain the formation of these linear loessial ridges, uniformly over a large area? The second is a question of geographic distribution: why, when the whole surface of the Palouse is underlain by loess, is linear topography found in the southwestern part and not in the northeast? Both questions has more than local implications, for if given conditions will produce linear hills in the southwestern Palouse, then similar hills should occur in loessial regions elsewhere if the same conditions are fulfilled.

Origin of the Linear Hills

Alternative Hypotheses

Alignment of topography can be produced by any of several agencies of erosion or deposition. Before stating the main argument, therefore, it is appropriate to consider certain alternative hypotheses and the reasons for rejecting them.

It is conceivable, first of all, that the loessial ridges were produced by erosion, but stratigraphic evidence proves that it cannot be so. Several deep road cuts through the crests of loessial ridges expose conspicuous layers of caliche, lying aproximately parallel to one another and to the present surface of the ridge. One such road cut about fifteen miles north of Walla Walla, Washington, displays at least six such layers, the deepest of which is over fifty feet below the surface. Because caliche is a surficial phenomenon, associated with soil-forming processes in the "B" horizon, it is necessary to conclude that these deep-lying layers mark the approximate surfaces of earlier ridges, which were stable long enough to permit caliche to develop. The parallelism of the caliche with the present surface makes it evident that the hills had essentially their present form throughout the time of loessial accumulation—in short, that the linear ridges were formed by accretion.

It is possible to narrow the range of inquiry still more by considering two further alternatives. On the one hand, linear landforms may predate the deposition of loessial material, the loess being merely a superficial blanket. This alternative contends that the present topography is a slightly altered copy of something older—that the linear pattern is not genetically related to the existence of loess, because the lineation was already there.

The second and contradictory hypothesis would hold that the alignment of topography was produced because loess accumulated most rapidly in certain elongate areas, eventually producing linear hills. Although this hypothesis does not reject the possibility of some pre-loessial alignment, it denies that the present topography is a copy of earlier lineation. This hypothesis asserts that the presence of loess was essential to the formation of these linear hills, and that without the loess there would have been no such alignment as is found today.

If lineation of topography existed before the loess accumulated, it is reasonable that such lineation should be visible in nearby areas which are not covered by the loessial blanket. Neighboring nonloessial areas of the Columbia Basin were examined, therefore, in an attempt to discover other types of linear topography, which, had they been covered by loess, might have produced aligned hills like those of the southwestern Palouse. Three types of nonloessial lineation were found.

One kind of alignment occurs where consequent streams flow parallel to one another down a steep regional slope. Such streams have produced a conspicuous linear pattern where they flow down the south flanks of the Horse Heaven Hills, an anticlinal ridge just west of the Palouse. If such stream alignment is to explain the linear pattern of the southwestern Palouse, however, one should find a steep regional slope there, either toward the south-southwest or toward the north-northeast. Furthermore, this slope should become gradually more gentle toward the nonlinear northeastern Palouse. No such slope exists, and the idea is rejected.

A second kind of aligned drainage occurs where subsequent streams have eroded headward along parallel joints in the Columbia River basalts. Joint-controlled stream channels are prominent features of a scabland tract along the lower Palouse River; they present an almost identical pattern at Wallula Gap, fifty-five miles to the southwest; and they are visible at several intervening points (Fig. 1). They have no apparent relationship with the loessial hills, however, for they trend in quite a different direction. Aerial photographs, moreover, reveal many places where joint-controlled channels disappear beneath a loessial cover and immediately lose all topographic expression.

Longitudinal sand dunes compose the third and last kind of linear landforms to be examined for possible relationships with the loessial ridges. Along the Columbia River, notably near Pasco, Washington, and Umatilla, Oregon, strong southwesterly winds have formed blowouts in shallow sand which overlies terrace and floodplain gravels. These blowouts advance downwind and leave behind them two straight ridges of sand, between which is a furrow which marks the blowout's earlier path. These dunes, similar to those which Hack has called "parabolic dunes," produce a strikingly linear pattern which, when seen from the air, looks as if a giant rake had been drawn across the surface. It is conceivable that such longitudinal dunes might have formed before the loessial blanket was deposited, and that the linear hills of the southwestern Palouse are really sand ridges with a loessial veneer. Today's active dunes are aligned in a slightly different direction than the loessial ridges (Fig. 1), but a change in wind direction within the past few thousand years could easily explain the discrepancy. There are two reasons, however, for believing that such longitudinal dunes have nothing to do with aligned topography in the southwestern Palouse. In the first place, all linear ridges should have cores of dune sand, but there is no evidence that they do. Wherever the base of the loess is exposed, it almost invariably rests directly on basalt; in no place was dune sand found at the contact. In the second place, the longitudinal dunes are of a totally different order of magnitude than the loessial hills. Whereas the Palouse ridges commonly measure two or three hundred feet from base to crest, the dunes in question are seldom more than ten feet high, and are usually much less. These dunes do not rise to great heights chiefly because the veneer of sand is thin. About twenty miles northeast of Pasco, Washington, the sand gradually becomes thicker, and the dunes grow higher, but as they do so, they cease to be either longitudinal or linear. Instead, large "transverse dunes" have developed, crudely scalloped in ground plan and aligned northwest-southeast. In sum, even though they have been blanketed by loess, neither longitudinal nor transverse dunes are likely to have formed ridges such as those in the southwestern Palouse.

The "Wind-Shadow" Hypothesis

Of the three kinds of linear topography to be seen in the Columbia Basin outside the loess-covered areas, all appear unrelated to linear ridges in the loess itself. It is reasonable, therefore, to set aside the notion that lineation in the Palouse is a contemporary copy of a pre-loessial alignment, and to consider the alternative hypothesis—that the linear ridges were formed because the loess accumulated more rapid in some places than in others.

If the wind is carrying loessial material in suspension, deposition will occur wherever wind velocity is sufficiently reduced. The eroded basaltic surface which predates the loess must certainly have presented many obstacles to the wind, and in the lee of such obstacles there would have been zones of reduced wind velocity wherein loess would accumulate more rapidly than elsewhere. Such zones—or "wind-shadows"—would be of elongate shape, tapering downwind from the obstacle. Hence, if silt-bearing winds blew again and again from approximately the same direction, an elongate ridge would develop in the wind-shadow of each obstacle, each ridge lying parallel to wind-direction and aligned with other ridges developing at the same time.

Evidence in Support of the Wind-Shadow Hypothesis

Three lines of evidence lend support to the wind-shadow hypothesis. The first is based on analysis of the drainage pattern, the second on examination of individual ridge forms, and the third on a reconstruction of past wind behavior.

1. Throughout much of the southwestern Palouse there is a marked tendency for small streams to be aligned in conformity with the topographic pattern. More sizeable streams, by contrast, show no apparent relationship to the trend of lineation (Fig. 1).

The wind-shadow hypothesis provides a reasonable explanation for this peculiarity of drainage. During the time when loess was accumulating, there must have existed a contest between eolian and fluvial processes for control of topographic form, eolian processes tending to produce a linear pattern, fluvial processes tending to keep the main pre-loessial pattern intact. In order for a stream to maintain its course against the encroachment of a growing linear ridge, a stream had to be large enough to erode the loess more rapidly than it accumulated. Even at times of greatest deposition the wind could make no progress in extending a fragile loessial ridge across a major stream channel. Upvalley, however, there must have come a place where streams, carrying water only at rare intervals, were so small that they could remove no appreciable amount of loess. If such a stream lay transverse to wind direction, its valley would act as a trap for wind-borne silt; eventually, the valley would be buried and drainage rerouted into parallel channels between the newly-formed linear hills. Stream valleys which chanced to lie parallel to wind-direction, however, would serve as funnels for the wind, and relatively little deposition would occur. In time, a characteristic drainage pattern would develop, where streams in their lower courses followed irregular paths, but in their headwaters followed the alignment of the linear hills. In short, the pattern would be much like that which is seen today in the southwestern Palouse, and which contrasts so sharply with the dendritic drainage of the northeastern part (Fig. 2).

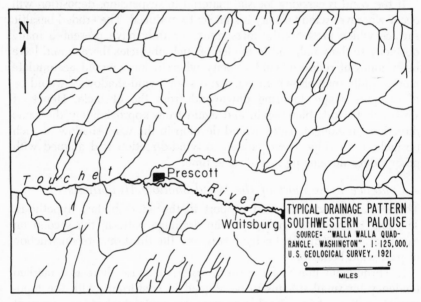

TYPICAL DRAINAGE PATTERN
SOUTHWESTERN PALOUSE
SOURCE: "WALLA WALLA QUAD-
RANGLE, WASHINGTON", 1: 125,000,
U.S. GEOLOGICAL SURVEY, 1921
0   5
MILES

FIGURE 2: Characteristic drainage pattern in lineated portions of the southwestern Palouse. Note that the alignment of drainage is best developed where streams are smallest.

2. The loessial ridges, when considered individually, likewise exhibit peculiarities of shape. Viewed in long profile, many of the ridges are consistently asymmetrical, terminating abruptly at their south-south-western extremities, but sloping off more gently toward the north-northeast. Such asymmetrical ridges are especially conspicuous where relatively large streams cross transversely the trend of loessial alignment and have cut into the underlying basalt. In such places, the clearly marked south-southwestern ends of the hills abut directly on the edges of the transverse valley, but as the ridges extend to the north-northeast, they lose identity very gradually. Where several such hills occur side by side, a distinctive topographic pattern results, the parallel ridges resem-

bling a row of banners with narrowed ends, streaming out from a flagpole in a strong south-southwesterly wind.

This peculiar pattern is clearly consistent with the wind-shadow hypothesis. The dissected basaltic walls of the transverse valley would confront the wind with a whole series of high obstacles, each with its wind-shadow, and each serving as a fixed point from which a loessial ridge might extend downwind. The shape of the ridge would conform to the characteristic shape of the wind-shadow, sharply outlined in the immediate lee of the obstacle, but increasingly diffuse with greater distance from it.

3. If the wind-shadow hypothesis is valid, the orientation of asymmetrical ridges clearly demands acceptance of a corollary proposition, namely, that silt-bearing winds must have blown from the south-southwest with great consistency. Absolute proof of such a proposition is obviously impossible, but field evidence suggests that it is not unlikely.

Although most investigators apparently believe that the loessial material originated from water-laid sediments to the south and west of the Palouse, opinion is by no means unanimous. Campbell, for example, has expressed the belief that the bulk of loess could not have come from the southwest, and suggests that northerly winds, possibly associated with a glacially-induced anticyclonic system, might well account for the deposition of silt. If Campbell's view is correct, the wind-shadow hypothesis is obviously untenable. In an attempt to determine the direction of silt-bearing winds, therefore, the loess itself was examined.

Determination of wind-direction was based on the premise that median grain-size of loessial material must decrease with increasing distance from the source area. Samples of loess were collected for grain-size analysis from twenty-three sites, composing a traverse across the Palouse from southwest to northeast. Wherever possible, at least two samples were taken from each site, one at about six feet below the present surface to reflect the most recent episodes of deposition, and a second at depths ranging from fifteen to thirty feet, representing earlier episodes. A base-line was then drawn at the southwestern margin of the Palouse, perpendicular to the trend of lineation, and the median grain-size of each sample was plotted as a function of distance from the base-line. The resulting graph shows the change in grain-size from southwest to northeast, both in surficial materials and in materials at depth. Also included in the graph were data collected by P. D. Krynine from two sites near Spokane, Washington, on the extreme northeastern margin of the Palouse.

The general decrease in grain-size from the southwestern to the northeastern Palouse shown by the graph is confirmed by statistical analysis. Data from other sources support the same conclusion. Rieger has collected samples along two east-west traverses from the Columbia River to the foot of the Idaho Rockies, and Kraszewski made a shorter east-west traverse in the region between the Touchet and Snake rivers. The results of both investigations support the thesis that loess from the southwestern Palouse is coarser than that in the northeast. Flint, likewise, has concluded "that the average grain-size (of the 'Palouse soil') decreases conspicuously from the Pasco Basin northeastward toward Spokane . . . , Pullman, and Colfax." In short, silt-bearing winds did not blow from the north or east for any appreciable span of time; almost certainly their main direction was southwesterly, or nearly so, as the wind-shadow hypothesis demands.

The hypothesis also requires that silt-bearing winds were highly consistent in direction, for if they had varied substantially, the location of wind-shadows also would have varied, and loessial ridges would never have formed. Direct proof of such consistency is obviously impossible without access to Pleistocene weather records, but data from three weather stations near the Palouse show that winds which carry dust today almost invariably blow from the same quarter. Records of dust storms for the period from January, 1949, to June, 1957, were obtained from the U. S. Weather Bureau Stations at Walla Walla, Washington, and Pendleton, Oregon. The direction and velocity of winds were tabulated for each storm, and the data recorded in graphic form. Similar data, collected at Spokane by Bryan for the period 1905–1925, were also plotted on the same basis. The consistency of wind direction during dust storms is obvious from an examination of all three graphs: at Walla Walla, 84 percent of all dust storms originate from one quarter of the compass; at Pendleton the figure is 88 percent, and at Spokane it is 95 percent. It cannot be maintained that contemporary wind behavior duplicates that of the past, and especially that wind direction was the same then as now. Present-day data, however, do show that silt-bearing winds of highly persistent direction cannot be regarded as unlikely in the past.

Linear Topography in Other Loessial Areas

Linear topography, evidently similar to that of the southwestern Palouse, has been noted by investigators in loessial regions elsewhere. W. L. Russell has described an area in the western Great Plains where at least 125,000 square miles exhibit a marked alignment of valleys and ridges in a northwest-southeast direction. Russell attributed the linear pattern to the concentration of wind-borne material downwind from surface irregularities. Although the brevity of Russell's analysis permits no detailed comparisons, his views concerning the origin of alignment in the Great Plains seem essentially to correspond with my findings in the southwestern Palouse.

Apparently similar lineation has also been recognized in the loessial areas of central Europe. Alfred Jahn has described "longitudinal streaks of loess" and "loess bridges" which extend across river valleys on the Lublin Plateau of Poland. Jahn refers to these linear features as "primary phenomena" which owe their origin to deposition of silt by easterly winds. Linear hills, called *zavieja*, also occur in the loess of Czechoslovakia. Their origin has been ascribed to deposition of wind-borne silt in the lee of pre-existing hills by winds which blew primarily from the southwest.

Recent Changes in Linear Topography

Most linear ridges in the southwestern Palouse are extensively dissected by small streams, and some have been altered almost beyond recognition. There is no doubt that at least some of these ridges were once continuous, for road cuts through ridge crests exhibit caliche layers, mainly accordant with the present surface, but abruptly truncated where tiny streams have eroded headward into the flanks of the ridges. The extent of dissection by very small intermittent streams indicates the possibility that the eolian processes which built the linear hills are no longer acting to perpetuate them. This possibility is supported by the certain knowledge that the loess has long since ceased to accumulate in the southwestern Palouse. It follows, if the wind-shadow hypothesis is valid, that linear topography has likewise ceased to form.

It might be difficult to convince a person who has experienced a blinding Palouse dust storm that silt is no longer being deposited. The testimony of persons familiar with the region, however, indicates that dust storms of present-day intensity were unknown before the 1890's when farmers first settled in the Palouse, broke the sod, and exposed the friable loess to the full blast of the wind. Intense as they are, the recent dust storms have produced only a negligible accumulation of loess by contrast with earlier episodes of deposition. Indeed, glacial drift and scabland channels are very nearly free of wind-borne silt, and Bryan has concluded that "the present dust storms probably deposit dust at a greater rate than at any time since the Wisconsin glaciation." With no renewal of the loessial blanket, fluvial processes would have gained the ascendancy everywhere, dissecting the linear hills at a rate far in excess of that previously, and in a manner which apparently continues at the present time.

Distribution of Linear Topography

This paper has raised two major questions, the first concerned with origin of linear hills as such, for which the wind-shadow hypothesis has been offered as an answer. The second question, now to be considered, asks why linear topography is distributed the way it is—widespread throughout the southwestern Palouse, but practically nonexistent in the northeast.

Either of two possibilities might explain the difference in distribution. The presence of linear hills presumably required (a) a certain kind of wind behavior, and (b) a certain kind of material. While it is practically impossible to reconstruct past wind behavior with any certainty, the velocity and direction of winds during present-day dust storms appear to be much the same in the northeast as in the southwest, and it may well have been so in the past. Loessial material, however, is not the same.

Forty-four samples of loess taken from linear areas show a range in median grain-size between 0.0270 mm. and 0.0405 mm., with an average of 0.0329 mm. The median sizes of twenty samples from nonlinear areas range between 0.0175 mm. and 0.0280 mm., with an average of 0.0232 mm. It would appear that lineation in the Palouse is associated with loess whose median grain-size exceeds 0.0270–0.0280 mm. Conversely, if median grain-size is less than that figure, linear topography does not develop. Russell suggests a similar situation in the linear ridges of the Great Plains, describing the material which composes the ridges as loess-like in appearance, but "slightly coarser" than ordinary loess.

It becomes possible, therefore, to rephrase the main question as follows: why is linear topography in the Palouse found only in association with coarse-grained loess? If winds of the past were similar to those which blow today (a supposition which is likely but not provable), the wind-shadow hypothesis provides a framework for a possible answer.

Since the linear hills are composed of relatively coarse material, wind velocity must have been relatively great in order to have carried it. Data from the Walla Walla Weather Bureau show that high-velocity winds today are extremely preferential in direction, whereas low-velocity winds are considerably more variable. If the same tendency existed in the past, wind-shadows would have been oriented consistently in the same direction when strong winds were blowing. Although silt would be dropped wherever wind velocity decreased below a certain point, the coarse fractions would be the first to be deposited. The presence of consistently aligned wind-shadows would cause just such reductions in velocity, thus resulting in the selective deposition of coarser fractions in the form of linear hills. These hills would necessarily be located closest to the loessial source area—in the Palouse, toward the southwest. Finer fractions, however, carried farther to the northeast, would be deposited only when winds reached a lower velocity, and such winds today are relatively variable in direction. With shifts in wind direction, the location of wind-shadows would also have shifted, and linear hills would never have formed.

13. Developmental Processes in Laterite Terrain in Amapá

John H. Vann

Geographers, along with many other people, including specialists of all kinds, have a tendency to apply what is well known about one area of the world directly to another area, without considering that there may be local or regional factors greatly altering conditions in the other areas. Vann suggests that this has been the case in studies of the development of erosional landforms in the laterites of northeastern Brazil. Here, he suggests, earlier field work has accepted the idea that the normal erosional cycle of streams is applicable to this area. Vann's position is that the field evidence he has uncovered suggests other hypotheses, and he proceeds to analyze the terrain and the conditions producing it to strengthen his thesis.

The processes leading to the formation of laterite, which is essentially a residual end product of weathering, have been discussed in detail in an extensive literature. The studies on which this literature is based were carried out by geologists and pedologists and have not been widely disseminated among geographers. Nevertheless, in this mass of information there is much that is interesting to the physical geographer. Especially intriguing, to the writer at least, are references to the morphology produced when the laterite is eroded. Wherever genesis of erosional landforms is discussed, except in a few instances, the cycle of erosion theory is invoked.

It is the writer's opinion, based on ten years of research in the American tropics, that the hypotheses used to explain the landforms of laterite terrain fail to account for what actually occurs. In much of the laterite terrain of the Guianas and Brazil the morphological characteristics of valleys are not consistent with the idea that the valleys were carved by streams through the processes of lateral corrasion and vertical erosion. The valleys have broad, flat bottoms and precipitous walls. Furthermore, many of them lack permanent streams capable of eroding valleys of their size and shape, and many contain a narrow bench along their walls. Such morphological peculiarities are especially characteristic of the valleys developed in the laterite terrain of Amapá, in northeastern Brazil.

SOURCE: *Geographical Review,* LIII (1963), 408-17. The author is a member of the staff of the Department of Geography, Louisiana State University.

The coastal State of Amapá is the northeasternmost political unit in Brazil. In this relatively isolated area several general landscape types may be identified: (1) a shore and strand landscape, composed of beach, mud flats, and clay wave-abrasion platforms, covered on the landward side by mangrove (*Avicennia nitida*); (2) a marsh and lake landscape, between the shore and strand zone and the uplands of the interior; (3) a savanna landscape, occupying ancient erosion surfaces between the eroded mountains of the interior and the marsh and lake zone; and (4) the mountains of the interior, covered with tropical rain forest.

This paper is mainly concerned with the savanna landscape. The savannas are developed on deeply weathered old erosion surfaces that rise abruptly from the marsh and lake zone and ascend in a series of broad, gentle steps to the foothills of the interior mountains. The steps are arranged in a belt that roughly parallels the coast. Across these erosion surfaces shallow, steep-sided, flat-bottomed valleys have been formed that in many places exhibit convex or straight sloping walls. The valleys have very steep headwalls that begin abruptly in the flat surfaces of the savanna zone. The vegetation cover of these surfaces is predominantly grass and sedge, with scattered trees of *Byrsonima* and *Curatella* and clumps or islands of palms. The valley bottoms are covered with gallery forest composed of trees typical of the tropical forest of this region or lines of plams along the watercourses (Fig. 1).

Laterite Profile

The soil of the savanna is a thick tropical laterite that caps the upper older parts of the surface, and almost pure medium to coarse quartz sand where the laterite has been removed by erosion. The sand is the result of long-continued weathering of quartz-rich granites and gneiss under the influence of a seasonally wet tropical climate. Rainfall across the savanna zone is more than a hundred inches and occurs mostly during the seven months January to July inclusive; the period August through December is markedly drier. Adequate, reliable climatic records do not exist for the territory, but during the period September to mid December, while the writer was in the field, only two inches of rain was recorded at Macapá, in the southeastern part of the zone. The air base near Amapá, about 210 miles north of Macapá and near the center of the length of the savanna zone, recorded 4.5 inches of rain in the same period. The total rainfall for the year was about 100 inches at Macapá and 188.5 inches at the Amapá air base. The precipitation contrast between the rainy and dry seasons is so great that the dry season is strikingly arid. Temperatures rise sharply because of a lack of cloud cover, and the heat added to the dryness of the air greatly increases evaporation and reduces soil moisture. The savannas give the impres ion of landscapes in the twenty-inch rainfall zone of the United States. nsects die off, grass becomes markedly siliceous, birds seek better-watered regions, and the vegetation turns brown and enters a growth est period. The countryside presents an entirely different aspect from hat during the wonderfully green rainy season.

Since laterite caps much of the savanna zone and is rocklike both in ardness and in porosity, surface runoff is impressive at times of rain. Brazilian engineers who constructed and maintain the Macapá–Amapá ighway informed the writer that runoff was so great that they figured : at 100 per cent in planning for road drainage. This is not wholly ecessary, since in the rainy season the writer observed some downward enetration of water through the laterite. However, the percentage unoff is very high on the hilltops covered with thick laterite, and soil ridity is a problem at all seasons except the wettest part of the year.

The processes now at work degrading the laterite-capped area are robably typical for all laterite-encrusted areas in Brazil. The classic aterite profile described repeatedly in the literature is well developed 1 Amapá. At the surface is a typical ironstone crust, beneath which lie 1e mottled zone and the pallid zone familiar to students of laterite.

The laterite of Amapá has been formed by pedogenesis on granite, ranodiorite, gneiss, and schist. The gneiss is especially high in silica nd breaks down into highly siliceous sands, which compose the pallid one at most of the localities in Amapá visited by the writer. In contrast, 1e mottled zone is composed in many places of an almost impervious lay, with which the laterite crust is in contact.

rosional Attack

ullying during the rainy season begins along scarps that separate the rosion surfaces, and the gullies grow headward in the manner familiar 1 badland topography. As the gullies widen and deepen with time, so 1at they penetrate the laterite crust, processes come into play that 1crease the rate at which valleys develop. Water penetrating down-vard through the vesicular and pisolitic laterite forms springs along the ase of gully walls when the gully is incised to or below the contact etween the laterite crust and the mottled clay. Springs undercut the ully walls by sapping, and the walls retreat by backwasting. A shallow, road, flat-bottomed gully with steep walls becomes a characteristic ypographic feature. Sapping also occurs at this stage around gully eads at the contact of the clay and the laterite crust, promoting head-ard retreat.

As the gullying process continues, considerable runoff in the wet sea-n eventually allows the gullies to work vertically downward through 1e mottled clay and the sands of the pallid zone until another mottled nd aluminized zone is reached beneath the sands of the pallid zone and directly above the parent rock. Backwasting and headward retreat are accelerated around the base of valley walls and valley heads at this lower level. Frequently, therefore, valleys that have been subjected to the influence of these combined processes for a long period of time display a narrow bench at the level of the contact between the laterite and the upper mottled zone. Here the laterite crust retreats above the mottled clay under the influence of long-continued spring sapping. Below this bench gullying erodes vertically into the mottled clay. The sand beneath the mottled clay stands in vertical walls after it is incised by gullying because ferruginous and siliceous cement binds the grains together. When gullying finally penetrates the sand to the second mottled and aluminized zone of clay, another spring line develops, and the retreat of the sand portion of the valley wall begins. A lower level flat develops. The older valleys show two spring lines, one at the base of the laterite crust and the other at the sand and kaolinized clay contact. A bench is formed by the spring line at the base of the laterite crust, and the flat valley bottom is formed by the second (lower) spring line (Fig. 1).

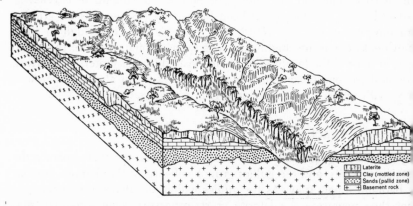

FIGURE 1: Block diagram of a typical sapping valley in the laterite terrain of Amapá.

In some places, especially where the laterite profile is developed on schist, the pallid zone does not contain large quantities of sand but is composed of clay, increasingly aluminized with depth. The valleys are therefore shallower, developing only to the base of the laterite, where they expand laterally by backwasting along the laterite-clay contact. Since the clay is compact, durable, and almost impervious, valley deepening by gullying is arrested or greatly slowed, and valley widening proceeds more rapidly than deepening. Broader, shallower valleys develop that lack the benches.

Valleys that develop by sapping and gully wash widen with time and coalesce to form ever-broadening, flat-bottomed depressions that contain marsh and swamp in the wet season. During the dry season they become savannalike meadowlands or thickets. These shallow, flat-bottomed, poorly drained depressions are referred to locally as *baixas* and are a conspicuous feature of the Amapá savanna country. During the dry season one may wander at will over the baixas. Boring with a soil auger down to thirty feet reveals fill of pale bleached sands three to six feet deep underlain by a mottled clay beneath which is a highly kaolinized clay. In the wet season the baixas fill quickly with clear, pure water to a depth of several feet and become herbaceous marsh, or, where covered by gallery forest, become swamps. Many aquatic plants appear, and fish and animal life invades the baixas from the coastal marsh zone and streams. Thus the baixas completely change character from dry to wet season. In them one may observe the fluctuation of the water table conducive to the formation of Marbut's "ground water laterite."

Landscape Development

If the peculiar landscapes of the Amapá savannas are to be understood, it is necessary to grasp the significance of the laterite crust as a control of morphology. The writer takes the position that the laterite of Amapá is the product of a former cycle of pedogenesis on the old, complex, metamorphic and igneous rocks of the ancient Guiana Shield. The character of the weathering profile indicates a long period of pedogenesis on formerly planed rock surfaces that culminated in the formation of a laterite crust.

Since the formation of the laterite, which was the illuvial horizon of a soil-forming cycle, the laterite crust has itself become a parent material. Today, where it has not been severely dissected or removed by erosion, it is being weathered into a new soil series. However, the formerly completed laterite profile is being strongly attacked by gullying and spring sapping with attendant mass wasting. Thus large areas of beveled surface truncate the laterite profile. A catenary development of soil series is found in the areas of truncated laterite profiles.

In Amapá runoff is so heavy over the laterite on hilltops and upper slopes that material weathered from the laterite is swept away almost as soon as it forms, leaving many bare laterite surfaces. It is this circumstance that has led some observers to the idea that laterite is still forming on the capped surfaces. In reality laterite is forming only at lower levels, in the baixas, and has long since ceased forming on the capped surfaces.

The crust that caps remnants of old dissected surfaces serves to protect the areas beneath from erosional attack. But even these areas are being slowly reduced by the attrition of gullying and spring sapping, so that in the future only smaller remnants of the surfaces with old rock outcrops will contain ferruginous crusts of the thickness and age now observable. The lithology and physical character of the laterite profile in large measure control the type of morphology that is developing now and will continue to control it as long as laterite profiles remain on old erosion surfaces. Of course, as the truncation of the laterite profile advances and more and more of the crust is removed, landform development will change accordingly. On the other hand, the present cycle of evolution as expressed in the formation of the present valleys and baixas is working toward the creation of a new lower surface similar to the ones it is destroying.

The writer's observations in Amapá tend to confirm the widely held opinion that laterite terrains require vast periods of time for their evolution. The development of the erosion surfaces on which the laterite crusts were formed also occurred very slowly. Whether or not they were peneplains in the classical Davisian sense is by no means certain. In view of present landform development in Amapá, there seems to be no necessity for supposing that the surfaces were formed by stream planation. The present large streams, such as the Rio Araguari, the Rio Tartarugal Grande, the Rio Fleichal, the Rio Calçoene, the Rio Cunani, the Rio Cassiporé, and the Rio Oiapoque, rise in the mountains and flow in deeply incised valleys across the erosional surfaces with their residual caps. There is nothing in the landscape associated with the rivers to suggest that they formerly planed such broad surfaces as those associated with the laterite. Indeed, all these rivers are operating under structural control until they enter the narrow Recent coastal plain, and it seems apparent that they have been confined to zones of structural weakness throughout the greater part, if not all, of their history. It seems much more likely that the surfaces with which the laterite is associated were formed in much the same fashion as the currently forming surface explained in this paper.

Age of Laterites

As for the age of the laterite and the erosion surfaces, they must both surely be no younger than Tertiary. It has been repeatedly demonstrated in the rich literature on laterite that the classic profile takes a long time to develop. Nearly all the papers dealing with the age of laterite assign it to the Tertiary (Miocene and Pliocene).

In view of the evidence from the literature and the field evidence from Amapá, where laterite profiles are fifty to sixty feet thick in places, it must be concluded that the presence of a mature laterite profile indicates at least a Tertiary age. Since the Amapá erosion surfaces on which the laterite profile occurs preceded the laterite in origin, they too must be Tertiary or older. Perhaps the surfaces were formed in the Eocene and the early Miocene and the laterite in the late Miocene and the Pliocene. It seems probable that the present cycle of valley formation described in this paper began in the Pleistocene and continues to the present. Perhaps it was initiated during periods of higher rainfall that accompanied the climatic changes of Pleistocene time. Although Pleistocene climatic changes may not have had as marked an effect on rainfall in the tropics as on that in temperate regions, it is probable that these changes increased rainfall somewhat in tropical climates with seasonal precipitation.

From the numerous descriptions of laterite terrain similar to that of the Amapá savannas it seems safe to assume that there is a laterite erosional morphology characterized by steep-sided, flat-bottomed valleys with convex and/or straight slopes on valley walls leading from flat-topped remnants of laterite capping on old erosion surfaces. However, whenever the origin of the old erosion surfaces is dealt with in the literature, they are usually stated to be caused by peneplanation. Notable exceptions are the statements of Radley and Mulcahy, who attribute the surfaces to slope retreat, and of Playford, who denies that peneplanation took place before laterite developed in Western Australia. Usually the valleys are said to be the result of uplift after peneplanation, which causes rejuvenation of erosion with attendant dissection. The writer submits that neither peneplanation nor uplift is necessary to produce this topography and suggests that laterite morphology is produced by a combination of gullying, sapping, and mass wasting, as has been explained by the interpretation of the field evidence from Amapá.

14. Some Aspects of Desert Morphology
R. F. Peel

Deserts, because of their relatively inhospitable environments, have resisted both intensive and extensive field work. As a result, many of our ideas of desert morphology have been developed from observations of the margins of the deserts or from the interiors of some of the smaller desert areas of the world. The Sahara, a desert region so vast that the entire United States could be placed in it, with large areas of desert extending beyond, probably has the ultimate in desert characteristics. In this selection, Peel has avoided conclusions derived from desert margins and smaller deserts and has sought to find underlying principles of all desert morphology. He takes strong exception to many gen-

*erally accepted ideas about desert landforms and conditions
and, using evidence from many deserts of the world,
makes a very strong case.*

Some sixty years ago W. M. Davis laid the foundations for systematic studies of the relations between climate and landscape by proposing three basic types of landscape cycle proper to humid, frigid and arid conditions respectively. In more recent years Davis's primary distinctions have been elaborated, on the one hand by the study of morpho-climatic regions, on the other by proposals for distinctive cycles appropriate to intermediate types of climate such as savanna, sub-arid, and periglacial; but if we review in broad terms the progress made in this field since Davis wrote his basic papers one thing stands out, and that is the relatively small amount of study that has been devoted to the arid lands in comparison with the other major divisions. Davis himself has been held in part responsible for this, in that by electing to call humid conditions "normal", and styling extremes of cold and aridity "climatic accidents", he created an unbalanced and misleading picture. But although his choice of terms may have been unfortunate, to blame him for the comparative neglect of dry-land studies is surely unwarranted. His attitude has at least had no such effect on his other "abnormal", the lands of ice and snow; indeed nothing so sharply underlines the neglect of the arid deserts as a comparison of the volume of study devoted to them with that devoted to the glacial regions. In the latter field we have by now almost a subject in itself, nourishing a vast literature of thousands of articles, several specialized journals, and shelves of weighty texts and major monographs. But the geomorphologist interested in deserts will find no single journal devoted exclusively to his interests, an article literature to be numbered only in hundreds, and no comprehensive textbook more recent than Johannes Walther's *Das Gesetz der Wüstenbildung* first published in 1900. And yet, as L. C. King and others have repeatedly stressed, by any definition the dry lands occupy a good third of the earth's surface, whereas glaciation, although expanded to cover about the same fraction during the Pleistocene maximum, today affects no more than about ten per cent.

It would be interesting, but would take us too far afield, to review the reasons for the comparative neglect of the earth's deserts. More pertinent to the present paper are the facts and their results. Until a decade or two ago the majority of the earth's great deserts, although civilization grew up around their edges, had remained astonishingly unknown in any exact and scientific sense. This interior of the Libyan Desert, for example, an area of size comparable to peninsular India, was effectively penetrated for the first time as recently as the late 1920's,

SOURCE: *Geography*, XLV (1960), 241–62. The author is head of the Department of Geography, University of Bristol, England.

and substantial tracts of it, as of the rest of the Sahara, still remain
very little known. Things have indeed been changing fast in the years
since the last war, particularly with the scientific surveys of arid
Australia conducted by C.S.I.R.O., UNESCO's Arid Zone Research
Programme, and the vast amount of prospecting and geological work
carried out in the Sahara in consequence of important oil and other
mineral discoveries—to say nothing of the employment of desert tracts
for nuclear experimentation. But little of the new information that has
resulted has yet found its way into our textbooks, and geomorphology
has entered into the investigations only in minor degree. It remains
true even today that for a large fraction of the earth's desert lands we
have no detailed and reliable topographic maps, no continuous geological surveys, and only the most generalized data on physiographically
important aspects of climate and hydrology. Specific geomorphological
studies, although increasing, are still few and far between in comparison
with the areas involved, and a large proportion remain of a reconnaissance character. Relatively few studies based on reliable measurement, whether of forms, conditions or processes, are as yet available.

The results of this situation are familiar enough. In the majority of
our textbooks the accounts of arid-land geomorphology remain brief,
somewhat standardized, and markedly unbalanced; inevitably so, since
they rely on limited material of varying age and reliability and on
studies and opinions far from evenly distributed or fully representative.
And in this last context it must be noted that in sharp contrast to most
of the arid zone one corner of it has been remarkably well studied, and
from it has poured out a copious stream of excellent descriptive work
and interpretative theory. This area is the "Arid Southwest" of the
United States, classic ground for the field geologist; but although the
American material is of the greatest value, it must be kept in correct
perspective. In various ways the "Arid Southwest" is not very typical of
the earth's great deserts, being much more diversified and in large
part only sub-arid; while in its totality it comprises only a small sample
of the whole. When we recall that the whole of the United States could
be comfortably placed inside the Sahara alone, with enough space left
over for several European states, it will be apparent that we should
be chary of basing world judgments too freely on what may well be true
of California and Arizona. This point must clearly be borne in mind in
reading many textbooks which, in the absence of other information,
necessarily tend to rely largely upon the American material.

The purpose of the present paper is to draw attention to this general
situation in dry-land geomorphology, and within that picture to illustrate
some of the uncertainties that beset us by discussion of a few selected
topics and features. These have been selected rather arbitrarily, and
limitations of space preclude any full discussion even of the few themes
touched on.

General Considerations

Since they owe their existence entirely to meteorological causes, the earth's present deserts include within their confines regions with all kinds of geological history, structure and tectonics; but although they include large tracts of mountains of various types it so happens that the greater part of the present deserts lie upon ancient land-surfaces of marked stability. Plains therefore, of varying character, altitude and origin, bulk large in their morphological make-up. In physiographic conditions the outstanding features are well known: a marked infrequency and irregularity of rainfall, both in time and place; typically dry air; strong daily insolation and nocturnal radiation; and a marked sparsity, amounting over great tracts to a total absence, of vegetational cover. With the latter goes a general absence of true soils, the superficial deposits remaining for the most part purely mineral and incoherent unless chemically cemented. These conditions are of course present in very variable degree, for just as no sharp boundary can be placed around the arid zones so they exhibit a wide internal range in degree of aridity. But in some measure the features mentioned are definitive.

In attempting to interpret the landscapes of desert tracts, however, a fundamental problem is how long conditions have been as we now see them; a problem which raises the question of how much of the present scenery is truly the product of current conditions and processes, and how much residual (though no doubt in some degree modified) from past periods of possibly quite different conditions. Elucidation of the climatic history is thus a matter of quite basic importance if we are to form any true appreciation of the scenery in arid tracts, and to this we must add an understanding of past geological history, for this also varies greatly within tht desert zones. More recent studies have indeed made it appear very doubtful if any attempt at formulation of broad landscape theories for the arid environment can be safely undertaken until we know a lot more about the past geological and climatic histories of the areas from which we must draw our evidence, but these matters will be touched on again later in this paper. For the moment it is convenient to confine discussion to present conditions and to the evolution of theories widely held.

The earlier scientific explorers of our deserts, seeing no surface water, experiencing no rain, and finding the scenery that met their eyes both unfamiliar and astonishing, concluded in some cases that they were traversing the unmodified floors of former seas, in others that the bizarre landscapes they encountered must have been carved out entirely by the actions of solar heat and wind. Closer studies however led to different conclusions, and for some time past most geomorphologists have been united in the opinion that apart from its patent importance as an agency of dust-removal and dune-building the part played by wind in creating the desert landscape is probably nothing like so great as pioneers like C. R. Keyes supposed, and that improbable as it might appear the dominant agency of land-sculpture throughout the desert lands remains flowing water. There is indeed much evidence to support this view, both in the field and in theory. Great tracts of our present deserts are dominated by features which can only be reasonably explained on a water erosion hypothesis, while it seems probable (if not entirely certain) that there is no spot within them on which rain *never* falls. The significant physiographic difference between the desert and the humid land can indeed in this particular be correctly stated as one of degree rather than kind, consisting essentially in comparative frequency of rainfalls; the average interval between being perhaps a week in the one, as against a year, five years or even ten or twenty in the other. Once rain has fallen in sufficient quantity to initiate runoff, the latter will patently be governed by the same physical laws in both regions (although the contrast in governing conditions may make it take different forms and produce somewhat different effects); and provided that no other active processes are working during the long drought spells in ways which obliterate and counter the occasional water erosion, the effects of the latter, although only occurring for short periods at lengthy intervals, may well be accumulative. Arguing in this way, and making due allowance for the lack of large-scale co-ordinated drainage systems and a single riverine base-level, one can reasonably arrive at a conclusion similar to that of Davis, that although the process may be disconnected, intermittent, and thus greatly slowed down, water erosion can continue to dominate the desert landscape cycle at least until it reaches a very advanced stage. But this assumes, of course, that no other processes acting more continuously, and perhaps in other directions, arrest or counter the progressive and cumulative effects of the occasional water action; and whether this is true or not is patently a key question in desert geomorphology.

Of such possible processes two are obvious; the one being wind erosion and transport, the other general weathering. It is not intended here to discuss the proved and possible contributions of wind action to desert landscape in any detail, although from every point of view we know all too little about them. Indeed, despite the major advances made by R. A. Bagnold and others in elucidating the mechanics of sand-movement and dune-construction, and the painstaking studies of soil-blowing by wind conducted in America and elsewhere, it is still perhaps true to say, as did Eliot Blackwelder, that the relative importance of wind "is one of the most important unsettled problems of desert geomorphology". But in general terms it would seem possible to summarize current opinion in the following way. Acting unaided on strong coherent bedrock wind has negligible erosive effect, although it may in some measure assist weathering by bringing in water vapour on the one hand or by evaporating water from the rock on the other; but when the surface formations are soft and friable, or when strong rocks have been weathered to a sufficient state of fineness and incoherency, wind has considerable powers of erosion by removal. J. A. Udden emphasized the tremendous theoretical capacity of wind in this respect long ago, and we have now a good deal of observational data from studies of soil-blowing in the American "Dust Bowl" and elsewhere to reinforce both theoretical calculations and the tacit evidence of vast quantities of exported dust redeposited as loess around the peripheries of many desert areas. This action, termed deflation, is almost certainly the most important erosive action of wind, far transcending the abrasive erosion effected by the coarser particles of sand-grade during their transport. The latter, the familiar "sand-blast" action, is clearly responsible for the production of distinctive fretted surfaces, the shaping of pebbles into dreikanter, and other small-scale effects, but no incontrovertible proof seems ever to have been advanced that it can carve out major landforms or contribute in important degree to general denudation. The combined erosive effects of wind thus seem to be controlled primarily by lithological considerations expressing themselves in the rate at which particles small enough for the wind to lift and carry away are released from parent rock, and if we leave aside unconsolidated surface deposits, this would seem to be essentially a function of rates of weathering. Weathering also interrelates intimately with the occasional actions of water in that during the long drought spells great quantities of rock wastes are created which, in their transport, rapidly abstract most of the available energy from the ephemeral streams and sheet-floods. According to may theories also, static weathering, assisted by gravity removal of loosened particles, plays a leading role in the slow retreat and shaping of steep slopes. Weathering processes are thus patently of fundamental importance in the slow evolution of desert landscapes, yet our certain knowledge about how they work and combine seems to be still somewhat confused and inadequate. Some discussion of this subject thus seems appropriate.

Desert Weathering

The relative absence of vegetation and soil exposes a large fraction of bedrock to direct atmospheric weathering in many desert locations, and in hilly ground the bare rock is typically littered with rock fragments and residues. From these the wind constantly sifts out the accessible finer particles as they form, carrying much of the dust right out of the desert zone and concentrating the slower-moving sand in particular localities. Impressed by the enormous quantities of rock fragments, often markedly angular, the apparent total absence of water, and the exaggerated temperature differences between day and night (often, for rock surfaces, of the order of 100° F.), earlier observers concluded that the dominant agency at work must be thermal shattering, operating through the cyclic stress differences imposed by repeated volumetric changes. These, it was argued, would tend rapidly to break up and detach the surface layers of bedrock, and would continue to attack loosened boulders and fragments even to the extent of reducing them to granular form by breaking the bonds between crystals or particles of minerals with different coefficients of thermal expansion. David Livingstone, with other early and more recent travellers, reported hearing rocks burst with pistol-shot reports under this action, and scientists like Walther, Ball, Hume and Lucas demonstrated that the stresses and strains involved were quite sufficient to produce the observed results. The same kind of process was invoked to explain the onion-skin exfoliation so commonly to be seen on massive crystalline rocks in the deserts. Serious doubts were first cast on this theory by the observations of D. C. Barton in Egypt and Eliot Blackwelder in America. Barton, studying ancient monuments in Egypt, found that weathering of the stonework was in general more pronounced in the Delta than higher up the Nile valley, and that on any individual monument decay was universally at a maximum on those parts which remained constantly in shadow, and least of all on surfaces directly exposed to the sun and to the maximum heating and cooling. These results he interpreted as implying that in constrast to previous theory insolation and radiation in anhydrous conditions produced no appreciable weathering effects, the main enemy being here, as elsewhere, moisture. Blackwelder's field observations in America, reinforced by a careful study of the Mormon Temple in Salt Lake City, produced a like result, and in a series of papers he urged that the thermal-shattering theory of desert weathering was quite mistaken, and that in deserts, as in the temperate humid lands, chemical weathering involving water was the real destroyer of rocks. This thesis he applied even to massive exfoliation. A further blow to the traditional theory was given by various laboratory experiments, including the often-quoted experiments of D. T. Griggs. In these, Griggs exposed a polished face of granite to some 90,000 fifteen-minute cycles of alternate heating and cooling over a temperature range of nearly 200° F. (far greater than anything experienced naturally in the deserts) and found the rock totally undamaged at the end. Repeating the same experiment but using a cold-water spray for the cooling part of the cycle, however, Griggs found that the whole block very quickly disintegrated.

Further studies have been made of these matters in recent years, but the conflicting statements still to be found in textbooks underline the fact that we have not yet established with any certainty the relative importance of different weathering processes in deserts. The occurrence of pebbles split as though by frost, no less than the angularity of many rock fragments, seems to support the thermal-shattering theory, and Dury has recently cited as evidence for it the spreading abroad and down-slope working of rock fragments. But a large volume of evidence has grown up pointing conclusively to the great importance of chemical processes. It is difficult to conceive how the many tor-like forms, pedestal rocks, rock pinnacles and arches, to say nothing of tafoni and rock cavities, could be formed by any purely mechanical process of weathering; and direct evidence of chemical decay is often to be found in the deep rotting of exposed rock surfaces especially of the plutonic igneous rocks. Pediment surfaces in the Mohave Desert were found by the writer in 1955 to be occasionally rotted to a depth of a foot or more, so that the power-scrapers used to level minor roads cut away that depth of bedrock without difficulty; and when climbing Gebel Kissu, a 5,000-foot granite peak in the southern Libyan Desert, the bare granite was found to be so rotted in places that holds crumbled away into sand. Deep cavities etched out on the undersides of granite boulders, the emergence of incipient rounded boulders from bedrock granite, and the rounding of those boulders when detached all point to chemical processes of felspar decomposition, and it seems clear that for the crystalline rocks at least this process is of major importance.

But such chemical decay implies the presence of water, and a second problem thus arises as to where the water comes from. Blackwelder appealed to the occasional rainshowers, holding that although after them the rock surfaces dried quickly, small quantities of water which had penetrated a short distance into the rock would remain and slowly attack the minerals. This is one possibility, and it must be remembered that in the high temperatures experienced quite small quantities of water mixed with air could be very active. But it seems likely that in many deserts precipitation of night dews may make a significant contribution. Relative humidity readings taken by the author in the Libyan Desert in 1938 showed astonishing increases up to 60 or 70 per cent by midnight after day minima of 10 per cent or less, and successful experiments conducted in Palestine with simple dew-traps support the possibility. The common "vermiform markings" to be seen on limestone fragments in lag gravels* (the German *Rillensteine*) have been at-

* The term *lag gravels* is widely used in American geological literature to describe the thin superficial coatings of pebbles or small stones which form the surfaces known as *desert pavement* in the New World, *reg* and *serir* in the Sahara. These surface gravel layers are formed by progressive wind removal of all the fine particles from mixed alluvial or other deposits, leaving the larger stones to accumulate on the surface. When the stones touch one another in a continuous carpet the underlying material is completely protected from further wind deflation (hence the term *armoured surfaces*), and the harder stones of old lag gravels are commonly highly polished by sand-blast and may be cut into dreikanter forms.

tributed to solution by dew films; and even if liquid dew were not precipitated, it seems likely that pervious rocks desiccated during the day will draw in large quantities of water in the vapour form at night, as L. A. Ramdas has shown to occur in desert soils in the Punjab. The apparent total absence of surface water during the daylight hours may thus have misled observers as to the possibilities of water-motivated chemical weathering even in the driest locations.

To these general comments it must be added that other processes may also be at work to varying degree. Many years ago J. T. Jutson stressed the importance as a weathering agency of the surface crystallization of salts drawn out of the rock in solution by evaporating water. For this action to be potent, larger quantities of water would be needed, and Jutson cited the process as being particularly important in eating away the feet of rock pedestals around the edges of the shallow and shifting West Australian lakes. The writer has wondered whether isolated "finger-rocks" noted in shallow desert depressions in southern Libya, and recorded elsewhere by other observers, which frequently exhibit a similar annular cavity near ground-level, may not have derived it in a similar way from former periodic wetting by some long-vanished sheet of water. This touches immediately on the question of former climatic conditions; but the possibility seems worth recording, since such rocks are often cited as positive evidence for the efficacy of ground-level etching by sand-blast. Again exfoliation, which is not of course confined to desert areas, has frequently been explained in part at least as due to spontaneous dilatation of rock masses through "unloading" as the originally super-incumbent strata were removed. In many cases this seems the most likely explanation, but various different factors may be involved in different cases.

Before leaving weathering brief mention may be made however of processes commonly observed in desert areas which may not be directly destructive to rocks, and may even be preservative. A wide variety of surface incrustations and mineral skins has been recorded, under the general term "desert varnish", although this should perhaps properly be restricted to a limited group. The true desert varnish presents intriguing problems to the mineralogist and rock chemist in terms of the physics and chemistry of its growth and the origin of the manganese which is so prominent a constituent of it, but it does not seem to have any particular physiographic importance save in cases where it may cover large expanses of rock and help to preserve them from destructive weathering. The much thicker hard blackish "rind" so commonly observed as an outer coating on loose blocks and fragments of sandstone in the Sahara however may have more significance. Often a quarter of an inch or more in thickness, composed largely of oxides of iron and manganese, and flinty hard, this crust when unbroken effectively protects the underlying material from all weathering and erosion, yet when broken it is found to have drawn out in its growth much of the cementing material from the inner rock which is left weak and is readily scoured away. Fragments, tubes, "cannon-balls", and other queer-shaped stones made of this material are often a major constituent of the lag gravels which cover much of the *reg* plains in the Nubian Sandstone areas of the Sahara, but it does not yet seem to have been established with certainty whether these fragments represent portions of formerly continuous surface rock-coatings, or concretionary structures which grew within beds of sandstone now weathered away. W. H. Hobbs claimed to have seen this crust widely developed over sandstones near Kharga, giving the rock the appearance of basalt, but more recent travellers in this region have not recorded it in this form, and opinion seems to favour an original growth within the parent rock. Studies of deep weathering in the moist tropics record growth astonishingly similar and the question is thus raised as to whether this black crust, though so typical of the desert, really originated in an arid climate at all.

The same kind of problem attends the last phenomenon of this type that can be mentioned; the much thicker superficial formations which have come to be known as "duricrusts". Described thirty years ago by Woolnough in Australia these occur as thick indurated formations, often 20 feet deep, bonded by cements which may be ferric, calcic or silicic and are often extremely hard and resistant. The American caliche is a formation of this type, as are the thick and tough silcretes described by du Toit, King, and Frankel and Kent in South Africa. In Western Australia the formations are more commonly iron-bound, and termed ferricretes. Physiographically these formations, where they occur, may be of considerable importance, for they seem to occur only on ancient erosion surfaces of marked lack of relief, but when the latter are uplifted and dissected the duricrusts form a protective cap-rock and as such contribute significantly to the development of characteristic flat-topped mesas and vertical-lipped escarpments. In themselves, however, these formations offer other interesting problems, for although found widely in deserts it is believed that they too may not be the product of truly arid conditions. Woolnough indeed concluded that the necessary conditions for their growth demanded not only a surface of minimum relief, but a savanna type of climate offering ample seasonal rains separated by long hot dry seasons. The ferricrete variety indeed may well be a kind of fossilized laterite; and the implication is that at the period of its formation Western Australia had a very different type of climate from that which now prevails. Some time ago Sandford recorded somewhat similar fossil laterite in the Libyan Desert again with the suggestion that at some earlier period this part of the Sahara enjoyed a savanna type of climate; and comparable formations have been recorded from the Ahaggar. If these suggestions are correct we may thus have here important evidence bearing on the question of the climatic history of our great deserts.

To complete these scattered comments on aspects of weathering brief mention must be made of the difficult question of relative rates— a matter on which we know all too little. Faced with the profusion of weathered debris, the traveller in deserts may initially conclude that weathering must be very rapid; but when one finds lower Paleolithic artefacts lying sharp and unburied although polished among the surface residues, a different picture is presented. We have little concrete evidence on which to base quantitative estimates, but comparatively it would seem that in most desert locations weathering is exceedingly slow; far slower than in comparable locations in the humid lands. This is indicated by the rapidity with which the "Cleopatra's Needles" have weathered since their removal to London and New York in comparision with the trivial damage they had received in 3500 years in their native Egypt, and even more perhaps by the remarkable degree of preservation of prehistoric rock-carvings and paintings on exposed rock-walls at many sites in the Sahara. Such evidence indeed tends to support the view that the drier the climate, the less the weathering, irrespective of temperature. Some attempts have been made to estimate weathering rates by study of the growth and decay of desert varnish over roughly dateable prehistoric petroglyphs but with inconclusive results. All that can perhaps safely be said at present is that weathering in deserts seems to proceed very slowly indeed; and the disharmony between this conclusion and the profusion of weathered debris suggests again the possibility of legacies from former conditions of different climate.

Landscape and Its Evolution: Major Features

Although desert landscapes exhibit a wide range of variation, it has long been agreed that apart from their lack of co-ordinated drainage systems and thus somewhat chaotic relief, the most distinctive feature is the marked angularity of much of the scenery. Mountainous tracts are typically harsh, sharp and jagged. Elsewhere the landscape may be made up of a number of separate, almost horizontal levels, more or less dissected, but joined one to another by steep straightish slopes. Or again, vast sensibly flat plains may predominate, sometimes virtually featureless, in other cases dotted with isolated and steep-sided hills which leap up out of the plain "like cliffed islands rising from the sea". The gently flowing curves which in our own countryside normally link hill-top with valley-floor and plain are little in evidence, and may be totally lacking.

Attempts to interpret the evolution of these strange types of scenery began, as earlier noted, with appeal to former sea-floors or to the sculpturing of wind, but in formulating his "Geographical Cycle in an Arid Climate" W. M. Davis visualized the dominant agency as occasional storm-floods aided by persistent weathering; the former dissecting and wearing down the "original mountains" and sweeping their wastes into the initial deformation basins, the latter assisting in the slow retreat of scarps and the reduction of the residual mountains. Ultimately, in old age, the tectonic basins would have been all filled in, the mountains reduced to tiny residuals or cut away altogether, and broad plains of arid erosion would develop dotted with low-angle rock domes marking the sites of the original mountains. Emerging out of this concept, and extensively discussed both by Davis himself in later papers and by many subsequent writers, came the theory of the initiation and evolution of low-angle erosional surfaces surrounding the dwindling mountains, the features to which W. J. McGee had somewhat earlier applied the term "pediments", and which have given rise to so much controversy ever since.

Since Davis wrote, no radically different overall cyclic scheme has been suggested, although opinion has swung over in favour of a more Penckian type of mountain-reduction by slope retreat, systematized by L. C. King in his pediplanation theory. Attention on the whole has centred more on specific landscape elements, such as the pediment and the forms and features of mountain-face slopes. Before turning to these, however, it is perhaps worth noting that although Davis claimed that his scheme was applicable to any type of initial surface, it was patently geared in substantial measure to the arid landscapes he knew best in the American Southwest. There, is the Basin and Range Province, the high degree of tectonic dislocation permits the scheme to be applied readily and convincingly; but it is not so easy to apply it to some areas in the Old World deserts where aridity may well have overtaken regions of marked stability and already reduced to a plains condition. This matter will be touched on again later.

The Pediment

So many papers have been written about pediments, and so many varying hypotheses advanced, that it would be impossible to give here any useful account of even the main ideas. . . . Despite the extensive literature, however, it seems doubtful if all the problems involved in pediment formation have been fully solved. The true pediment has been defined as a gently shelving mountain-foot slope, faintly concave up-wards and steepening toward the mountain, and carved out of bedrock, though commonly carrying a thin veneer of detritus in course of transit. Its slope may increase from perhaps half a degree or less at the outer margin, where it usually disappears under an alluvial blanket, to 5 or even 7 degrees at the inner margin. It is often remarkably smooth and undissected; almost straight in transverse profile (parallel to the mountain-foot); and at its inner margin connects, often in a remarkably sharp and clean-cut angular junction, with the rough weathered mountain-face rising behind it at any angle which may exceed 30°. The general form of the typical pediment makes it appear certain that it has been superficially planed off, if not entirely cut, by flowing water; yet it also appears certain that it can only have grown to its present dimensions by a progressive backward retreat of the original mountain-face which has maintained its contrasting steep angle. The main agency responsible for the mountain-face retreat would appear to be overall weathering, assisted in the removal of its products by direct gravitational sliding and rolling, wind action, and probably above all by rain-wash during storms. From the foot of the mountain-slope further removal of this material is conceived to be mainly the work of flowing water, which in its progression planes off and grades the expanding pediment. But during prolonged and extensive retreat it is not entirely clear how the sharpness of the angular junction between the two surfaces is maintained and how water-flow having the correct volume, load, and flow characteristics can be so suddenly and uniformly supplied at the head of the pediment as to smooth and grade it right back to the foot of the mountain-slope.

Various suggestions have been made to answer these problems, but only one or two can be touched upon here. W. J. McGee, the discoverer of the pediment, suggested that sheet-floods, those distinctive phenomena of the desert, had been the agency responsible for planing off and developing the smooth pediment surfaces, but S. Paige pointed out that for water to adopt the sheet form of runoff demands the prior existence of a smooth gently inclined surface no less than appropriate loading conditions. McGee, he argued, had confused cause and effect. This point is mentioned because several more recent writers on pediments have advanced arguments which seem to verge on the same debatable ground. L. C. King, who has extended the concept of pediments far beyond its original homeland and indeed claimed that features genetically similar can form in the humid European environment, although his broad "pediplanation" theory was first developed and applied to sub-arid lands in Africa, has argued that the dominant agency responsible for both mountain-face (or escarpment) retreat and pediment formation and extension is surface water-flow; the sharp contrast between the two slope forms in inclination and surface character being due to a sudden change in the volume and nature of the runoff. On the mountain-face the runoff is of the "rainwash" type, a network of thin, ever-changing and intertwining threads of water incapable of effective linear erosion but in aggregate very effective in washing down to the slope foot particles loosened by weathering. With the augmentation in volume downslope, however, at a certain point the character of the runoff changes from what N. M. Fenneman called "unconcentrated wash" into "concentrated wash", with much greater erosive and transportive capacity. This "change-over" line marks the junction between mountain-face and pediment, and downslope from that line the rock is carved away into a smooth upwardly concave graded slope, whose undissected character results from the heavily loaded condition of the runoff which forces it to act in the manner of a braided stream with constant lateral migrations and planation, or even as a sheet-flood, with dominantly laminar flow. Quoting King: "But, as the angle of slope falls off . . . threadflow soon becomes incapable of removing the volume of precipitation: the threads join up into sheets . . . and a land-form is needed that can dispose of sheet-flow. *This land-form, adapted to, and moulded by, sheet-flow of water is the pediment.* It can dispose of the large volume of water produced by a thunderstorm of intensity 3 or 4 inches per hour more efficiently, more quickly, and with less damage to the landscape than any other topographic form: it is the answer to the thunderstorm and the cloudburst."

King, both from his own observations, and from those of T. J. D. Fair that he quotes, leaves no doubt that the general character of runoff flow *does* alter at the slope-junction; but it could be expected to do so as a result of the sudden change in slope-angle if this had been caused in other ways, and it is not easy to visualize how such a sharp and sudden change-over in nature and result of runoff could develop along such a regular line without some pre-existing break in the topography. J. A. Mabbutt, treating pedimented forms in Little Namaqualand, recognizes this hen-and-egg difficulty, in that he suggests that the smooth pediment surfaces themselves are in part the result, in part the cause, of the sheet-wash type of runoff which crosses them; but the mechanics of development and maintenance of the sharp angular junction of the two slope forms still seems to the writer to present difficulties not wholly explained. If we are to treat the whole profile, mountain-face and pediment together, as a continuous unit dominantly developed by surface water-flow throughout, there is little in current stream-profile theory to suggest an explanation. E. Yatsu has presented interesting evidence of stream-profiles in Japan which display angular breaks (or at least the linkage of two different exponential curves) which he attributes to the dominance of two markedly different grades of load material with a lack of material in the size ranges between them, but it is not easy to see an explanation of the pediment form in these terms. If, on the other hand, we consider that the mountain-face retreats primarily under weathering (as many have held), and that the pediment, apart from its surface smoothing by flowing water, develops essentially by weathering retreat of the mountain-face slope-foot, equal difficulties arise in explain ing how the junction-line remains so even and regular in level, and so sharply cut. Space will not permit development of these themes, but it seems that despite all that has been written about it, the pediment landform has not yet been fully and convincingly explained in terms of physiographic processes. Tuan's conclusions about the Arizona pediments, which he has recently studied in detail, although revealing a number of morphologically different types and favouring the kind of evolution originally suggested by A. C. Lawson rather than that championed by D. W. Johnson, do not materially extend our understanding of the mechanics.

But apart from the tantalizing problem of how pediments develop, questions arise as to how essential a feature they are of desert landscape in general, and therefore of whether general landscape evolution theories which incorporate pediment generation are of universal validity. True pediments very similar to the American examples have been recognized and described in various parts of the Old World deserts, but there is much evidence to suggest that in many parts of arid Africa, for instance, they are little in evidence or even totally absent. S. Passarge, writing of the *Inselberglandschaft* of the Kalahari, stressed that the "island-mountains" had no surrounding belt of transitional hills and no intermediate slope separating their steep flanks from the plains, and in many parts of the Sahara, photographs reveal tower-like hills and mountains rising from the surrounding flat plains without the intervention of any recognizable pediment. Features of this type are particularly well developed in the massive older Palaeozoic sandstones from which the dissected Tassili plateaux have been carved, as in the Ajjer region, in Ennedi, and around the flanks of Tibesti. Without detailed ground investigation it is difficult to know how much a superficial flattish cover of blown sand may contribute to the "marine stacks" impression of these features, but in the neighbourhood of hills such sand, unless built into recognizable dunes, is likely to be thin; and in the southern Libyan Desert the writer noted substantial inselberg mountains not only lacking any recognizable pediment, but also in some cases being possibly surrounded by a slight annular depression comparable to that surrounding some of the haystack inselbergs of Nigeria. Unfortunately this visual impression could not be checked by measurement on the ground, and the writer is not aware of any detailed studies based on measurement conducted in the regions of extreme aridity in the Sahara or elsewhere which might throw light on this question. Indeed, as was stated at the outset, a recurrent difficulty in trying to assess the validity of existing theories of desert landscape is lack of sufficient reliable field data to allow us to judge how well they fit the existing facts; and the pediment is of course only one of the range of landforms to which this element of uncertainty is attached. Lacking basic surveys we cannot even say with any precision and certainty what *are* the dominant landforms in the Sahara or Arabia; and until adequate measurements of forms, and related geological information, are available on a much wider scale than at present it might well be held a waste of time to debate interpretative theories. But whether the flat surfaces around "haystack" inselbergs in the Libyan Desert are truly very low-angle pediments or not, attention might again be drawn to a basic difficulty inherent in many of the general theories relating to the evolution of arid landscapes. Nowadays almost all ideas incorporate in some measure the notion of lateral retreat of steep slopes "parallel to themselves"; but to allow this to happen, the steep slopes must themselves have been created by some other agency as a starting-point. In the Basin and Range Province of the American Southwest such steep initial slopes can be credibly provided on the thesis of multiple block-faulting; but in areas like the Sahara the available geological evidence would seem to rule out this possibility over large areas. Lacking a "starting-point" in the shape of steep slopes created by tectonic dislocation, how can they be provided? L. C. King, in applying his thesis of successive cycles of pediplanation to the whole African continent, suggested a possible answer by postulating a series of continent-wide uplifts. These would cause deep incision of the trunk rivers, whose over-steepened valley-slopes would then slowly retreat laterally across country for hundreds of miles, leaving in their wake the familiar level plains. Doubts have been expressed about this idea on quantitative grounds, even supposing the basic mechanism to be correct; but in the Saharan region one might ask in addition where are the major rivers from whose overdeepened valleys the steep slopes could have migrated? It is difficult to envisage any satisfactory scheme in terms of the present geography; but again the question arises, could not the necessary deep stream-valley erosion have been accomplished in some former era of wetter climate, of which most traces have since been obliterated? This possibility directs one's thoughts beyond pediments, residual inselbergs, needle rocks, and retreating escarpments to the vast plains which surround them, and some brief discussion of these important features may be attempted.

Desert Plains

In presenting his "Arid Cycle" in 1905 W. M. Davis devoted some space to discussing the possible mechanisms by which extensive plains could be developed under arid conditions. He realized that in this context American evidence was inadequate, and in his discussion relied a good deal on Passarge's descriptions of arid South Africa. While admitting that under conditions of *total* aridity wind would be the only available agency of erosion, and that the later stages of his cycle would probably be much more arid than the initial, Davis found it difficult to imagine wind alone cutting the land surface down towards a smooth and level condition, since he thought that wind would tend to eat out the softer formations and thus create hills and hollows rather than obliterate relief. This tendency, however, he felt might in practice be counteracted by the persistence of occasional local rains and runoff which would wash wastes into any incipient wind-cut hollows and so counter the differential wind erosion. The whole surface, in old age, might thus be slowly worn down to create a true plain of desert erosion which could lie at any altitude in relation to the sea.

Whether any of the great plains which characterize a large fraction of our major deserts have indeed originated in this way remains a problem by no means fully resolved; but for areas where studies have been made in the field, opinion in general seems to be against Davis's suggestion. In the Sahara, for instance, some of the large featureless surfaces lie across enormous spreads of alluvial material, from which wind has sifted off the surface "fines" to leave a protective coating of *reg* gravels. Such surfaces are clearly in large measure of constructional origin, whatever the form of the buried rock-surface; and the same is true of the great clay plains common along the southern fringes of the Sahara described by Dresch and others. In other areas, level plains have a surface coating of wind-blown sand, which again contributes to their level featureless appearance, but probably only in small measure since away from dune-fields and ergs the sand is likely to be a thin veneer. In others again, however, the bedrock is widely exposed at the surface. On this latter type some examples carry a variable sprinkling of residual haystack hills, but others are totally smooth. One such is the great Selima Sand Sheet on the Egypt–Sudan border, an area of several thousand square miles whose surface is for the most part of a billiard-table smoothness. The whole area, so far as survey data are available, would seem to slope very gently towards the north and east, but at average gradients of only 2 to 3 feet per mile, and although its surface is uniformly covered by a flat sheet of blown sand this, where plumbed, has been recorded as only about a foot thick. Essentially therefore this area would seem to be a vast erosional plain cut across the Nubian Sandstone rocks, of quite extraordinary smoothness, extent and levelness. How are such vast erosional surfaces, which have also been recorded in Arabia and other of the great deserts, to be explained?

Various possibilities are theoretically open; but few writers have favoured the wind as a major agency. As Davis quite rightly observed, where we can identify evidence of true wind erosion on a large scale in the deserts it is in the form of sculptured features—yardangs, flutings and hollows—and there seems no physical reason why wind should erode towards a level surface. Davis's suggestion that occasional water-action would fill in any incipient wind-cut hollows with detritus is moreover scarcely convincing, since no such action would seem to have hampered the excavation of the great wind-excavated hollows described by Berkey and Morris in the Gobi Desert, or the vast Qattara Depression south of Alamein which has also generally been ascribed primarily to wind erosion. Indeed, the occasional inflow of runoff water into such hollows has been claimed as a contributory factor in their excavation, in that it leaves residual moisture in them which assists a more rapid weathering of the bedrock. We know all too little about the long-term and large-scale actions of wind to be certain but the balance of evidence seems to be against it as a primary agency in the creation of large-scale desert plains, although it may have contributed in important degree to the removal of material from them.

Of other possible explanations some have looked to marine agencies, either in the sense that the rocks forming these great plains are marine sediments uplifted without sensible distortion or tilt, or, where the rocks are patently bevelled by the surface, that sea-waves during slow subsidence cut the surface to its present perfect planation. Evidence is too scanty to warrant discussion of these possibilities, save the remark that in the interior Sahara neither seems very likely; so we are left with the possibility that the plains were subaerially eroded, but not essentially by the wind. This means that they were water-cut, either by flowing rivers (as peneplains) or by the processes of scarp-recession and pedimentation envisaged by King. The exceedingly low gradients which appear to obtain on some of the surfaces raise questions as to the feasibility of either process, but fuller quantitative data are necessary before this point could fairly be argued. The more obvious difficulty, that both processes would demand considerable surface water-flow, and hence a more humid climate than now obtains, is, however, less real than it seems, for as hinted at several earlier points, considerable evidence is accumulating that most if not all of our great deserts have experienced periods of much wetter climate in the past. To this basically important aspect of the whole subject attention must now be directed.

Climatic Change

It has long been realized that, quite apart from questions of any minor changes during historic times, all the great deserts have probably experienced phases of more humid climate in the more remote past. The evidence is of many kinds, but in the Sahara for instance there is the presence of numerous old lake-beds, now totally dry and often with the lacustrine mud deposits largely stripped away again by wind; the old strand-lines denoting former, much larger lakes in the major depressions, for instance the Chad basin, that of Bodele, and the basin of the middle Niger; and the multiple, ancient water-courses radiating out from the mountains, like the Igharghar and Tafassasset systems from Ahaggar, all today dry and often blocked by invading sand-dunes.

Biological evidence includes the presence of "relict faunas" including various tropical fish in the Algerian waterholes, the surviving small crocodiles in the pools of Tibesti and Ennedi, and (until they were exterminated) the elephants and lions of the Atlas. The profuse archaeological evidence, in particular that provided by rock paintings and engravings, demonstrates not only that man was able to live freely over most of the Sahara throughout much of prehistoric time, but that an abundant big game of the tropical savanna type inhabited it, and that in Neolithic times there was sufficient grazing for men to herd cattle in areas now totally sterile. All this points to the occurrence during Quaternary times of periods of substantially different climate. What is much less certain is how much wetter the climate was, when, and for how long. From various lines of evidence, opinion widely favours at least two separate pluvial periods, probably separated by periods of considerable aridity, and it is generally assumed that these, like the East African pluvials, were related to the climatic oscillations which produced glaciation in higher latitudes; but the problems of duration, intensity and correlation are by no means fully solved. In the present context, however, the immediately important question is whether, if we are correct in attributing much of the present landscapes to water action, this action took place predominantly or even entirely in some areas during the Pleistocene pluvials, and is hardly continuing at all under present conditions. To adopt this hypothesis would resolve the difficulties of some who have found it difficult to imagine the present intense aridity of large tracts of the Sahara permitting the kind of processes envisaged by Davis to operate effectively at all; but it would mean also that we are looking today at what is effectively a fossil landscape hardly changing except for very slow weathering, the highly infrequent local flood, and the constant sand-moving actions of the wind. This may well be a substantially correct picture; for W. Meckelein and his companions, in their study of northern Libya in 1954-55, felt justified in dividing that area into coastal steppe, semi-desert, and extreme desert zones and found that whereas there were plentiful signs of water-action (present or past) in the two former, no certain signs of recent water-action at all were found in the third, which they concluded was a region in which relief was being *conserved* rather than destroyed or created.

If we apply this hypothesis to the major lineaments of the landscape, a difficulty might appear in the question of whether the Pleistocene pluvials were of sufficient duration to permit water-controlled processes to sculpture the landscape to the degree that we must infer. But are we confined to Pleistocene pluvials? Recent studies in the Ahaggar open up much wider vistas. There French geomorphologists, after an extensive study, conclude that throughout the whole of the Ahaggar there is little or nothing in the scenery, save sand dunes and patination on the rocks and pebbles, which can realistically be ascribed to the processes proper to aridity. Little trace can be found of wind erosion; the massive crystallines, volcanics, and sedimentaries alike are carved up into a system of water-formed valleys; the granites, particularly at higher levels, are deeply weathered and rotted by processes which seem to demand much more moisture than is at present avaialable; and some suggestions of frost-action and nivation have been recorded. Even lower down, in the fringing plains, these authors saw a striking likeness between the inselberg-dotted plains and those familiar to us in the savanna lands; and their conclusion is that the whole of this landscape, apart from superficial details, is in essentials relict from Tertiary and in part from even earlier times and was carved under conditions of abundant seasonal rainfall of the savanna-land type. Aridity, they claim, as preserved this essentially fossil landscape, as it has preserved the alluvial spreads on the great *reg* plains, spreads which, in their structure, show clearly that they were laid down dominantly under considerably more humid conditions.

These conclusions, although they undermine many of our notions about the "arid landscape cycle", are clearly in line with a number of the points made earlier in this paper, and if similar interpretations have general validity, many of the difficulties and apparent contradictions earlier discussed disappear. A great deal more study will obviously have to be done in a variety of areas; but it is becoming more and more evident that we are in no position to build up new theories of landscape evolution under aridity by inference from studies of our present desert landscapes until we have a much more certain and complete picture of their climatic background than has hitherto been available.

Sand and Dunes

Little has been said about wind-blown sand in the deserts, a major subject in itself; but here at least, it might be thought we have a field in which the phenomena are purely the product of current conditions. This is patently in large measure true; but without attempting to enlarge on the many intriguing problems relating to the building of desert dunes, a subject which R. A. Bagnold's brilliant work has done so much to clarify, certain broad questions remain unanswered which do again bring us in contact with problems of past climate. In the Sahara, although some sand is present in most places, the major dune-systems are concentrated in particular regions: the great ergs and sand-seas. What is the origin of all this sand, and why is it so largely concentrated into particular areas? Bagnold himself has argued that the bulk of the sand comes from the breakdown of arenaceous rocks, and this is probably correct, since the Sahara is rich in sandstones, themselves in some cases built in part of consolidated ancient dunes; while the great concentrations have been explained on the theory that the active sand has been released by wind-sifting from vast alluvial accumulations, some of which may underlie the great ergs. Oil-well borings, some of which have been made in erg areas, may tell us more about this. There is then the intriguing pattern of the great belts of longitudinal dunes, which fall into enormous arcuate systems spanning the whole breadth of the Sahara. These must surely be governed by the dominant flow of the air-streams across the desert from north to south, but much more meteorological data will be necessary before wind directions and dune trends can be correlated in detail over the whole region and Bagnold's theories about the building of the great seif systems fully tested. Anomalous trends are known, however, especially along the southern fringes of the Sahara where A. T. Grove has made an initial study of the relations between the orientations of live dunes and those of older dead systems. Such studies, when more fully extended and based on more certain knowledge of the relations between wind and dune trends, may well throw important additional evidence on past climatic conditions. Other important problems relating to dunes involve fuller understanding of the factors which determine the variable behaviour of sand in different situations; why it builds dunes here and spreads abroad there and why the different characteristic shapes of dunes occur where they do. And finally, quantitative problems, such as the average rates at which dunes of different types grow, extend, and migrate, invite a great deal more study. Such problems are not only of great interest in themselves. They have obvious practical implications; and again, as has been suggested many years ago, if we knew more about the rates at which the huge dune systems of the Sahara have grown, they themselves might be able to reveal further clues about the climatic past of the region.

Conclusions

The topics touched on in this paper have ranged widely, and the writer is well aware that the discussion of them has been incomplete and at times incautious. His purpose will however have been fully served if the paper has drawn attention to the great gaps in our knowledge of the geomorphology of a good third of the earth's lands, and to the dangers inherent in much of the interpretative theory that has been produced about desert landscapes. Almost every new study underlines the importance of giving full recognition to local and regional differences in past geological history, structure, and lithology; and as knowledge grows, so it becomes ever clearer that basic importance must be assigned to reconstruction of the past climatic history before we can safely finalize our ideas about the nature and significance of any hypothetical "arid cycle". Much information points to the conclusion that the greater the aridity, the less actually happens apart from the actions of the wind; and it seems increasingly probable that a great deal of the scenery in our great deserts is essentially relict from earlier periods, some possibly of great antiquity and quite probably of very different climatic conditions. The great problem for the future would seem to be to assess how much of the scenic evolution can truly be ascribed to the present desert phase, and until that is established, attempts to produce any definite "cycle" of landscape evolution under aridity by inference from the features in our present deserts would seem both dangerous and premature.

15. The Floodplain and the Seashore, A Comparative Analysis of Hazard-Zone Occupance

Ian Burton and Robert W. Kates

For better or worse, and often the latter, man appears to have a desire to live on landforms that are frequently threatened and occasionally overtaken by disasters. Volcanoes are perhaps the most notorious offenders of this type, but nobody seems to be leaving their fertile slopes. Both floodplains and seashores also qualify as this type of landform. Although efforts have been made to control or reduce the ravages of high water, success has been limited— so limited, in fact, that Burton and Kates have serious doubts about the wisdom of applying expensive preventative and ameliorative measures through federal action.

The United States is in danger today of embarking on a large-scale and costly program of coastal defense against storm hazard comparable with the program of flood control that has been operating in river valleys for the past quarter of a century. Federal legislation passed in 1936, and subsequently, has been largely the reason for the heavy investment in flood-control engineering works, to the neglect of possible alternatives. Yet appraisals of the flood-control program are in general agreement that despite federal expenditures of about five billion dollars, average annual damages from floods have continued to rise. Nor is a brighter prospect

SOURCE: *Geographical Review.* LIV (1964), 367–85. Dr. Burton is a member of the staff, Department of Geography, University of Toronto, and Dr. Kates is on the staff, Department of Geography, Clark University.

held for the future. The Chief of Engineers stated in 1960 that at the present rate of expenditure flood protection will "just about keep up with the increase in flood damage that may be anticipated by 1980 as a result of flood plain development over the next two decades."

A repetition of the same course of action with respect to coastal flood problems seems likely. The storm of March 5–8, 1962, on the east coast of the United States focused attention on coastal storm damage. One informed official recently remarked that it seems unlikely Congress will be satisfied that it has done its duty by coastal constituents until an Atlantic Wall has been built from Maine to Mexico!

It is feared that more than one billion dollars could be spent on coastal protection by the federal government alone in the next fifteen to twenty years without any assurance that storm damage would be reduced; in fact, it might well be that average annual damages resulting from storms and saltwater flooding would be increasing by the 1980's. Because of long-term sea-level fluctuations and other factors, a program to "contain" the sea would seem to have as little chance for success as King Canute's attempt to command the waves.

Human Adjustments

A variety of human adjustments have evolved in response to flood hazards in river valleys, of which engineering works are the most prominent. Others are permanent or emergency evacuation of population and property; bearing the losses with or without public relief; rescheduling of production so as to have low inventories at times of highest hazard; elevation of land; alteration of structures to make them flood-resistant; insurance; regulation and change of land use. . . .

Adjustments are also possible in coastal areas. The Chief of Engineers has declared that "in most cases, . . . on exposed reaches of shoreline, the principal reliance for reduction of damage from hurricane floods will probably have to rest with adequate warning service, proper building codes, evacuation plans and routes, and with the zoning of more hazardous areas."

Thus there would appear to be a clear need for careful guidance in the human occupance of hazardous coastal areas. Such guidance will be more effective if based on studies of the rate of coastal development and the processes by which this development is advanced. The need for study applies to much of the United States coastal zone, though public interest usually centers on areas of spectacular damage, such as the New Jersey coast, or on areas of controversy, such as Fire Island, New York, and Assateague Island, Maryland-Virginia, for which highway and bridge construction is being debated.

The writers have recently turned their attention to problems of coastal areas, beginning with a reconnaissance of parts of the east coast of the United States from Boston to Cape May, New Jersey. A major conclusion emerging from this work is that new damage potential is being created at an accelerating rate, by occupance of coastal areas subject to high winds, wave action, and saltwater flooding associated with storms. This occupance, however, is uneven and diverse. It appears to be influenced by a variety of factors, physical and cultural, but the relationships are poorly understood.

Basic to a better understanding of coastal occupance is some assessment of the rate of development in hazard areas. Indications may thus be obtained regarding rates of expansion over the next twenty to twenty-five years and the locations of areas of most rapid growth. A partial answer to the second of these questions is available. It seems reasonable to assume that the most rapid coastal development is occurring on the northeast coast in the urbanized area from Massachusetts Bay to the Potomac Valley, which Jean Gottmann has called Megalopolis. Therefore, the need for better understanding of coastal occupance is probably nowhere greater than on the shores of this giant conurbation. It is not clear, for example, whether the rates of coastal development exceed those which might be expected elsewhere in Megalopolis or whether they are merely what might be expected in view of the rates of urban expansion being recorded in the conurbation as a whole.

Definition of Hazard Areas

In order that rates of enchroachment may be established, the complex problem of defining the areas of hazard must be solved. As an interim measure, an arbitrary contour level may be selected, but a more satisfactory definition could be gained from a careful study of the factors that determined the height of surge in recorded storms. It may ultimately become possible to calculate theoretically the probable maximum elevation of tidal damage for given stretches of coast.

Storm-surge elevations at a given level of probability may be derived from empirical relationships established by the National Hurricane Research Project of the United States Weather Bureau. . . . Thus the hurricane experience of 1900–1956 would suggest that there is a probability of 0.01 of receiving a hurricane with a central pressure as low as 931 millibars or lower, and such a hurricane would generate maximum storm surges ranging from 12.5 feet to 14.5 feet, depending on where it crossed the coast from Maine to Maryland. However, in view of the considerable local variability in depth of inundation, it is desirable to produce maps showing areas of hazard and other technical information similar to that now being issued by the United States Geological Survey, the Army Corps of Engineers, and the Tennessee Valley Authority.

The Process of Development

The definition of hazard areas and the establishment of rates of development are only preliminary. The greater need is for knowledge of the processes. The role of private, public, and corporate bodies in the creation of new damage potential is little understood; so is their role in urging expensive protection policies on government agencies after major catastrophes. Understanding is lacking of the attitudes and the perception of hazard prevalent among coastal developers, businessmen, and residents. Hopefully, studies directed toward increased knowledge of the problems would provide the basis for more intelligent use of the nation's coastal resources and would also provide guidelines for the formulation of sound public policy and planning in areas with regulations for shore protection and coastal land use.

In order to establish a body of concepts dealing with development processes and possible adjustments in areas of high hazard, a systematic comparison has here been attempted between the characteristics of floodplains and those of coastal areas with reference to their suitability for human occupance. The comparison is made largely on a priori grounds, supplemented by the coastal reconnaissance described above.

Hydrologic Features

The causes of coastal and riverine floods are dissimilar. Rivers flood by the addition of water through excessive runoff from the drainage basin or blockage in the channel. In coastal flooding the effect of precipitation is negligible, there is no equivalent of the ice-jam flood, and the main factor is wind-driven water, which rarely enters the riverine flooding pattern.

Although causally unlike, river and coastal floods have some similar or analogous characteristics. The *height* (or depth) of flooding, as measured by stream or tidal gauges, is a useful measure in both. Height of flooding can be more easily compared from place to place in coastal areas because mean sea level provides a uniform frame of reference; in riverine areas, height is relative to an arbitrary local datum. Among the factors affecting height, length of fetch is in part analogous to size of drainage basin. A number of characteristics of flooding and occupance are related to size of drainage basin, and similar analyses can be made of coastal areas, using length of fetch.

For any given storm pattern over a drainage basin or a coast, height of flooding varies with the set of prior or associated conditions. Just as saturated or frozen ground increases runoff and produces a greater depth of inundation, so the coincidence of storms with high tides increases coastal flooding. Tidal fluctuations can be predicted with greater precision than associated or prior conditions related to riverine flooding, but both need careful consideration in any estimate of maximum hazard. Estimates of height have assumed great importance in river flooding because of their value in the construction of stage-damage curves. As study of coast protection develops, height of storm tides is likely to be recognized as one of the more important variables.

In addition to height, six other measures have been found useful in describing river floods: (1) velocity (the average speed of flow of floodwaters); (2) discharge (the volume of water per unit of time); (3) range (the maximum variation in the height of a stream at a given point); (4) duration (the length of time that the river exceeds flood stage); (5) seasonality (the concentration of flood events within a part of the calendar year); and (6) flood-to-peak interval (the time lapse between flood stage and the maximum peak, or crest.

Velocity can also be measured in coastal floods, and in both types it is an important variable, to which the amount of damage is directly related. *Discharge* has had more limited use, with reference to tidal inlets and the measurement of littoral currents.

Range varies considerably both in river and in coastal floods, but it is our impression that extreme ranges are more frequent along major rivers. Associated with the range is the extent of the area subject to flood. Floodplains several miles in width may be inundated, and analogous to such flooding is the inundation of extensive flat coastal areas. An outstanding example of a greater saltwater flood occurred on the north European coast and in eastern England in February, 1953. More commonly, however, flooding is limited to a narrow strip of land along the river or the seacoast. Where the hazard area is a narrow strip, and where similar land resources are available close by without the attendant hazard, there seems little reason to place residential or industrial property in the path of possible future floods. Yet this has frequently happened, both in river valleys and, as examination of new communities on the south shore of Cape Cod suggests, in coastal areas. Some purchasers of such property have been ignorant of the risk or have underestimated it.

Duration of flooding on floodplains is related to size of drainage basin and may be several days or even weeks, as in the backwater flooding in the delta of the Mississippi River. In a coastal area, "duration" may have the same meaning as in riverine areas with respect to slow-draining tidal marshes or a somewhat different meaning with respect to tide changes. Since a storm tide represents an increment over normal high tides. Storms that persist through several tidal changes are exponentially more severe than those of shorter duration. The duration is shortest with hurricanes and longest with extratropical storms. Thus it was the duration of the storm of March 5–8, 1962, through three successive high tides rather than the height of the storm surge that was the major damage factor.

The duration of a flood affects occupance in a variety of ways. In urban areas prolonged floods increase indirect losses, such as the loss of business and wages resulting from delays, and the loss due to continued submersion, which weakens structures, warps floors, and the like. Duration is of even greater importance in agricultural areas, since crops that might have been partly salvaged after a short flood become total losses if the floodwater does not drain rapidly away.

The recoverability of losses due to the duration of a flood is a matter of considerable dispute. The business of a retail store in an urban area on the floodplain may be interrupted for several days, but when the flood has receded, the lost business may be recovered, since sales may be above normal for a period. But the manager of a business in a coastal resort who is forced by flood damage to close early in the season cannot recover his losses in the same way. "Purchase" of the commodity he supplies has been diverted elsewhere or prevented, and not merely postponed.

Seasonality of floods permits adjustments, which may reduce damages, provided the seasonality is recognized and understood. For example, some farmers make deliberate adjustments by late planting or early harvesting to avoid having valuable crops in the ground during known periods of high hazard. A similar opportunity is provided by a well-defined season of hurricanes on the east coast, from August 1 to September 15, which contained 60 percent of the recorded occurrences from 1887 to 1956. For example, those who wish to have a summer cottage on the beach in an exposed part of the coast could use a trailer or mobile dwelling, which would be removed to a safer place with the onset of the hurricane season or with early warning of an approaching hurricane. The danger lies in the unexpected, out-of-season storm, which may increase damage by catching floodplain or coastal residents unaware. However, improved forecasts and their dissemination seem to be reducing this danger.

A long *flood-to-peak interval* provides the time needed for pressing into action a variety of emergency adjustments to river floods. It also permits extended measurement and observation, leading to greater accuracy and dissemination of flood forecasts. Conversely, flash floods give little or no warning, and damage may be correspondingly increased, with possible loss of life. In coastal areas the growing threat of an offshore hurricane compares with a rising flood in major rivers, and an extended period of observation permits hurricane warnings to be widely disseminated well in advance. In some coastal areas, however, especially where storms may develop quickly and unexpectedly, tidal inundations occur much more rapidly and may in effect be almost instantaneous, a situation comparable with flash flooding.

Geomorphic Factors

The hydrologic characteristics of floods are affected by the configuration of the land surface. It is helpful, therefore, in examining flood-hazard areas to be able to classify them according to their geomorphic characteristics. Ohya and others working at the Ministry of Construction in Japan have developed a classification of flood types on this basis. A classification of types of agricultural floodplain occupance in the United States has also been formulated. Here we have attempted to classify coastal types and to relate them to their floodplain equivalents or analogues (Fig. 1). The typology is unlike other coastal classifications in that it is based on those characteristics which seem to us to be

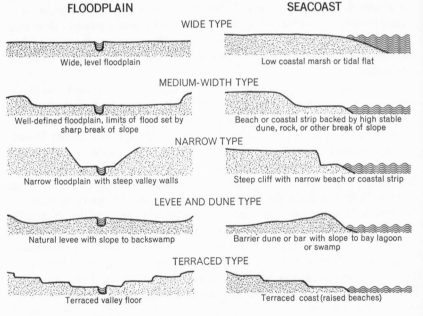

FLOODPLAIN   SEACOAST

WIDE TYPE

Wide, level floodplain   Low coastal marsh or tidal flat

MEDIUM-WIDTH TYPE

Well-defined floodplain, limits of flood set by   Beach or coastal strip backed by high stable
sharp break of slope   dune, rock, or other break of slope

NARROW TYPE

Narrow floodplain with steep valley walls   Steep cliff with narrow beach or coastal strip

LEVEE AND DUNE TYPE

Natural levee with slope to backswamp   Barrier dune or bar with slope to bay lagoon
                                                          or swamp

TERRACED TYPE

Terraced valley floor   Terraced coast (raised beaches)

FIGURE 1: A comparative typology of floodplains and seacoasts.

important for human occupance. To the coastal geomorphologist it will probably appear meaningless. Nor is the comparison with river floodplains intended to have genetic or morphological implications. This is a purely anthropocentric typology believed to have significance for present and potential occupance. It is not comprehensive but merely representative of some of the more common kinds of floodplain and coastal terrain. It is based mainly on width and slope of the flood-prone area and presence or absence of natural protection, such as levees and dunes or terraces and raised beaches. Each main type can be subdivided by size class of material (boulders, gravel, shingle, and so on) or susceptibility to erosion, factors that have important implications for occupance.

Wide Type

In an analysis of data from 104 cities with flood problems it was found that width of floodplain was directly related to size of city but inversely related to frequency of flooding. It seems likely that the reverse obtains in coastal areas; that is, where the coast is low and flat and the area subject to flooding is extensive, floods may be expected to occur more frequently, and large cities are noticeably absent. Floodplains and sea-coasts of the wide type may be expected to share problems of high water table and poor drainage.

Medium-Width Type

Where hazard zones are smaller and well defined, it is surprising to find their use expanding and little concern apparent. Such, however, has been the case on urban floodplains and, though not yet observed, could conceivably be in process in coastal areas also. An example of the medium-width type is the stretch of coast included in the Cape Cod National Seashore. The high stable dunes provide a splendid view for the residents who live on top of them, without flood hazard. However, no evidence has been observed of expansion down the front face of the dune in such areas or onto the beach itself.

Narrow Type

The narrow floodplain in the steep-sided valley is difficult of access and often remains free from dense settlement. When settlement does take place under the press of local circumstances, buildings are crowded on the floodplain, and the potential for a devastating flood is created. An example is the village of Lynmouth in north Devon, England, a small community crowded into the mouth of a narrow valley, which was virtually wiped out in August, 1952, by the rapid rise of a small stream following a torrential storm concentrated over its small watershed. Set-tlement is normally absent from the analogous coastal type, though the village of Hallsands is situated in such a position on the south Devon coast and has suffered severe storm and flood damage, perhaps asso-ciated with increased hazard due to offshore dredging.

Levee and Dune Type

Levees, dunes, and bars afford a degree of protection against high water levels, but they are not invulnerable, and severe damage may result when they are breached by man or nature. Property on the crest is destroyed in the area of the breach, and considerable volumes of water may flow through and inundate large areas. One characteristic of coastal occupance appears to be unique: there is no riverine analogue to the prevalent and continued destruction of coastal dunes to provide improved scenic views or building sites.

Terraced Type

Terraced river valleys are common and provide safe sites for human occupance. Only the lowest terraces are subject to flooding, and that infrequently. Less common, but equally valuable as safe sites, are marine terraces, which may command a view of the ocean without undue exposure to its dangers.

The Role of Engineering

In certain river and coastal situations, engineering works can be constructed to protect vulnerable areas. Where earth or sand can be used, artificial levees and dunes can be constructed. Floodwalls in some cities, and seawalls on some coasts, protect high-value property against damage. The dam has no exact equivalent in coastal engineering, though a hurricane dam is under construction at the mouth of the Providence River to protect the city of Providence, Rhode Island, and a plan is under study to build such a dam at the mouth of Narragansett Bay. Coastal harbor walls and jetties are more common, but they do not strictly compare with dams.

It is worth stressing that there are great technical unknowns in both riverine and coastal engineering. The effects of a dam on a downstream river channel, or of a groin on a beach from which the littoral current is being deflected, are only partly understood. However, there appears to be greater uncertainty in coastal engineering, related in some fundamental way to the magnitudes of energy that can be dissipated on the coasts.

One conclusion emerging from studies of river floods is that protection against floods of a low order of magnitude but high frequency of occurrence may encourage more rapid development in hazardous areas and thus increase the damage potential for less frequent but higher-order floods. It is possible, therefore, that where protection in coastal areas is not accompanied by new zoning laws or building codes, further encroachment may be stimulated there also.

However, our coastal reconnaissance leads us to suggest that the reverse may likewise be true. If removal of a barrier dune (levee and dune type) increases the amenity of a coastal site by giving more houses a view of the ocean, further development may take place, with a resultant increase in the frequency of damage. Conversely, the obliteration of an ocean view by construction of an artificial dune may reduce amenity value and slow up development.

Construction of levees in agricultural areas may have what has been described as the "levee effect." Managers of farms severed by the levee may be tempted to farm the land between the levee and the river on a speculative basis and may be better able to do so because of more secure farming behind the protection of the levee. A coastal analogue is the construction of a house on the sea slope of a barrier dune, especially where this is a speculative venture in the hope of quick returns from high rents during a few storm-free seasons.

Watercourses are canalized in both coastal and riverine areas. Ditches pierce natural levees to provide improved drainage for backswamp areas, but they may also act as inlets for water from the main river, which flows into the backwaters and accentuates the flood problem. A coastal analogue is the construction of canals to provide waterfront sites for dwellings that may be hundreds of yards or even several miles from the open ocean; in this manner many more coast dwellers are able to keep a boat close to the house and sail out to sea. These same canals, however, provide avenues up which seawater can be wind-driven far inland and cause severe flood damage in previously safe localities.

Cultural Features

In an assessment of what adjustments should be made in floodplain settlement to minimize flood damage, the factors must be considered that induce men to settle on floodplains and remain there in spite of a demonstrated hazard. It is helpful, therefore, to compare the locational advantages of floodplain sites and coastal sites.

River valleys have played a traditional role as corridors, particularly through dissected terrain. They provide low-incline routes for highways and railroads as well as the medium for waterborne transport. Installations associated with these transport arteries, and activities benefiting from nearness to them, have tended to locate close to the river, and often on flood-prone land.

Coastal margins rarely provide such convenient paths. More normally, coastal settlements serve as termini. Coastwise movement of people and goods may result in the development of ports, but these are isolated settlements, and their sites are often selected for shelter from the ocean, so that storm damage is low. So far as transport utility is concerned, coastal settlements have a greater opportunity for judicious selection of sites, and by virtue of the nature of their business and their high degree of awareness of the potential force of the sea, they have a strong motive for seeking out places where they are protected from its full force.

The association with transport is only one of the locational advantages of rivers and coasts. In the case of rivers, easy disposal of waste, the supply of water, the opportunity to develop power, and the comparative advantage of level land for building have historically influenced settlement. With the deterioration in the quality of river water, the reduction in the adequacy of waterpower for modern industrial needs, the substitution of other modes of transport, and the advent of earth-moving machinery, much of the historical motivation for floodplain settlement has declined or even disappeared. Settlement itself has not declined, however, and continues, by inertia, to expand from its original foci.

Coasts possess some of the same advantages. Easy disposal of waste is an increasingly important asset of coastal location. The waste products from human activity, though still small in relation to the capacity of the ocean, present a growing problem, especially in estuaries and bays that provide a terminus for river-borne waste.

In most places the ocean is not considered a source of water supplies. Continuing technical advances in the process of desalinization, and the rising cost of "fresh" water, suggest circumstances in which coastal locations could become highly favored, though not in the near future. Opportunity to develop power has also been absent in coastal areas. Modern technology, however, is changing this assessment of coastal resources. In the Rance estuary of northern France power stations are under construction that will use tidal fluctuations to turn the turbines. Similar plans have been developed for Passamaquoddy Bay, on the Maine–New Brunswick border.

The comparative advantage of level land cannot be said to exist to any great extent in coastal areas. But two other inducements are of great significance—access to the resources of the sea and recreation. Fishing is of paramount importance and leads to the settlement of coastal areas that would otherwise be devoid of human habitation. As in the location of coastal settlements directed primarily to trade, sites were formerly selected that would minimize the effect of storms. Advances in coastal engineering now permit greater flexibility and attention to markets in the construction and expansion of port facilities.

Undoubtedly the main attraction of coastal areas today lies in their opportunities for recreational use. This is a relatively minor factor in riverine situations, but on the coast it is the dominant reason for the rapid expansion of settlement in the past decade. An important aspect of the recreational amenity is proximity to the sea. The most favored sites overlook a fine sandy beach, with easy access to warm, calm water. There is a large extent of such seacoast in the eastern United States, and a thin ribbon of settlement (only in specially favored places is coastal settlement dense, and rarely does it extend far inland) tends to spread out along it. A situation is rapidly being reached, therefore, in which all seafront lots suitable for recreational use will be developed to some degree, so that wherever a storm or an exceptionally high tide strikes, some damage will result.

In both riverine and coastal locations the particular damage patterns we have observed appear somewhat random. There is a systematic variation in some of the factors at a particular place, but when all factors are considered, a random pattern is perhaps the most accurate description of the resulting damage.

The effect of flood damage on property values and on the social and economic status of the communities affected is complex. There is evidence to indicate that after heavy damage a community may never completely recover its former status. Examples are the decline of Narragansett Pier, which is attributed to the hurricane damage in 1938, and the more rapid decline of floodplain neighborhoods reported by Roder in his study of Topeka, Kansas. On the other hand, rather poorly constructed buildings or sea defenses may be replaced by more substantial structures after a storm. Evidence of high-quality reconstruction after the March, 1962 storm was seen along the New Jersey coast in August from Cape May to the Barnegat Light.

It has been observed that on river floodplains awareness of flood hazard is, in part, a function of the number of floods experienced. Also, farmers are known to have a keener awareness of hazard than city dwellers. Our impression, after interviews with a number of managers of coastal property, is that they too have a greater awareness of the hazards of storms than is common among city dwellers on river floodplains. Even the seasonal coast dwellers, who see the sea only in its usually more placid summer mood, seem to share this heightened awareness. The presence of the sea, the impact of the tide on the imagination, the increasingly widespread ownership of boats, and the minimal knowledge of the weather that may be associated with such ownership all contribute to this awareness. The city floodplain dweller with no knowledge of flood hazard is common. The coast dweller without a little knowledge of storm potential has not been found.

Nevertheless, coast dwellers, while showing a more realistic appreciation of what is possible, tend to be optimistic in their assessments of the frequency, likelihood, or probability of storm damage. They also tend to underestimate the possible severity of such damage. It might be safe to forecast that increased coastal protection will develop an even greater sense of confidence, without a corresponding increase in security.

If our appraisal of the coastal flood problem is correct, it follows that there is urgent need for further research and for greater understanding not only of the nature and degree of the hazard itself but, especially, of the process and rate of settlement in hazard areas. Such understanding may help to promote a more rational approach to the management of coastal lands.

16. Man as a Geomorphological Agent: The Example of Coal Mining

Arthur Doerr and Lee Guernsey

As this earth becomes increasingly crowded with men, their impact on the total landscape is bound to become greater. We tend to think of landforms as being produced by the mighty forces of nature, either by cataclysmic events of short duration, or as the result of processes at work, slowly forming the landscape through the centuries, millenia and eons. Man's role as an agent of landform development means work on a relatively limited scale and over what are extremely short periods of geologic time. Nevertheless, man is in many ways, but usually not deliberately, and frequently not consciously, creating new landforms and landscapes. Doerr and Guernsey have selected one of the more evident patterns of landforms developed by man and show us how it is accomplished. They view the results, as most of us do, as not particularly pleasing but nevertheless as visible physical facts.

Geographers, geomorphologists, and geologists have probably long recognized that man is a geomorphological agent, but they have been remiss in publishing analytical studies of man's influence on landforms. Some of man's *physical* landscape alterations are dramatic in impact, whereas other effects are far more subtle and difficult to observe. A complete examination of man's geomorphological influences is a stupendous task. It is not the purpose of this paper to investigate all the ways in which man acts as a geomorphological agent. Rather our purpose is to describe the effects of coal mining in the United States upon landforms and associated phenomena.

To this end it is necessary to inventory the mining regions from an areal standpoint; to recount the geomorphological effects of coal mining, specifically, where practical, and otherwise qualitatively; to postulate

SOURCE: *Annals of the Association of American Geographers*, XL (1956), 197–210. Dr. Doerr is on the staff, Department of Geography, University of Oklahoma, and Dr. Guernsey is a member of the Department of Geography, University of Louisville.

concerning coal mining–geomorphological relationships; and to speculate concerning the future course of coal mining and its influence upon
the physical landscape.

Common-sense hypothesis and later field verification disclosed that
the influences of underground mining and strip mining on the physical
landscape, while both distinctive, are separate phenomena. Hence the
influences of underground and strip mining are discussed separately.
Further, field investigations verified previous suppositions that landform
features resulting from coal mining are far more conspicuous in an area
of low initial relief. Mountainous regions are initially so gross in relief
that immediate mining influences are little more noticeable than a mole
hill on a level plain. It should be remembered, however, that subtle
influences are evident and can be detected even in rugged terrain.
Finally, it is obvious that the imprint of mining upon the landscape is
becoming more significant as man continues to meet the coal fuel needs
of the United States.

Location of Past, Present, and Future Coal Mining Areas

At present, coal is mined in commercial quantities in twenty-eight states
and more than four hundred counties. Thirty-seven counties each produced more than 5,000,000 tons in 1952. Each year approximately
500,000,000 tons of coal are removed from beneath the surface along
with countless tons of waste rock and debris. Of this total, about four-
fifths is produced east of the Mississippi River. Obviously, then, coal
mining has had a more significant geomorphological influence in the
eastern part of the United States than in western sections. However,
the locus of coal production will probably continue its westward shift
because of increased western fuel demands and an eventual depletion of
eastern coal reserves. As coal production expands geographically, the
influence of man upon the physical landscape will become more widely
recognizable.

Geomorphological Effects of Underground Coal Mining

Underground coal mining has always been of much greater significance
than surface mining. In recent years, however, surface mining is becoming increasingly important. While strip mining has had a more noticeable geomorphological significance, underground mining has had, and
will continue to have, considerable geomorphological importance. Landform features resulting from underground mining are conspicuous landscape features in areas of heavy production.

Soon after mining has begun, small mounds or hillocks, composed of waste rock or slack, are formed. These hillocks may be conical or oriented along a longitudinal axis. These mounds of waste materials vary considerably in height, depending upon the size of the mine, the quality of the coal, and the lateral extent of the land used for the refuse pile. Piles of refuse arranged along longitudinal axes are commonly about twenty feet high and occasionally may be as high as forty feet. On the other hand, if all the waste material is piled in the same place, the resultant conical-shaped hill (in general appearance much like a small parasitic volcanic cone, and certainly as noticeable as a kame) may reach heights of 75–100 feet.

The refuse piles which are oriented along longitudinal axes tend, after a short time, to develop swampy pockets in the space between succeeding ridges. These marshy areas are transitory and disappear with dry weather. Sides of the ridges are rapidly gullied and minute alluvial fans are deposited on adjacent flatter areas. Some of the hillocks disappear quickly, but one of the authors has observed sizeable ridges still in existence after fifty or more years.

The cone-shaped hillocks develop a miniature radial drainage pattern, and as years progress, begin to look increasingly like a small eroded cinder cone. Since both the cone-shaped and longitudinal hillocks contain poisonous wastes, they often remain without vegetation for twenty or thirty years. In addition, toxic materials carried to adjacent areas may poison vegetation and eventually result in accelerated erosion in these contiguous areas.

Waste materials which are burned at the surface produce noxious fumes, and as these fumes combine with atmospheric moisture, they may produce sulphurous or sulphuric acid which will destroy vegetation within the immediate vicinity. Occasionally underground mines will start to burn and must be sealed up. Eventually, if the coal seam is near the surface, smoke and sulphurous fumes will issue from the ground in a fashion not unlike that of fumaroles.

Other geomorphological effects are associated with subsidence, or man-induced faulting. "Squeezes" resulting from the collapse of a mine roof may cause earthquake-like tremors. Such minor tremors are frequently felt in areas of underground mining, and occasionally a sharp jolt is felt.

The effects of squeezes are instantaneous and at the same time permanent. After the squeezes, cracks may appear at the surface, small hills may disappear, swamps may be formed, and drainage may be temporarily deranged (on rare occasions, permanently deranged). In short, this man-induced faulting may result in many of the features associated with normal diastrophic faulting.

Other more subtle changes which occur in underground workings are due to exposure of subterranean strata to the atmosphere. Undoubtedly the rate of weathering is increased, which probably facilitates subsidence. When mine pillars have weathered away, continued settling may alter physical and cultural surface features radically.

History and Techniques of Strip Mining

The strip mining of coal began more than one hundred years ago. The first diggings were made by pick and shovel; later animal-drawn slip scrapers were used. Only outcropping coal or seams covered by thin soft overburden could be mined by these crude methods. Obviously, shallow mining and crude implements left little geomorphological imprint upon the land. About the turn of the century, steam shovels were used in scattered areas. In 1914 stripping was responsible for the removal of 0.3 percent of the coal mined in the United States, but this percentage had increased to almost 25 by 1949, and there were 1,761 strip pits operating in more than 220 countries of this country during that year. Larger equipment, introduced to increase strip mine production, has left more distinct topographic marks on the landscape.

During the past two or three decades some of the largest earth-moving equipment in the world has been used to remove overburden from above coal seams. Today, practically all strip coal mining is done on a large scale by electric or Diesel-powered shovels and draglines. The removal of coal is a relatively simple process, and the procedure is nearly uniform throughout the United States.

The first cut is made at an outcropping seam of coal in hilly terrain or at the limit of the leased or purchased property on level terrain. The overburden from the first cut is piled on the ground next to the area to be strip mined. In some cases the dragline simply digs down to the coal seam. In other areas a large shovel and dragline work in parallel-tandem operations. In this latter operation the dragline makes no attempt to work down to the coal, and the shovel removes the remainder of the overburden. In either operation the exposed coal is loaded into trucks by a loading shovel. The coal is then taken to a beneficiation plant and marketed.

Meanwhile the dragline operates continuously. At the end of the first cut the direction is reversed and a new cut is made parallel to the first, the overburden from the new cut being dumped into the first cut from which the coal was loaded. Thus the process continues as a cut-and-fill sequence until the last cut is made. The operation of strip mining equipment is rather methodical for any given terrain, coal seam, and method of mining, and the resulting surfaces in comparable original terrain have the same characteristics.

Geomorphological Effects of Strip Mining

Strip mining leaves the surface topography in a series of nearly parallel ridges and valleys. The actual width, height, and steepness of the ridges vary with the character and thickness of overburden, the unstripped terrain, the equipment and methods used, and the age of the banks.

When the depth of the coal seam is shallow, the local relief of the stripped terrain is naturally low. The strip mining of shallow coal seams leaves a vertical distance of from two to six feet from the bottom of the valleys to the ridge tops, and the relief between the last unfilled cut and the adjacent ridge may reach 20 feet. As the spoil banks age, the local relief is lessened by erosion and settling. In strip mining coal to a depth of 60 or 80 feet, ridge crests may be 50 feet apart, and the slopes are as steep as the angle of repose of the overburden. This means that the ridges will have a slope measuring from 30 to 80 percent. Extreme local relief of as much as 100 feet may be attained between the last unfilled cut and the adjacent ridge.

Disposal of the overburden alters the terrain more than is immediately obvious, since the volume of the excavated spoil is greater than the original volume. Consequently the spoil banks cover more land than the surface actually mined. The first ridge is piled on unstripped land and as a result is higher than adjacent ridges. In contrast, the final cut is a long deep pit with a vertical high wall on one side and a steep bank on the other.

The size and arrangement of ridges and valleys are partially determined by the mining equipment and methods. When power shovels or draglines are used singly, a high proportion of the rock strata immediately above the coal seam is placed on top of the spoil. This usually creates steep, sharply serrate ridges and conical banks, which, because of their steep slope, are subject to rapid erosion.

With tandem operations (those in which draglines and shovels are used jointly), the upper part of the overburden can be placed on top of the lower strata. Thus the surface spoil material has a higher proportion of soil and is more homogeneous in composition than when the dragline is used alone. However, these spoil banks are subject to excessive settling and severe erosion, in spite of the fact that their relief is less pronounced than on banks created by the single unit method. Further variation in the character of stripped land is developed because of the contiguous or non-contiguous location of stripped areas and irregular property boundaries.

Flat plains facilitate the stripping of entire blocks of land, whereas in rough dissected plains or hill lands normally only two or three cuts are made. In hilly areas, stripping is usually done on the contour. As coal seams in rough terrain usually dip into hillsides, it is practical to strip a band of only 100 to 300 feet. The total length of the cut varies from a few hundred to thousands of feet. On rare occasions entire hill tops are removed, and the spoil banks which are piled down slope normally do not exceed 20 acres in size.

Weathering and Erosion

The type of overburden which makes up the spoil banks varies considerably in different parts of the United States. Most frequently the sedimentary stratum above the coal seam is shale, and it, in turn, may be covered by other sedimentaries and/or glacial till, outwash material, or aeolian deposits. Obviously the character of the overburden is significant in weathering changes and soil formation.

The initial cut removes most of the soil and weathered parent material. As succeeding cuts are made, the overburden is composed of increasing amounts of unweathered material. Stripping, in effect, turns the soil horizon upside down and caps it with rock which originally capped the coal seam. The resultant conglomeration of material is much different from the original soil type.

Material making up the spoil surfaces includes sands, silts, and clays as well as sandstone, shales, and limestones. The majority of spoil banks are composed of loamy material and silty shale. Soil accounts for only about 30 percent of the total. These banks sometimes contain enough silt and clay to insure high water retention near the surface, but if rock fragments are dominant at the surface, run off and percolation are rapid.

Since material from immediately above the coal seam is usually thrown on top of spoil banks, a radical change in soil acidity often occurs. Frequently the overburden contains pyritic material which breaks down on exposure to air and moisture to iron sulphates, which are, in turn, altered to sulphuric acid. These acid spots usually appear as moist, roughly circular patches on spoil banks. This increased acidity precludes vegetative growth and at the same time kills beneficial microorganisms. It should be pointed out, however, that the overturned overburden is usually richer in phosphorous and potash than the original top soil of the stripped area.

Since newly formed spoil banks are devoid of vegetation, the bare surface lies exposed to the full ravages of weathering and erosion. Disintegration is especially rapid during the first few years after exposure of overburden with freezing and thawing, ice wedging, and burrowing causing a rapid deterioration of the surface rock material. Decomposition does not proceed as rapidly as might be supposed, since there is a general absence of organic acids, and the pyrites are located patchily. However, oxidation and hydration do occur with some rapidity, since newly exposed rock materials are usually not particularly resistant.

It is difficult to make a generalization about the rate of weathering, since much depends on the climate, type of rock exposed, mining methods, and the absence or presence of highly sulphurous material. As a rule of thumb it can be stated that weathering is more rapid in humid areas which experience considerable temperature extremes and where the coal or overburden is heavily laden with pyrites.

The rate of erosion is strongly influenced by slope of the spoil bank and texture of the overburden material. New spoil banks do much settling and slipping during the first five years of exposure. During this period the tops of ridges become rounded, the valleys are flattened, and the gradient of the slopes is reduced.

Increasing amounts of glacial till, loess, and alluvium increase the proportion of soil, improve the texture, and affect the erodibility of spoil bank surfaces. Valley strip mining generally results in more soil in the spoil surfaces than hillside strip mining, because of the greater proportion of alluvium in the overburden. Loessal banks are prone to severe gully erosion. Spoil banks mined in areas of glacial till are generally porous and well drained. Sandy spoil banks often contain enough alluvium to give them a slush-like consistency during rainy periods, and as a result mud flows are common in this type of stripped area. Then, after drying, the sandy spoils become compact and temporarily recemented.

As a general rule it may be stated that sandy spoils erode most rapidly, and shales erode the slowest. High clay content makes the shale more cohesive than sand and hence less subject to erosion. Gravelly till tends to resist erosion, but once a gully begins on a glacial till bank, it will cut rapidly.

Great quantities of earth are usually eroded away from spoil banks. In level terrain, miners and farmers often establish a diversion ditch to save adjacent fields from being covered by waste eroded from stripped sections. However, when rolling terrain is strip-mined, the mine waters are usually drained into a stream. Such a stream will frequently become overloaded, and its normal gradient and stage in the erosion cycle will be altered. Stream pollution from dissolved chemicals is commonplace.

Establishment of Lakes

Within the rough dissected topography created by strip mining, water often collects between the ridges and on partially graded areas. As a result, numerous small, intermittent, shallow ponds are formed. In addition, the abandoned runways, roadways, and final cuts usually become filled with water and form lakes as much as 80 feet wide and 50 feet deep. These lakes are not stagnant, since the water constantly circulates through the spoil banks; however, exposed coal of relatively high sulphur content often contaminates the water coming in contact with it. If this occurs, the water becomes a solution of weak sulphurous acid or contains other toxic elements. As a general rule, strip pits near the bottom of hills contain less toxic water and offer better chances of success with fish than those on the higher slopes.

Changes of Vegetation

Immediately after being formed, spoil banks are bare of vegetation. The physical conditions previously discussed affect the rate with which spoil banks are revegetated naturally. In general, spoil banks become covered with natural vegetation very slowly because of poor seedbed conditions on their surface. Woody plants generally begin to invade spoil banks within three years. A thin cover of herbaceous plants may also develop along with the pioneer trees and shrubs, but generally it is about twenty years before a tree cover occurs naturally.

As a consequence of the slow rate of natural revegetation, many states require that coal operators revegetate the barren spoils. By carefully selecting the species and sites, tree plantings have been made with a survival rate of more than 60 percent. Physical benefits derived from reforesting spoil banks include reduction of erosion, addition of organic matter to the spoil, and lowering the rate of moisture evaporation.

Contrary to popular opinion, grading the spoil banks does not aid plant growth. Rather, a poorer growth of trees on graded strip-mined lands is caused by poor aeration and moisture conditions due to the compaction from the weight of grading machinery. Surfaces have been reported to be compacted to depths of two feet as a result of the use of heavy machinery. Graded banks dry more rapidly during periods of drought than ungraded because graded banks cannot absorb what little rain falls. On the other hand, when there is heavy rainfall, graded banks tend to become waterlogged because of a lower percolation rate.

Extent of Strip Coal Mining

It is difficult, perhaps impossible, to ascertain the exact number of acres which have been strip mined in the United States. The problem is made difficult because accurate records of acres stripped are rarely kept. The principal interest lies in the amount of coal produced, rather than the area stripped. By inductive reasoning, however, it is possible to arrive at a reasonable estimate.

For example, the total amount of strip-mined coal from 1914 through 1954 was approximately 1,905,710,000 tons. This means that an area of about 380,000–400,000 acres has been stripped for coal in the United States since 1941. At present the strip-mined area is increasing at the rate of about 20,000 acres per year. Undoubtedly this rate will increase, since the percentage of coal mined by stripping methods is showing a steady rise.

Since levelling of spoil banks is negligible in most areas and weathering and erosion of stripped areas is slow by human standards (although rapid when considered from a geomorphological standpoint), the spoil heaps will become even more apparent features of the landscape Similarly, thousands of acres of land which have been undercut by underground mining will begin to feel the effects of subsidence after props begin to rot out of abandoned mines.

Conclusions

Man's removal of coal for fuel has resulted in a change in the physical landscape. By underground mining, man causes accumulations of rock debris near the mine mouth which form longitudinal or conical hillocks Earthquake-like tremors due to subsidence frequently occur. Man-induced faulting results in temporarily deranged drainage patterns, occasional depressions, and other surface modifications. Where underground fires have begun in coal seams near the surface, fumarole-like features are occasionally seen. Many other subtle chemical and physical changes affecting the rate of weathering also occur due to underground mining, but it is difficult to ascertain their significance or extent quantitatively.

By strip mining, man makes an even more obvious imprint upon the landscape. Modified ridge-valley terrain is developed, soil profiles are disturbed, buried rock strata are exposed to surface weathering, lakes are formed, and the spoils are made barren of vegetation.

Continued heavy fuel demands in the United States will result in more widespread influence of man upon terrain. Coal mining is but one of many examples of man's role as a geomorphological agent.

IV. BIOGEOGRAPHY

The biotic elements of the physical earth function interdependently with all life forms as well as with the inanimate elements in what could be described as a single gigantic system. Although the geographer and other scientists tend to treat some of these various elements as separate entities, there are direct and indirect connections and relationships between and among all of them. Because vegetation and animal life have been traditionally independent fields of study, biogeography is coming to imply a more ecological and systemic approach to the elements of the so-called biosphere and their relationships to other elements of the earth. The two articles in this section present a global view of biogeography—that is, the biosphere as one of the great systems of the unity of the earth. Subsequent separate sections on vegetation, soils, and animals consider these divisions of biogeography in greater detail.

17. The Importance of Biogeography
K. C. Edwards

Professor Edwards feels that biogeography is "more concerned with the world of plants than with that of animals." As has been suggested, the importance of both of these elements and a systemic approach to their ecology constitutes a principal contribution of biogeography. By its very nature and subject matter, biogeography appears to require a much stronger foundation in the biological sciences than has been found in the traditional undergraduate and graduate training of geographers. It may be, therefore, that biogeographers are biologists first and geographers second. Whatever their background and training, the work and contributions of biogeographers are of increasing importance in understanding the complexity of the contemporary world.

It might well have been expected that on this occasion I should speak, according to my bent, on some topic within the field of human geography. Instead, I feel it is high time that some recognition should be given to recent advances made in that "underdeveloped" division of our subject which is largely concerned with non-human organisms. The

Source: *Geography*, XL (1964), 85–97. The author is professor of geography at Nottingham University, England.

claims of biogeography to hold a more significant place in present-day geography are compelling and, to my mind, irrefutable. Research in this field is attracting an increasing number of able workers and, as their results are assimilated into the main content of geography, the subject becomes correspondingly enriched. To use a current expression, biogeography is one of the growing points of geography, and one has only to mention a few outstanding scholars in other countries, such as C. Troll in Germany, H. Gaussen in France, A. W. Küchler in the U.S.A., V. N. Sukachev and the late L. S. Berg in the U.S.S.R., to realize how wide has been the interest in this field during recent years. British geographers too have made, and are continuing to make, constructive contributions, and one result of their efforts has been the appearance of a basic textbook, *Vegetation and Soils* by Dr. S. R. Eyre, the first substantial work of its kind by a British author since those of Marion Newbigin more than 30 years ago.

Biogeography was formerly regarded as more or less synonymous with plant and animal geography. In practice, however, it is more concerned with the world of plants than with that of animals. This is partly because animals, like man, are ultimately dependent on plants for their existence; and it is partly because animals, unlike plants, do not exhibit the same close relationship to environmental conditions. Largely for this reason, animal ecology as a branch of zoology has progressed on very different lines from those of plant ecology, on which biogeography greatly depends. It is fair to add that plant geography as understood by geographers cannot as yet be matched by a corresponding animal geography. Among zoologists the distributional aspect has been mainly considered from the standpoint of evolutionary forms and their progressive dispersal in relation to changes in land and sea masses. The division of the world into six zoological "realms" by A. R. Wallace in 1860 was made on this basis and not on ecological principles, yet so far as mammalia are concerned, it has remained in use with modifications to this day. Wallace's line dividing Australasian fauna from that of Asia—a relic of schooldays among some of us older people—was, however, one of the earliest boundaries in biogeography. It was T. H. Huxley who gave the name Wallace's Line to this boundary. Later investigations have shown the actual demarcation to be much less sharp. We should also remember that Wallace, who died before the ideas of Wegener and Joly became current, rejected the notion of land bridges, which are now assumed to have played a leading part in the dispersal of animals and plants.

The Soil/Vegetation Complex

If the study of vegetation is one of the leading objectives of the biogeographer, the general importance of his field is surely obvious. After configuration the vegetation cover is the most conspicuous and the most universal of all the observable phenomena on the solid portion of the earth's surface. By far the greater part of the land area conveys to the human eye an impression of greenness—earth's green mantle, to use A. G. Tansley's eloquent term—even though under certain conditions the greenness may verge to yellow, brown, or grey. This is so commonplace that we take it for granted, yet the vegetation cover is the fundamental manifestation of the fact that so far as we known our planet is unique. It would seem inevitable then that geographers should seek to develop an understanding of the inter-relations between plants and the conditions under which they grow, particularly in terms of their spatial variation. To illustrate the intimacy of relationships between organisms, though not in this case among plants, I need only refer you to that notable example of ecological folklore, "On Ilkla' Moor baht 'at"!

Now since plants cannot be studied apart from the soil in which they grow and the climatic conditions prevailing within and above the soil, biogeography must include a knowledge of pedogenic processes and soil types as well as of actual, as distinct from generalized or abstract, conditions of climate. Bearing in mind, however, that climate affects both soil and vegetation, it follows that biogeography is concerned with the soil/vegetation complex as its central objective. The soil with its organisms and micro-organisms together with the plant cover constitute a true biosphere, the nature of which is of such fundamental importance to man that its investigation by geographers should be regarded as no less important than, for instance, the study of land forms. A case could even be made for it taking precedence over the latter, admittedly not as a logical procedure but as an alternative and certainly refreshing approach to either physical or cultural geography.

As with other geographers who specialize in the systematic branches, the biogeographer profits by the use of concepts derived from related specialist fields. Examples of these are the hydrological cycle, evapotranspiration and the soil catena. But the traffic need not be altogether in one direction. Professor L. Dudley Stamp in *Taxonomy and Geography*, a publication probably unknown to many geographers, has shown that biologists and ecologists have much to gain from co-operation with geographers, not least with regard to techniques of mapping.

Development of Plant Geography

At this point it seems appropriate to refer to the relationship between plant geography and plant ecology. While Humboldt himself as an eminent naturalist, often regarded as the founder of plant geography, perceived vegetation not merely from the floristic standpoint but also in terms of plant communities, it was only towards the end of the nineteenth century and after, in the era of post-Darwinian biology, that the foundations of modern ecology were laid. Among a number of works by continental botanists published shortly before 1900, two in particular should be noted. One was A. F. W. Schimper's famous *Plant-Geography upon a Physiological Basis*, which appeared in 1898, and the other E. Warming's *Oecological Plant Geography*, published three years earlier. While Schimper related the broad types of vegetation to physical factors and to climate in particular, Warming approached the subject from a more strictly ecological angle. He gave currency to the term "ecology" (invented previously by the German biologist E. H. Haeckel), adopted the concept of plant communities and initiated the idea of climax in what he called the vegetation of equilibrium. For a long time, however, the plant composition in each of the main vegetation types was regarded as static rather than dynamic. The dynamic view embodied in the principle of plant succession was firmly established by the American botanist F. E. Clements in a monumental work published in 1916. In our own country over the past 40 years no one has rendered greater service to plant geography than Professor A. G. Tansley, not only in connexion with British vegetation but also in achieving a final break from the floristic tradition in favour of modern ecological ideas. We can now distinguish plant geography in the sense of biogeography, based on an ecological approach, from the geography of plants, which is more specifically a branch of botany as represented by the well-known work of R. O. Good, *The Geography of Flowering Plants*. All teachers of geography, incidentally, should be familiar with the excellent little book by A. G. Tansley and E. Price Evans, *Plant Ecology and the School*.

The factors concerned in accounting for the character and distribution of plant communities are well known, but one or two of them deserve comment. These factors are, of course, climatic, physiographic (altitude, slope and aspect), edaphic and biotic, the last including man as well as animals and other organisms. To these should be added the historical factors which relate to previous changes in the distribution of land and sea, changes in surface features, past climates, and the like. The effects of the Quaternary Ice Age upon the vegetation of the British Isles, on which a good deal of work has been done, illustrate the importance of historical influences, as does the probable effect of Neolithic cultivation upon vegetation in the loess areas of Central Europe. All these are environmental or external factors and are the concern of the ecologist and biogeographer alike. To the botanist, however, internal factors are also to be recognized, but these relate, chiefly with regard to individual species, to highly specialized aspects, such as plant genetics (gene content and chromosome endowment) and dispersal mechanisms.

It must be stressed that the external or habitat factors are interactive, and while it is sometimes justifiable to regard one or another a exerting a predominant influence upon distribution, it is seldom that a single factor operates independently of others. This is where over-generalization most frequently arises. Thus in England the common beech is known to thrive best on calcareous soils, but there, in our teaching, we often leave the matter. This gives a wrong impression, for while it is true in northwest Europe, towards the southeastern limit of its range, as in the Balkans, the beech is either indifferent to calcareous soils or actually shows a preference for non-limestone soils.

Biogeographical Problems

Modern work in biogeography has thrown light on many problems relating to the origin and distribution of vegetation types, and new evidence is often conclusive enough to demand the rejection or modification of long-cherished ideas. During the past 25 years, for example, geographers and ecologists have devoted considerable attention to one of the long-recognized but least understood of the major vegetation types, the savanna. As a result, the commonly held view that tropical grasslands are the product of climate alone is now challenged because of evidence presented by different investigators showing the importance of edaphic and biotic factors, the latter including human interference largely through the age-old practice of burning. In 1938 the German geographer H. Lautensach expressed doubt as to how far the savanna should be regarded as a natural grassland. On the other hand, in 1956, C. Troll restated the case in support of climate as the overriding factor. In this country Dr. M. M. Cole, through her studies in Brazil, Central and South Africa, and Australia, has adopted a new approach to the problem which depends primarily upon recognizing the dynamic nature of both vegetation and the physiographic aspects of habitat. This is a truly ecological approach, acknowledging time as an essential factor in vegetation development.

Even with regard to the tropical rain forest, usually considered to be a stable community, investigation has shown that, at least in some areas, the climatic climax may be subject to modification. For, in the process of regeneration, young offspring of the dominant trees tend to be scarce or even absent, and the composition of the upper storey of the forest may eventually be changed by the seedlings which are likely to replace them.

Another example of new light shed upon an old generalization is that concerning the northern boundary of the great boreal forests. In broad terms this has long been identified with the isotherm 10° C (50° F) for the warmest month, but Professor D. L. Linton has recently drawn attention to the results of air-photo surveys carried out in the Soviet Union which indicate a different state of affairs. Instead of a continuous boundary, long fingers of tundra penetrate into the forest, mainly along the ridges, while tongues of forest following the valleys reach far into the tundra; also outliers of forest occur in the tundra and vice versa. Even more significant is the dynamic nature of the boundary. The forest limit has certainly retreated since early post-glacial times, but its present position hardly reflects the climatic factor alone. In many places man himself has contributed to the recession by burning, felling, and reindeer-herding. Other factors likely to accentuate the advance of the tundra are seed losses due to removal by wind and water and low rates of germination, which tend to restrict tree-growth.

These ideas put forward by Soviet scientists have lately received support from air surveys of the Canadian "Barrens". From the interpretation of these it appears that ground conditions here are now more important than climate in determining the forest limit.

Quite apart from the precise nature of the tree-line and its stability is the improbability of temperature control in terms of the 10° C isotherm for the warmest month, for except in a few places this does not closely accord with the forest limit. As Professor A. A. Miller has remarked, in stressing the importance of warmth duration measured in terms of accumulated temperatures, "a tree does not live and reproduce by July temperatures alone." Professor Miller also notes the confusion of ideas among climatologists, some of whom, including Köppen, make use of vegetation in formulating a classification of climates but in so doing are really distinguishing vegetation regions delimited by climate. Surely climatic types can only be based on climatic criteria.

One further instance may be given to show how biogeographical investigation directs attention to changes now taking place. This refers to the cedar forests of the Middle Atlas in Morocco. It has recently been shown that in parts of this mountain range current geomorphic processes have a marked effect upon the plant cover. The removal by erosion of Quaternary detrital deposits which mantle the slopes, thus exposing the schistose rocks beneath, appears to inhibit the natural regeneration of the cedar but encourages the spread of other conifers, especially the Aleppo pine. On the other hand, in places where the superficial material is not under attack, cedar regeneration continues unaffected.

In some of the less-developed countries problems of economic growth, when viewed in relation to one another, can be seen basically as different aspects of one major problem which is essentially ecological in character. In this connexion Uganda affords a good illustration. Here the improvement of living standards must depend for some time to come on progress in agriculture, both in subsistence cultivation and cash cropping. Due largely to an unbalanced diet, much of the population of 6 million suffers from protein deficiency resulting from an over-dependence on starchy foods, such as banana, cassava, and maize. Yet there are some 3¼ million cattle in Uganda, though these are mainly of poor-quality Zebu type. Cattle distribution is closely related to the non-occurrence of the tsetse fly of which serious infestations affect the herds from time to time in well-populated areas. Tsetse control and ultimate eradication are therefore essential to the improvement of both livestock health and human well-being. Among the human population the existence of sleeping sickness, which is transmitted by the fly, is now restricted to the comparatively small area of south Busoga. As a result of official anti-tsetse measures, many districts are closed to cattle-keeping. In some non-infected parts the Department of Agriculture, operating on behalf of the Tsetse Control Department, has encouraged resettlement by giving assistance in the form of land units of up to 20 acres per family. The settlers are responsible for clearing, but the methods employed seldom result in the bringing of more than 2–5 acres into cultivation, consequently the bulk of the holding is left in forest or scrub, which may readily become a breeding ground for tsetse. In other parts, forest conservation policy appears to be at variance with both settlement and tsetse-control aims.

One other important factor is the part played by the traditional practice of burning, a subject of continuing controversy in Uganda as elsewhere. The question as to whether, in respect of the dry season, burning should take place early or late has a significant bearing on vegetation growth, tsetse-breeding habits, and land-use needs.

Thus in Uganda there would appear to be a conflict of views inherent in the present situation, not because any of the measures for improvement are unsuitable in themselves, but because they tend to be applied as independent policies without adequate co-ordination. To view the problems as the inter-related aspects of a complex ecological situation might well provide a more effective solution. To the biogeographer the issue, stripped of its political and administrative elements, is basically concerned with a rational treatment of the plant cover.

Biogeography and Economic Vegetation

Does the study of economic vegetation form part of biogeography? In the broadest sense it does, for cultivation and organized grazing represent the maximum influence of man as a biotic factor. On the other hand, if the emphasis is to be placed on techniques of production and various economic considerations, the biogeographer may well yield place to the agricultural geographer. Yet from the historical standpoint there are points of interest for both.

Early man was nurtured in forest surroundings, and he has ever since spent much of his energies in clearing the natural forest to provide room for his crops and animals. That he started to do so at all was not only because he required open ground for sowing, but equally because his crop plants, to produce a harvest, demanded sunshine. Man's food crops were heliophiles, in contrast to the shade-tolerant plants which grew within the forests, offering him only what he could collect.

The earliest form of cultivation was by planting, which depended on vegetative or asexual reproduction. The use of seed followed much later, but in either case, by his methods of domestication, man created new varieties for his use. The appearance of man-induced plants, or cultigens, affirmed that man himself had become a formidable agent in vegetation development, a rôle further accentuated by the part he played in the wide dispersal of such species. Thus man became what Carl Sauer termed the "ecologic dominant" over many parts of the world. Vavilov and other Russian scientists have attempted to trace the geographical origins of the principal cultivated plants, basing their work on the idea that areas which to-day exhibit the greatest diversity of genetically related species and varieties are most likely to have been the areas of origin. This view is consistent with, though not a direct application of, the controversial Age and Area theory of the botanist J. C. Willis. Vavilov suggested that five such hearth areas can be recognized, all falling within the tropics and the warm temperate zone: southeast Asia, southwest Asia, Ethiopia, the Mediterranean basin, and Middle America, extending from Mexico to Peru. Later he added an area in China, but this only demonstrates the degree of uncertainty on this matter, which is still speculative.

Another close link between plant geography and the study of economic vegetation is the concept of plants as indicators of land potentiality. It is interesting to note that A. J. Herbertson, writing in 1897, accepted this idea and added, "How much waste of money and time might have been saved to settlers in most of our colonies if a systematic floral (i.e. plant) survey had been made." There is more than a hint of groundnuts here!

The Eucalypts Become Exotics

To illustrate the application of ecological principles to problems of dispersal in economic vegetation, we can hardly do better than refer to a particular genus originating in the southern hemisphere. If Europe's gift to Australia was men, Australia's gift to the world is trees, namely the great family of eucalypts (Myrtaceae). Until little more than a century ago when seedlings were successfully raised in southern Europe, the eucalypts were confined to their native habitat in Australia. To-day these trees with their characteristic greyish-green foliage and untidy strips of bark can be observed in many parts of the world, often in strangely unexpected places, fulfilling numerous purposes. They screen the wayside stations along the railroads of the Pampas and the new roads of Israel, they give shade to citrus-fruit farms in California and Arizona, they are grown for firewood in Ethiopia and the Nilgiri Hills of southern India, they help to stabilize the coastal dunes of Andalusia and the Cape of Good Hope, and as ornamental trees, they adorn the streets of cities from Lisbon to Canton.

In a belief, not fully substantiated, that eucalypts are effective in draining swampy land, they have been greatly used in reclamation schemes. Many were planted in the Pontine Marshes, perhaps also as an anti-malaria measure, and at the present time they are a feature of drainage projects in southern Turkey. One species, *E. robusta,* has been grown in Uganda for the same purpose, notably in the small valleys of Kampala, which were swamp-ridden until about 30 years ago.

It is mainly for the production of timber and fuel, however, that eucalypts are cultivated. Their adaptability to different climatic conditions encourages their use in areas of sparse natural woodland or in others where shortage has resulted from the excessive reduction of indigenous forest. If the yield from Australia itself is included, the present output from all areas makes the eucalypts the world's most valuable source of hardwood timber. In parts of South Africa especially in the Transvaal, under summer rain conditions, plantations cover 500,000 acres, chiefly *E. saligna.* Large tracts of this species, grown for use in the mines, clothe the *veld* around Johannesburg. In the Brazilian state of São Paulo, with its more uniform rains, large-scale production is again to be found, while an example of extensive eucalypt afforestation in an area of winter rain is that in the U.S.S.R. on the slopes of the Caucasus confronting the Black Sea.

The introduction of eucalypts into Ethiopia is of special interest. In that country frequent changes in the location of the capital during past centuries were the direct result of fuel shortages resulting from forest destruction. In 1885 the emperor Menelik, anticipating the move to Addis Ababa, which took place in 1896, established plantations of Australian gum trees in the district. These have been maintained ever since and still supply the city with much of its fuel. Moreover, every town and village in Ethiopia is now dependent upon its local reserve of trees (*E. globulus*) for fuel, timber and other materials. This species, the only one which proved successful, has become an essential element in the economy, and in serving the needs of the greater part of a nation of 15 million pople, it may well claim a unique place in the history of afforestation.

Brazil is the leading country for the production of eucalypts as exotics, with two areas of major importance, one in São Paulo and the other in Minas Geraes. In the former, cultivation started at Jundai in 1903 to supply fuel for the Paulista Railway. The railway company still maintains a reserve of some 5 million trees, although on this heavily used line diesel-electric locomotives have already reduced the need for wood.

In Minas Geraes, near Belo Horizonte, vast hillslopes are covered with young eucalypts to provide charcoal for smelting the famous iron ore (itabarite) worked in the district. Owing to the high cost of carrying coal and coke from distant sources, charcoal is the normal blast-furnace combustible, but its use soon depleted the native forests. The raising of eucalypts, mainly E. *saligna* and E. *robusta,* which reach a size suitable for cutting in about 7 years, has now ensured a continuous supply of fuel amounting to well over a million tons annually.

Having outlined some of the facts relating to the establishment of the eucalypts as exotics in many parts of the world, in little more than a century, some explanation of their successful dispersal is required. The adaptability of these trees to different climates has already been mentioned, but this characteristic can only be explained with reference to their family history and not merely to their geographical origin. For the genus dates from far back in Eocene times and continued to evolve, with the emergence of different forms and species, in response to changing physical conditions throughout the rest of the Tertiary era. The length of time involved, quite as much as the prolonged isolation of the Australian continent, is an essential factor in accounting for the great number of species, of which there are over 500, as well as their adaptability. This also explains why not all species are uniformly adaptable as exotics. The development of many drought-resistant types in Australia, however, has proved a major advantage in permitting their introduction to other regions which are too dry to support indigenous trees. Other than certain types like the snow gum of the Snowy Mountains of Australia, it is their general inability to withstand frost which prevents their cultivation in the cool temperate zone, although a few individuals have survived in the British Isles despite occasional severe wintry spells.

The long period of adjustment to changing conditions in Australia has also enabled the eucalypts to thrive in a great diversity of soils. Some species are distinctly alkali-tolerant, and this, too, greatly extends the range of possible habitats. The famous Tasmanian blue-gum E. *globulus* grows well in many types of soil and, largely for this reason, is now the most widely cultivated of all.

As exotics the eucalypts are almost invariably raised from seed. This is an important ecological consideration, for by this method plantations are kept free from pests to which the trees are susceptible in their native environment. One further characteristic of special economic importance is the exceptional rate of growth, which often amounts to 10 feet a year for several years. Thus with about 600 different species and varieties available to suit a wide range of physical conditions, this huge family exhibits a remarkable versatility among plants used in the service of man.

Conclusion

It is now time to summarize the main conclusions arising from this very inadequate attempt to assess the importance of biogeography. First, being concerned with the phenomena of the biosphere, including the relations between man and the rest of organic nature, it is obvious that biogeography occupies a basic position within the total field of geography. The facts of plant (and animal) distribution, moreover, are themselves facts of geography in that they help to differentiate the earth's surface, besides being inescapable factors in the human environment.

Secondly, just as geomorphology emphasizes the dynamic nature of landform development, so biogeography demonstrates the ever-changing character of the soil/vegetation complex. Its findings frequently bring to light new relationships and in so doing reaffirm the need for continued investigation.

Thirdly, by its very nature, biogeography affords an effective means by which other aspects of our subject may be integrated; and in this respect it offers immense possibilities in both teaching and research. Let no one think that biogeography is marginal to geography proper, even though some of its aspects appear highly specialized. On the contrary, it is more likely to enhance the unity of geography than some other branches of the subject.

Fourthly, so far as application is concerned, biogeography has its part to play as an aid in formulating policy for land development. This was ignored in the case of the Tanganyika groundnuts scheme, and the omission was clearly a factor contributing to its failure. With world population continuing its upward trend, the need for a constant review of soil/vegetation relationships in the interest of land productivity becomes ever more pressing. Allied to this, though it has not previously been mentioned, is the application of biogeographical studies to problems of conservation. Damage to landscape takes many forms, and there is an increasing demand for persons trained in the principles of ecology not only to undertake field investigations but, no less important, also to teach those principles to others. In the University of London the introduction a few years ago of a postgraduate course in conservation, under the joint auspices of University College and the Nature Conservancy, was a welcome innovation in this regard, involving co-operation between three departments in the College, those of Botany, Zoology and Geography.

Whether or not, as geographers, we explore the possibilities of using biogeography as a means of integrating the different aspects of our subject, biogeography with its relevance to man as a living organism, as Ratzel long ago pointed out, provides an essential link between physical and human geography.

18. The Ecosphere

Lamont C. Cole

An important contribution of the biogeographer (or biologist-geographer) is the essential ecological approach to life problems of the earth. By examining how all living organisms on the earth interact with one another and with their inorganic environment, we may be able to estimate, if not determine, the total life-supporting capacity of the earth. Obviously, such studies as this contribute to our understanding of one of the greatest problems confronting man—the significance of which goes far beyond the periphery of biogeography and enters the social and geopolitical fields as well.

Probably I should apologize for using a coined word like "ecosphere," but it seems nicely to describe just what I want to discuss. It is intended to combine two concepts: the "biosphere" and the "ecosystem."

The great 19th-century French naturalist Jean Lamarck first conceived the idea of the biosphere as the collective totality of living creatures on the earth, and the concept has been taken up and developed in recent years by the Russian geochemist V. I. Vernadsky. The word "ecosystem" means a self-sustaining community of organisms—plants as well as animals—taken together with its inorganic environment.

Now all these are interdependent. Animal life could not exist without plants, nor plants without animals, which supply them with carbon dioxide. Even the composition of the inorganic environment depends upon the cyclic activity of life. Photosynthesis by the earth's plants would remove all of the carbon dioxide from the atmosphere within a year or so if it were not returned by fires and by the respiration of animals and other consumers of plants. Similarly nitrogen-fixing organisms would exhaust all of the nitrogen in the air in less than a million years. And so on. The conclusion is that a self-sustaining community must contain not just plants, animals and nitrogen-fixers but also decomposers which can free the chemicals bound in protoplasm. It is very fortunate from our standpoint that some microorganisms have solved the biochemical trick of decomposing chitin, lignins and other inert organic compounds that tie up carbon.

A community must consist of producers or accumulators of energy (green plants), primary consumers (fungi, microorganisms and herbi-

SOURCE: *Scientific American*, April, 1958, pp. 2–7. Reprinted with permission. Copyright © 1958 by Scientific American, Inc. All rights reserved. Available separately at twenty cents as offprint No. 144 from W. H. Freeman and Company, 660 Market Street, San Francisco, California. The author is professor of zoology at Cornell University.

vores), higher-order consumers (carnivorous predators, parasites and scavengers), and decomposers that regenerate the raw materials.

Communities vary, of course, all over the world, and each ecosystem is a composite of the community and the features of the inorganic environment that govern the availability of energy and essential chemicals and the conditions that the community members must tolerate. But the system that I wish to consider here is not a local one but the largest possible ecosystem: namely, the sum total of life on earth together with the global environment and the earth's total resources. This is what I call the ecosphere. My purpose is to reach some conclusions on such questions as how much life the earth can support.

Organisms living on the fact of the earth as it floats around in space can receive energy from several sources. Energy from outside comes to us as sunlight and starlight, is reflected to us as moonlight, and is brought to earth by cosmic radiation and meteors. Internally the earth is heated by radioactivity, and it is also gaining heat energy from the tidal friction that is gradually slowing our rotation. On top of this, man is tapping enormous amounts of stored energy by burning fossil fuels. But all these secondary sources of energy are infinitesimal compared to our daily sunshine, which accounts for 99.9998 per cent of our total energy income.

This supply of solar energy amounts to 13×10^{23} gram-calories per year, or if you prefer, it represents a continuous power supply at the rate of 2.5 billion billion horsepower. About one third of the incoming energy is lost at once by being reflected back to space, chiefly by clouds. The rest is absorbed by the atmosphere and the earth itself, to remain here temporarily until it is reradiated to space as heat. During its residence on earth this energy serves to melt ice, to warm the land and oceans, to evaporate water, to generate winds and waves and currents. In addition to these activities, a ridiculously small proportion—about four hundredths of 1 per cent—of the solar energy goes to feed the metabolism of the biosphere.

Practically all of this energy enters the biosphere by means of photosynthesis. The plants use one sixth of the energy they take up from sunlight for their own metabolism, making the other five sixths available for animals and other consumers. About 5 per cent of this net energy is dissipated by forest and grass fires and by man's burning of plant products as fuel.

When an animal or other consumer eats plant protoplasm, it uses some of the substance for energy to fuel its metabolism and some as raw materials for growth. Some it discharges in broken-down form as metabolic waste products: for example, animals excrete urea, and yeast releases ethyl alcohol. And a large part of the plant material it ingests is simply indigestible and passes through the body unused. Herbivores, whether they are insects, rabbits, geese or cattle, succeed in extracting only about 50 per cent of the calories stored in the plant protoplasm. (The lost calories are, however, extractable by other consumers: flies may feed on the excretions or man himself may burn cattle dung for fuel.)

Of the plant calories consumed by an animal that eats the plant, only 20 to 30 per cent is actually built into protoplasm. Thus, since half of its consumption is lost as waste, the net efficiency of a herbivore in converting plant protoplasm into meat is about 10 to 15 per cent. The secondary consumers—i.e., meat-eaters feeding on the herbivores—do a little better. Because animal protoplasm has a smaller proportion of indigestible matter than plants have, a carnivore can use 70 per cent of the meat for its internal chemistry. But again only 30 per cent at most goes into building tissue. So the maximum efficiency of carnivores in converting one kind of meat into another is 20 per cent.

Some of the consequences of these relationships are of general interest and are fairly well known. For example, 1,000 calories stored up by the algae in Cayuga Lake can be converted into protoplasm amounting to 150 calories by small aquatic animals. In turn, smelt eating these animals produce 30 calories of protoplasm from the 150. If a man then eats the smelt, he can synthesize six calories worth of fat or muscle from the 30; if he waits for the smelt to be eaten by a trout and then eats the trout, the yield shrinks to 1.2 calories. If we were really dependent on the lake for food, we would do well to exterminate the trout and eat the smelt ourselves, or, better yet, to exterminate the smelt and live on planktonburgers. The same principles, of course, apply on land. If man is really determined to support the largest possible populations of his kind, he will have to shorten the food chains leading to himself and, so far as practicable, turn to a vegetarian diet.

The rapid shrinkage of stored energy as it passes from one organism to another serves to make the study of natural communities a trifle more simple for the ecologist than it would otherwise be. It explains why food chains in nature rarely contain more than four or five links. Thus in our Cayuga Lake chain the trout was the third animal link, and man the fourth. Chains of the same sort occur in the ocean, with, for example, a tuna or cod as the third link and perhaps a shark or a seal replacing man as the fourth link. Now if we look for the fifth link in the chain we find that it takes something like a killer whale or a polar bear to be able to subsist on seals. As to a sixth link—it would take quite a predator to make its living by devouring killer whales or polar bears.

We could, of course, trace food chains in other directions. Each species has its parasites that extort their cut of the stored energy, and these in turn support other parasites down to the point where there is not enough energy available to support another organism. Also, we should not forget the unused energy contained in the feces and urine of each animal. The organic matter in feces is often the basic resource of a food chain in which the next link may be a dung beetle or the larva of a fly.

I estimate that the maximum amount of protoplasm of all types that can be produced on earth each year amounts to 410 billion tons, of which 290 billion represent plant growth, and the other 120 billion all of the consumer organisms. We see, then, that the availability of energy sets a limit to the amount of life on earth—that is, to the size of the biosphere. This energy also keeps the nonliving part of the ecosphere animated, largely through the agency of moving water, which is the single most important chemical substance in the physiology of the ecosphere.

Each year the oceans evaporate a quantity of water equivalent to an average depth of one meter. The total evaporation from land and bodies of fresh water is one sixth of the evaporation from the sea, and at least one fifth of this evaporation is from the transpiration of plants growing on land. The grand total of water evaporated annually is roughly 100,000 cubic miles, and this must be roughly the annual precipitation. The precipitation on land exceeds the evaporation by slightly over 9,000 cubic miles, which therefore represents the annual runoff of water from land to sea. It is astonishing to me to note that more than one tenth of this total runoff is carried to the sea by just two rivers—the Amazon and the Congo.

Precipitation supplies nonmarine organisms with the water which they require in large quantities. Protoplasm averages at least 75 per cent water, and plants require something like 450 grams of water to produce one gram of dry organic matter. The water moving from land to sea also erodes the land surface and dissolves soluble mineral matter. It brings to the plants the chemicial nutrients that they require and it tends to level the land surface and deposit the minerals in the sea. At present the continents are being worn down at an average world-wide rate of one centimeter per century. The leveling process, however, apparently has never gone on to completion on the earth. Geological uplift of the land always intervenes and brings marine sediments above sea level, where the cycle can begin again.

The rivers of the world are now washing into the seas some 4 billion tons of dissolved inorganic matter a year, about 400 million tons of dissolved organic matter and about five times as much undissolved matter. The undissolved matter represents destruction of the land where organisms live, but the dissolved material is of greater interest, because it includes such important chemicals as 3.5 million tons of phosphorus, 100 million tons of potassium and 10 million tons of fixed nitrogen. In order to say what these losses may mean to the biosphere, we must review a few facts about the chemical composition of the earth and of organisms.

Every organism seems to require at least 20 chemical elements and

probably several others in trace amounts. Some of the organisms' re
quirements are rather surprising. *Penicillium* is said to need traces o
tungsten, and the common duckweed demands manganese and th
rare earth gallium. There is a European pansy which needs high con
centrations of zinc in the soil, and several plants in different parts o
the world are so hungry for copper that they help prospectors to fin
the mineral. Many organisms have fantastic abilities to concentrate th
necessary elements from dilute media. The sea-squirts have vanadiun
in their blood, and the liver of the edible scallop contains on a dry
weight basis one tenth of 1 per cent of cadmium, although the amount o
this element in sea water is so small that it cannot be detected b
chemical tests.

But the exotic chemical tastes of organisms are comparatively un
important. Their main needs can be summed up in just five words-
oxygen, carbon, hydrogen, nitrogen and phosphorus, which account fo
more than 95 per cent of the mass of all protoplasm. Oxygen is the mos
abundant chemical element on earth, so we probably do not need to b
concerned about any absolute deficiency of oxygen. But nitrogen is a
different matter. Whereas protein, the main stuff of life, is 18 per cen
nitrogen, the relative abundance of this element on the earth is only on
10,000th of the earth's mass. It is apparent that our land forms of lif
could not long tolerate a net annual loss of 10 million tons of fixe
nitrogen to the sea. Fortunately this nitrogen loss from land is reversible
so that we can speak of a "nitrogen cycle." Organisms in the sea conver
the fixed nitrogen into ammonia, a gas which can return to land vi
the atmosphere.

Carbon also is not in too abundant supply, for it amounts to les
than three parts in 10,000 of the total mass of the earth's matter. Bu
once again the biosphere profits from the fact that carbon can escap
from the oceans as a gas—carbon dioxide. This gas goes through a
complex circulation in the atmosphere, being released from the ocean
in tropical regions and absorbed by the ocean waters in polar regions
Because some carbon is deposited in ocean sediments as carbonates
there is a net loss of carbon from the ecosphere. But there seems to b
no danger that a shortage of this element will restrict life. The atmos
phere contains 2,400 billion tons of carbon dioxide, and at least 3
times that much is dissolved in the oceans, waiting to be released i
the atmosphere should become depleted. Volcanoes discharge carbo
dioxide, and man is burning fossil fuels at such a rate that he has bee
accused of increasing the average carbon dioxide content of the atmos
phere by some 10 per cent in the last 50 years. In addition, lots o
limestone, which is more than 4 per cent carbon dioxide, has bee
pushed up from ancient seas by uplifts of the earth.

The story of phosphorus appears somewhat more alarming. This ele
ment accounts for a bit more than one tenth of 1 per cent of the mas

of terrestrial matters, is enriched to about twice this level in plant proto-plasm and is greatly enriched in animals, accounting for more than 1 per cent of the weight of the human body. As a constituent of nucleic acids it is indispensable for all types of life known to us. But many agricultural lands already suffer a deficiency of phosphorus, and a corn crop of 60 bushels per acre removes 10 per cent of the phosphorus in the upper six inches of fertile soil. Each year 3.5 million tons of phos-phorus are washed from the land and precipitated in the seas. And un-fortunately phosphorus does not escape from the sea as a gas. Its only important recovery from the sea is in the guano produced by sea birds, but less than 3 per cent of the phosphorus annually lost from the land is returned in this way.

I must agree with agriculturalists who say that phosphorus is the critical limiting resource for the functioning of the ecosphere. The sup-ply is at least shrinking (if dwindling is too strong a word), and there seems to be no practical way of improving the situation short of wait-ing for the next geological cycle of uplift to bring phosphate rock above sea level. Perhaps we should also worry about other essential ele-ments, such as calcium, potassium, magnesium and iron, which behave much like phosphorus in the metabolism of the ecosphere, but the evi-dence clearly indicates that if present trends continue, phosphorus will be the first to run out.

This brings me to the close of a very superficial summary of some of the physiological processes of the ecosphere. There are drastic over-simplifications in this treatment; the importance of some processes may be overestimated, and others (*e.g.*, dumping sewage in rivers and oceans) may not have received enough attention. The figures for the total quantity of energy received by the earth, for total annual precipi-tation and for the total supply of some chemical element, may overlook the very irregular distribution of these resources in time and space. Much solar energy falls on deserts and fields of snow and ice where it cannot be used by plants, and much precipitation arrives at unfavorable seasons or in such torrents that it does more harm than good to organ-isms. Yet I believe that there may be some merit, both intellectual and practical, in attempting to scan the entire picture.

Our survey suggests that man may be justified in feeling some real concern about the problem of erosion. It should also make us aware of the important role played by organisms that we might otherwise ignore or even regard as pests. The dung beetles, the various scavengers and the termites and other decomposers all play important bit parts in this great production. At least six diverse groups of bacteria are absolutely essential for the proper physiological functioning of the nitrogen cycle alone. Man in his carelessness would probably neither notice nor care if by some unlikely chance his radioactive fallout or one of his chemical sprays or fumes should exterminate all of the micro-organisms that are capable of decomposing chitin. Yet, as we have seen, such a tragedy would eventually mean an end to life on earth.

Finally, it is interesting to ask how large a role man plays in the physiology of the ecosphere. The Statistical Office of the United Nations estimates the present human population of the earth at 2.7 billion persons. Each of these is supposed to consume at least 2,200 metabolizable kilocalories per day. This makes a total food requirement of 22×10^{14} kilocalories per year. I have estimated that all of the plant growth in the world amounts to an annual net of 5×10^{17} kilocalories, of which not more than 50 per cent is metabolizable by any primary consumer. Thus if man were to feed exclusively on plants he would require almost exactly 1 per cent of the total productivity of the earth.

To me this is a very impressive figure. There are more than one million species of animals, and when just one of these million species can corner 1 per cent of the total food resources, this form is truly in a position of overwhelming dominance. The figure becomes even more impressive when we reflect that 70 per cent of the total plant production takes place in the oceans, and that our figure for productivity includes inedible materials such as straw and lumber.

If human beings were to eat meat exclusively, the present world population would require 4 per cent of all the flesh of primary consumers of all types that the earth could support—and this means that much of our meat would be insects and tiny crustaceans. I suspect that the human population is already so large that no conceivable technical advances could make it possible for all mankind to live on a meat diet. Speaking as one who would like to live on a meat diet, I can't see very much to be optimistic about for the future. This opinion, however, cannot be expected to alter the physiology of the ecosphere.

V. VEGETATION

Original or natural vegetation cover or lack of it plays an important part in the appearance and utilization of an area. Plant species differ with varying climate, soils, drainage, landform, elevation, and conditions of human use. Nevertheless, the vegetation cover is one of the best visual indicators of climatic variation, and the widely used Koeppen system of climatic classification is to a great extent based on vegetation differences. A knowledge of plant distribution over the surface of the earth in its relation to the above factors is of vital concern in the understanding of the past and present of any region.

There are two recognized approaches to the geographic study of plants. One is plant ecology, the study of the distribution of plant communities or associations and their relations to the physical and cultural environments. Plants tend to reflect changing natural conditions of an area; thus vegetation realms of various scales have been identified, although in most cases man has disturbed the original vegetation.

The second approach is floristic plant geography, which concerns itself with the distribution of plant or taxonomic units, such as families and species. Here the interest is focused on the characteristics of individual plants or groups of plants that affect their distribution. Some families or species are found in very limited areas, whereas others are almost worldwide and extend across some climatic and natural boundaries.

The economic importance of natural vegetation is, of course, considerable. And from natural vegetation through many centuries, even millenia, has come the crops that man grows and consumes. Finally, as it grows in the forests of the world, natural vegetation contributes both timber and a variety of other tree products. The selections following cover a wide variety of vegetation types and uses.

19. Forests and Human Progress
Raphael Zon

The 25 per cent of the earth that was originally covered by forest has played various significant roles in the history of man. "The primary stages of social development were reached in arid and treeless climates," according to Zon who presents here an excellent discussion of the relation between forests and the progress of civilization. Only recently

*has man been able to conquer forests on a large scale—in
some cases so completely that former forest areas are now
the most densely populated portions of the world. The
problem has developed, however, of maintaining forest
resources adequate to fill man's many needs, and at the same
time clearing sufficient land for crop cultivation to feed
larger and larger numbers of people. Ruthless cutting
has taken place in the areas where timber was the best "crop"
for the poor soil or steep slope. Forest conservation was
developed only after human domination of the forest became
too complete.*

Forests have had an important effect on the distribution of mankind
over the earth's surface. They have deeply affected the spiritual and
religious life of the tribes living within them or nearby. They have
been a source of raw material indispensable to the economic development of the human race. The relations between forests and man are
manifold and varied throughout the course of human progress from
the primitive stage to the present highly developed economic organization.

There may be recognized three stages in the relation of man to
forests:

(1) Civilization dominated by forests.
(2) Civilization overcoming the forests.
(3) Civilization dominating forests.

Just as we had the stone age, the bronze age, and the iron age at the
same time in different parts of the earth, so we have simultaneously the
three stages of the relation of man to the forest. Thus in central Africa
and South America man in his relation to the surrounding forests is in the
first stage; in a considerable part of North America and in Asia he is in
the second; and in Europe and in parts of the United States he is
already in the third.

Civilization Dominated by Forests

If no attempt is made to go back into the mode of life of our simian ancestors, whose abode must have been the forest, and our survey is
confined to the beginnings of civilization in Europe, Asia, and America
one fact stands out clearly; namely, that the forests in the early stages o

SOURCE: *Geographical Review*, X (1920), 139–66. The author has served with
the United States Forest Service, was director of the Lake States Forest Experiment
Station, and has been a forestry professor at the Universities of Minnesota and
Wisconsin.

human progress did not offer favorable conditions for the settlement of primitive man; on the contrary, they were always an element inimical to the spread of mankind over the earth.

The first and most striking evidence that this is so is the fact that only few traces of prehistoric man are found in densely forested regions. The chief memorials of Neolithic man in Britain, for instance, are found on the moorlands which in these ancient times appeared as islands of open habitable land above the vast stretches of swamp and forests. A study of the occurrence of human settlement from the earliest Stone Age tells the same story, namely, that the cradle of human civilization was not a primeval forest.

The first great nuclei of population, the seats of the earliest recorded civilizations both in the Old and in the New World, originated in arid regions, at best only scantily covered with forest. In the Old World the Egyptian, Babylonian, Assyrian, and Phoenician civilizations arose in hot and dry regions in climate not unlike southern Arizona and New Mexico. Within the "rainless belt" extending across North Africa, Arabia, Persia, and on through Tibet into Mongolia, or from the borders of it, have come all the conquering races of the Old World.

Similarly in the New World the nations which developed a high degree of civilization were those in the arid regions of Mexico and Peru —the Aztecs and the Incas.*

Primeval Forests an Obstacle to Human Migration and Colonization

Forests have acted as barriers to human colonization in all parts of the world. In the Alleghanies as well as in tropical West Africa the forest for many decades delayed the penetration of the white man into the interior of the continent: It took the American colonists about 200 years to reach the crest of the Appalachians. It prevented the spread of the Hamites from North Africa southward and stopped the movement into the Congo region of the cattle-keeping aristocracies such as the Bahima, which had a social, political, and military organization superior to other tribes. In the heart of the Congo forest no traces of an ancient population have been found. All the evidence points to the comparatively recent penetration of man. The expansion of the Inca Empire from the high plateaus of Peru and Boliva eastward was limited by the impenetrable forests of the headwaters of the Amazon River. Attempts to penetrate down the eastern valleys brought feeble results. In contrast is the

* Remains of the Maya civilization are now found in the dense tropical forest. Huntington however suggests that this civilization arose and flourished during a time of drier climate. The succeeding moister period favored the growth of that type of heavy forest so inimical to human progress. Ellsworth Huntington: The Climatic Factor as Illustrated in Arid America, *Carnegie Instn. Publ. No. 192,* Washington, D.C., 1914.

southward expansion of the Empire—to or beyond the river Maule—by roads where neither the frigid heights of the Cordillera nor the inhospitable desert proved so formidable as the barrier of the forest. The history of the Spanish conquest is similar: the forest continued to mark the boundary of effective control. Indeed much the same is true today.

The Ancient European Forests

The Romans, the greatest colonizers of olden times, were forced to stop in their expansion and Empire building at the boundaries of the dense, virgin German forests whose inhospitable and somber nature was pictured in dark colors by such ancient writers as Tacitus, Pomponius Mella, and Marcellinus, who spoke of the forests as of something horrid and inaccessible and unsuited for human habitation. The more recent European historians, such as Gradmann for instance, consider the boundary of the Roman Empire as coinciding with the western boundary of the coniferous forests of southern Germany. The strategic genius of the old Romans clearly perceived that it was not the German mountains themselves, which were only moderate in height, that formed the bulwark of the ancient Teutonic freedom but the vast primeval forests with which they were clothed. In their writings they referred to the *saltus* (break or forest) and not to the Montes Germaniæ.

Just as the Romans were compelled to stop in their colonizing activities at the boundary of the virgin forests of central Europe, so the successive later waves of the nomadic tribes which moved from the eastern prairies westward—Huns, Magyars, Avars, and the like—broke up when they reached the barrier of primeval forests. The routes of migration in western and central Europe were largely determined by the openings in the primeval forests.

The difficulty with which primeval forests could be penetrated made them always an obstacle to all great historic migrations of man. On the grasslands pack animals could be used, and here the wheeled cart originated. In the primeval forest where a path must be hacked out with the aid of ax and knife man must be his own burden bearer. Three or four miles a day is the average rate of travel in such forests. Not infrequently man depends here on the animal trails. Mammoth and rhinoceros in the ages past were the first trail builders in the forests of central Europe, just as the elephants are breaking trails now in the African and eastern Asiatic forests to be later followed by man. The bear trails served as roads for the Teutons in the primeval forests of Europe, just as they are now doing in the forests of Kamchatka and Siberia for the hunters of fur animals. In North America, as Humboldt remarks, the "bison pointed out to man the best roads through the Cumberland Mountains." In medieval Europe the wild cattle broke the first trails in the forest, just as in our own western forests the cattle trails were the first which many of us traveled.

Forests of the North

In the northern forests the main obstacles to the movement of man are vast swamps and muskegs. In winter the snow cover usually improves the facilities for movement. Light sleds, skis, and snowshoes are then the chief means of travel. In summer, however, this advantage of the northern forest over the tropical one is lost, and it is necessary to use the rivers for roads. Where these rivers are often interrupted by rapids or falls, light transportable canoes had to be used, as they are still being used by the North American Indians. Such means of transportation, although they are of great help, are not, of course, sufficient or adequate for easy communication. For this reason all world trade routes have always kept away from virgin forest regions. Not a single transcontinental railroad has yet been cut through the forest region of the Amazon or Congo, and such railroads as the Trans-Siberian and the Canadian Pacific skirt only the southern boundaries of the virgin boreal forests.

Middendorff in his travel through eastern Siberia was surprised at the scarcity of wild game, which became abundant only toward the steppes and in the vicinity of human habitation. In his travel through the forests he found an insurmountable obstacle in the vast swamps. In winter when they are frozen over it is possible for men to enter the forest and cut wood, but it is out of the question to establish a permanent dwelling on the unstable ground. The swamp forests, therefore, are not inhabited. Even where the soil is not swampy the foot sinks deep in decaying vegetation, while fallen, dead, or diseased trees lie athwart the dense upright trunks and thus impede movement. Darwin, in his ascent of Mt. Tarn in Tierra del Fuego, encountered difficulties of a similar character.

The records left by ancient writers regarding the primeval forests of central Europe agree with descriptions given by modern travelers of the forests of the north which still remain intact. Pliny presents a picture of the primeval forests of central Europe which is not unlike that given by Middendorff of the primeval forests of eastern and western Siberia. He speaks of gigantic trunks capable of holding up thirty men in the water, of oak roots lifted like arches or forming mounds of earth, and of great islands of wood floating on the rivers; just as the rivers of Siberia today are cumbered with trunks of trees uprooted and accumulated in huge natural rafts, so that to travel even by water is difficult.

Dense, extensive forests are perhaps the most formidable of natural barriers. Areas which otherwise would be easy of access become unfriendly and inaccessible when covered with high and dense forest vegetation. Mountain slopes which if cleared would be accessible are inaccessible when covered with a dense forest. As Arrigo Lorenzi has pointed out, even the low and twisted forest vegetation characteristic

of the dolomite region of the eastern Alps—and that of the San
Bernardino Mountains of southern California might also be instanced
—presents a serious obstacle to travel.

The Sparse Population of the Forest

Comparison of a map showing the density of population or settlement
with one showing the distribution of the principal natural types of vegetation, such as desert, forest, grassland, shows at a glance that the most
scattered population is found in the deserts and in the large stretches of
primeval forest. This holds true of the northern forests of the temperate
region and the tropical forests of the Amazon and of northern Australia,
where the density of population is less than one per square mile, as well
as of the Congo forest and the primeval forests of southeastern Asia,
where the density of population is also very low. This belt of sparse
population is clearly distinguished from adjoining prairie or otherwise
treeless regions, where the density is considerably greater. Similar maps,
only on a larger scale, for individual countries show that the timbered
belt in the mountains has a thin population while the valleys below
are densely populated. Even the alpine meadows above the timber line
may have a denser though temporary population. In the timbered belt
are found only a few huts of hunters and wood-choppers.

A primeval forest at the lower stages of human civilization is of little
importance as a source of trade. The local demand for wood material is
fully supplied from the fringes of the forest region. The export of large
quantities of wood is out of the question because demand and means of
transportation are lacking. There remains only hunting and grazing. It
is true that throughout the Middle Ages hunting and pasturing of swine
in the forest were not insignificant sources of revenue to many a king.
This, however, was also possible only on the outskirts, since the interior
of the dense and dark primeval forests is unfavorable even for wild animals. Everyone who has traveled through the virgin Douglas fir forest
of Puget Sound has been impressed by the lack of animal and bird life.
An occasional squirrel or chipmunk is about all that one is likely to see
for days. The primeval forests of Asiatic Russia, the so-called Siberian
taiga, and the tropical *selvas* of South America support very few wild
animals. This is less true of temperate broad-leaved forests, where
abundant mast of beech and oak furnish food for animals and often for
men. Such poverty and inaccessibility of the virgin tropical and northern
coniferous forests make them almost entirely unsuited to human settlement. In the early colonial history of America the virgin forest was in
true sense of the word "No Man's Land."

·   ·   ·   ·   ·

Civilization Overcoming the Forest

So much for the influence of the forest upon man. This influence was greatest when mankind was at comparatively low stages of civilization. At a certain stage there begins a reverse influence, namely, that of man upon forests.

Primitive man, possessing crude stone implements only, found but few parts of the earth's surface which were neither too barren nor too heavily forested to be suitable for his habitation. It is true that in recent times societies have to the greatest extent developed, both in size and complexity, in temperate forested regions. This, however, is not inconsistent with the fact that the first large human societies arose, and the primary stages of social development were reached, in arid and treeless climates. The earlier phases of progress had to be passed through where the resistances offered by natural conditions were least; only when the arts of life had been advanced did it become possible for societies to develop in regions where the resistance was greater; and it was only further development in the arts of life, with the further discipline in co-operation accompanying them, that enabled subsequent societies to take root and grow in regions where climatic and other conditions offered relatively great difficulties. At first man is the slave of his environment and only later becomes to a certain extent its master.

First Steps in Destruction of the Forest

The primitive nations could not change to any marked degree the forest cover of the earth. Their tools were too crude, and, moreover, their activity was rarely concentrated at the same place for any length of time because their mode of life was largely nomadic. The primitive agricultural system, kaingin making, of the Philippines could never have brought about the destruction of the forests, since the cultivator's efforts were never centered long enough at one place. For this reason the effective influence of man upon the forest in the early days was confined to localities where it existed under very adverse conditions of climate or soil, as for instance on sand dunes, on the edge of the prairie or desert, or at its upper or northern limit. The Batusi and other peoples have encroached on the northeastern edge of the great central African forest. Today Ruanda is practically deforested. The remnants of the ancient forests that remain on the hill tops are regarded as sacred by the natives. In Europe we find that man early succeeded in crowding out the forest in the Mediterranean region, where at best it had a hard struggle to maintain itself. This operation can be traced back even to classical antiquity.

The dense forests of central Europe did not give way before the efforts of the Romans or the ancient Teutons. Only in the Middle Ages, beginning with the era of Charlemagne, when there arose an imperative need for more room, did the Teutons succeed in clearing any large areas of the dense forests. This clearing was not the work of individuals but was the result of many concentrated and persistent efforts on the part of the religious and knightly orders.

Extent and Character of the Process of Clearing

Some idea of the extent and character of this process may be gleaned from a study of the geographic names of different settlements. There are in Germany alone not less than 6,905 names of places which indicate their origin in forest regions. An analysis of such names reveals also the part which different nationalities have taken in the colonization of forest regions and shows whether settlement took place on open land or on cleared forest land. In Bohemia, for instance, just as in the northern German lowlands, all areas poorly stocked with timber from time immemorial were occupied first by Slavonic nations, which had come to these lands long before the arrival there of the Teutons. The latter, therefore, were forced, as latecomers, to provide for themselves places of habitation amid the dense primeval forest by cutting it off, burning, and clearing the land for fields. In the same way the Romans in colonizing the Alps occupied the open places and left untouched the forested regions of southeastern Austria, which for a long time waited for colonists to come there from Franconia and Thuringia to turn them into fields and orchards. The same story has been repeated in the last century in southern Brazil. The creoles and negroes took possession largely of the prairie sections, leaving the forests to the nomadic South American Indians. The present settlement of the forest regions began only after the arrival there of European colonists who, not finding any more open land, began to clear the forest for settlement; and now some of the originally forested land is more densely populated than the open prairie.

Along the Atlantic shore of Central America the forests began to be cleared for human settlement only after the arrival there of negroes; and on the Island of Formosa clearing took place only through colonization by the Chinese, who, after having cleared the western part of the island, took possession of the entire island and crowded the original population to the eastern part of it.

The earliest settlements in the forest were comparatively small. In Germany the extensive clearings are of a later date than the barbarian invasions, and only the areas which were by nature more or less clear of forest were inhabited in antiquity. Likewise in independent Gaul, especially north of the Loire, cleared and inhabited lands were like small islands encircled by vast forests. A striking example of the islandlike character of clearings in the forest may be seen today to the south and southeast of Munich. Such small settlements, when made by a people of comparatively high civilization carrying on agriculture according to improved methods, may last a long time if the extent of the forest territory is very great in comparison with the population. Cultivation on a large scale involving the clearing and agricultural development of enormous areas of land was made possible only in modern times when man became armed with powerful machinery for removing trees and stumps.

The Forest as a Supplementary Source of Food

In the earlier settlements the surrounding forests served as a supplementary source of food for the primitive agriculturist. The cultivation of small parcels of cleared land was supplemented by grazing of stock in the oak or other adjoining forest. The forest also furnished acorns as food for animals and even men, while the wild animals provided meat and hides. During the period of such early agricultural settlements the forest was often protected from destruction because of its value as a hunting ground and as a source of food. There are many evidences of the economic importance of wild edible fruits in the forest in the early settlements of primitive man. In the prehistoric settlements the remains of beech mast have sometimes been found in heaps. Poets and writers of antiquity have preserved the record of the epoch in which the inhabitants of the country surrounding the Mediterranean were fed on acorns and other fruits of the forest. Aside from the Arcadians, called by other Greeks "the acorn eaters," and the statements of Pliny about bread made of acorns, there are many historic evidences of the importance of the acorn in the early economic life of Europe and at a later period. Even today the acorns of various species of oak are an article of food in all the Mediterranean countries. Cultivation of land within the forest, coupled with the gathering of wild fruits, is still going on in many parts of the world, as for instance among the peasants of Siberia and the Indians of North America.

As the gathering of wild plants is displaced gradually in the course of economic evolution by the regular production of cultivated crops, stock raising supersedes the hunting of game. As an intermediate stage from hunting to stock raising there is often domestication of animals, as for instance the breeding of foxes, in a state of semi-domestication, in certain islands of the Bering Sea and in Newfoundland; or the raising of bees in the forest of the Ural Mountains, which is a step in advance of the gathering of wild honey as carried on, for example, by the Veddas but is not rational apiculture with food supplied by properly selected and cultivated crops. In the primitive horticulture of the primeval forest it is customary to cut down the trees in the portion of the forest destined for cultivation, then to burn all the wood or at least the branches and underbrush. The ashes serve as fertilizer; the ground is broken, and the seeds, shoots, or tubers are planted. To remove the roots of the trees would be too difficult a task for primitive implements; hence the fields are very imperfect. The peasants of eastern Russia, as well as some agricultural colonists in South America, burn the forest and cultivate the ground for some years, merely to abandon it and repeat the same process every ten or fifteen years. Periodical change of the soil is necessitated by the lack of fertilizer and proper working. It corresponds to the rotation of crops in scientific farming. When one clearing is abandoned, another is opened, and, since the products cannot be abundant owing to inadequate preparation of the soil, the cleared areas are large compared to the small number of people to be supported by them. But such areas are in no sense comparable to those under intensive cultivation. They have the character of oases scattered through the unexplored forest and are exposed to its perils. Wild animals, for instance, may destroy in a few hours the fruits of prolonged toil. The size of the clearing may also depend on the need of the crops for light and space.

Exploitation of Forests the Chief Cause of Their Disappearance

Extensive as this form of agriculture may be, it in itself would not be sufficient to have reduced the forested area of the world to its present size. It is the increased need for the products of the forest itself, particularly its timber, that has made the heaviest inroads upon it. Next to food, wood has been one of the most important factors of civilization, particularly at the time when iron, brick, and other structural materials were either unknown or little used.

In the early stages of economic development, the forests furnished man with fuel for overcoming the rigors of winter cold. It furnished fuel also for metal working, and a number of secondary products such as charcoal, pitch, ashes, gallnuts, some of which were more widely used in the past than they are now. In places where intense cold causes a heavy growth of fur on the wild animals, man has made use of materials produced in the forest for tanning the hides, thus providing himself with clothing and with covering for his primitive tents. At a higher stage of civilization and with the development of means of communication and transportation, the products of the forest are no longer merely the means with which to satisfy immediate needs; they become commodities of widespread use far beyond the forest boundary. Many industries which were dependent upon wood as fuel found their location in the forest. Thus the occurrence in the same areas of forests and mineral deposits gave rise to metallurgy and the art of glassmaking. In France about the fifteenth century, before the invention of high ovens, metallurgists and glassmakers took up their abode in the forest. In the Middle Ages an entire forest population employed exclusively in industries growing out of the use of wood lived in the forests of France. Kilns, charcoal furnaces, forges, glass furnaces, limekilns, and establishments where wood was worked up gave a peculiar aspect to the forests of that time.

Pallas describes the metallurgic industries connected with the forests of Russia in the Ural Mountains from which the necessary charcoal was obtained. In the forests of Russia also the coexistence of fur-bearing animals and plants producing tanning material has given rise to village industries, chiefly tanning. The forests of the eastern United States were once extensively used for charcoal making in connection with the iron industry.

Rivers as an Aid in Exploitation of the Forests

The penetration of the forests and the development of forest industries have been greatly favored by rivers. Watercourses penetrating forest regions are the natural means of access and with their banks constitute the first zone of attack on the phalanx of the forest. This was the case in Europe; the Rhine and its tributaries formed the principal routes by which extensive openings could be made in the German forests, and in the time of the Romans special corporations transported the felled trees on rafts. The same was true in Italy during the Roman epoch, when the Aniene, the Liri, and the Chiana served as means of transporting wood from the Apennines, and wood from the Alps reached Rome by way of rivers and the ocean.

The vast territory included between Hudson Bay and the Saskatchewan River was revealed to missionaries and fur dealers—*voyageurs, coureurs de bois*—by way of the St. Lawrence River. The development of our lumber industry in the early days would not have been so rapid had it not been for the proximity of the New England forests to the coast and the large number of navigable streams, such as the Penobscot, St. John, Androscoggin, St. Croix, and others. Wherever roads are lacking, wherever the rivers are not navigable, the forest cannot serve broad economic ends; in that case the primitive organization remains and the forest furnishes only a local means of livelihood, as is the case in the interior of continents or at high elevations.

In northern Russia forests are still intact because of lack of railways and roads; while the inland location and lack of communication with the coast, together with the long periods during which the rivers are frozen, present obstacles to the development of a wood-exporting industry. Much more favorable are the conditions in the adjoining Scandinavian peninsula, where from the time of the earliest commercial relations with neighboring countries forest products have played a very important part.

The modern development of railroad systems, however, is reducing transportation by water in many regions. Thus in the Vosges Mountains, as well as in our Lake states and Pacific Coast states, transportation by water is dying out altogether.

Psychological Influences

The psychological influence of the forest on primitive peoples has already been noted. At higher stages, when man sets himself to overcome the forest, he feels its influence none the less surely. Many of the specific pioneer traits of our own original settlers in this country may be traced to their battle against the forest on the slopes of the Alleghanies to provide a place for settlement. The hazardous work of hewing farms out of the virgin forest has bred a race of men of sturdy character and of enormous enterprise and self-reliance. It is true that life in the forest was not conducive to the cultivation of the graces of life characteristic of high culture. The virtues of the backwoodsman were those of a strong animal nature—courage, pertinacity, resourcefulness. In the delightful "Letters from an American Farmer," by J. Hector St. John de Crève-coeur, written in 1783, we find a realistic description of the influence of the forest environment upon the character of the so-called back settlers.

It is with men as it is with the plants and animals that grow and live in the forests; they are entirely different from those that live in the plains. . . . By living in or near the woods their actions are regulated by the wildness of the neighborhood. The deer often came to eat their grain, the wolves to destroy their sheep, the bears to kill their dogs, the foxes to catch their poultry. This surrounding hostility immediately puts the gun into their hands; they watch these animals, they kill some . . . they soon become professed hunters. . . . The chase renders them ferocious, gloomy, and unsociable.

In spite, however, of coarseness and even brutality, these people were undeniably men. No weaklings were produced by the life of the forest. The boundless woods with the long stretches of swamp land, the rough trails, the isolated homesteads sometimes miles away from the nearest neighbor bred unwillingness to co-operate with others for common purposes or to submit to any kind of discipline.

During the slow process of hewing their farms out of the forest, the settlers were compelled to rely for many necessities on their own skill with the ax. From the forest they obtained all the material for the construction of their cabins, from the puncheon floor to the shingles of the roof and the moss that calked the crevices of the walls. All these, together with the rude furniture, they got from the trees on their homesteads. The forest also supplied them with meat to vary the monotony of salt pork, itself made from hogs that found every bit of nutriment in the spontaneous products of the forests.

The back settlers, however, in the course of time lost much of their coarseness and produced leaders such as Henry Clay, Jackson, Benton, Cass, and scores of others, who for over half a century helped to shape the destiny of their country. In Abraham Lincoln this type of leader, purged of all the repulsive characteristics of the early type, found its highest expression. The old characteristics of the back settlers disappeared in him and "nothing remained but the pure metal—strong, keen, tempered to perfection, and yet at other times as soft and pliable as gold without alloy."

The entire ancient history of Sweden may also be reduced to the same struggle with the primeval forest. It is the colonization of the forests of northern Russia that has developed in the Russian people the necessary qualities which enabled them to spread to Siberia and take possession of it.

If of all the present nations, the Anglo-Saxons, the Teutons, and the Russians display the great colonizing capacity, may it not be attributed largely to their original impenetrable forests, in the struggle with which they have developed the persistence and unrelenting energy required for pioneer work?

Deforestation and the Progress of Civilization

With the growth of population and the spread of civilization the world's forested area has been progressively reduced. At present there is still under forest about five billion acres; if the brush land is included, considerably more, probably one-fourth of the entire land area. About another fourth of the land surface is covered with desert and tundra, which must be excluded from the possible area of human habitation. Therefore the land area available for human activities is none too large. If we compare the relative amount of the land under forest in the different regions of Europe which have comparable climatic and other conditions for timber growth, we find that England has only 4 per cent of its land in forest; France, 18 per cent; Belgium, 17 per cent; Germany, 26 per cent; Austria, 30 per cent; Russia, 32 per cent; Sweden, 40 per cent; and Finland, 60 per cent. These figures express also, although in inverse ratio, the relative density of population of these countries. In these figures, as in a mirror, is reflected the progressive movement of human civilization.

Other factors may undoutedly act as a modifying influence. Legal protection of woodlands may have had some effect in preventing indiscriminate deforestation as agriculture, commerce, and industries have developed; but in a broad way the extent to which the forest is cleared is in direct relation to the density of population and therefore to the conditions of civilization.

While it would be misleading to lay down, as a general law, without any qualification, that the decrease in forested area and human progress always go hand in hand, it is nevertheless true that up to the present time the countries having the most highly developed economic organization have also a greater population and a proportionately reduced forest area. This was true in ancient times as it is true now. Thus, for instance, the deforestation of ancient Greece at its highest period of development had progressed much farther than that of the southern end of the Apennine peninsula—at that time in a lower stage of development. The Hellenes then looked upon Italy as a densely forested country. Thus Alcibiades, exiled from Athens, in the discourse delivered to the Lacedaemonians, urging them to aid Syracuse, which was menaced by the Athenians, advised: "Build many triremes in addition to those we have, for Italy has wood in great abundance."

Reforestation Following Decline of Civilization

As the progress of ancient civilization, of which agriculture was an essential part, tended to the destruction of the primeval forests, so conversely, with the passing of this civilization, with the decadence of empire and the return to barbarism, the forests, aided by pestilence and devastating wars, gradually restored themselves. In a most striking description of the devastation of Italy Lucan states that brambles and trees spread over untilled ground at the time of the Antonines. After Venice was invaded by the Marcomanni and after the spread of pestilence accompanied by floods, earthquakes, and swarms of locusts, the population of Italy was greatly decreased, and the forests spread over the abandoned territory. In Roman Italy in the time of Augustus, according to the most probable estimates, the population numbered about 6,000,000, and the area of land under agriculture, which was a combination of field crops with pasture in oak forests, was comparatively large. As this area gradually decreased, the forests, no longer checked by the ax and the depredations of grazing animals, spread again over the natural domain which had been taken from them for agricultural purposes. In the great crisis of the third century, desolating wars further aggravated the conditions. Lactantius, speaking of the exorbitant taxes levied by Diocletian, mentions that the colonists abandoned their fields and that the fields then became covered with forests. Incursions of the forest upon cultivated fields reached to the very walls of the cities and even to the centers of inhabited places.

In his history of the forests of France, Maury mentions ruins dug up in the dense forests of the eastern region, and on the top of a ridge near Orleans was found in the midst of a forest a Roman *castrum* destroyed by the Vandals. In the Government of Smolensk in Russia fields and towns abandoned in 1812 as a result of the Napoleonic invasion, and later during the famine of 1840 to 1850, were very soon overgrown by forests. Similar cases are found throughout the United States from Virginia to Florida, where forests sprang up on fields abandoned after the Civil War. Even in New England with the migration of the population westward many abandoned fields have come back to forest and today are being cut over for the second and third times. If the climate is favorable and there is no interference from man, a few decades are sufficient for fields to become changed into dense forests.

The Struggle Between Man and Forest

Cook in speaking of the effect of agriculture on natural vegetation in Central America says:

Many localities which are now occupied by apparently virgin forests are shown by archeological remains to be regions of reforestation. Thus in the Senahu-Cahabón district of Alta Vera Paz relics of two or three very different types of primitive civilization indicate that as many ancient populations have occupied successively the same areas which are now being cleared anew by the coffee planters as though for the first time.

It does not yet appear that any considerable region of forest has been explored in Central America without finding similar evidence that the present forests are not truly virgin growth.

And again, speaking of the evidence of antiquity as exemplified by the crumbling of large earthenware pots of an earlier civilization, he continues:

We cannot know how long it has taken the pottery to crumble, but we can at least contrast the condition of these decayed pots with other pieces of pottery placed in caves of the same district in later prehistoric ages, which still appear fresh and new, as though recently burned. And yet the bones beside these apparently new pots have also crumbled nearly to dust, and there has been time for the surrounding country to be occupied with old forests of hardwood trees, like true virgin growth.

He also mentions terracing of the land as showing that agriculture was formerly extensively practiced and notes the presence of a type of terrace evidently designed "to hold drainage water and prevent erosion . . . [being] frequently met with in the heavily forested region in eastern Guatemala."

What is regarded by some geographers as evidence of a civilization that had arisen in the primeval forest is nothing but the remains of a civilization which succeeded in clearing the forest; with the decline of this civilization and favored by a warm and moist climate, the forest again took possession of the land.

In regions, however, where the climate is unfavorable or where there is even slight interference on the part of man, the return of the forest is slow, the land is either merely run over with brambles and vines or becomes virtually a desert. Thus in the region of Friuli there are ruins of medieval castles destroyed during the last years of the Venetian Republic but not yet overrun by forest vegetation except ivy. Bishop Ennodio relates that the fields of Italy at the time of the wars between Theodoric and Odoacer were stripped of their indigenous covering and were overgrown with thorny plants. In many uncultivated areas which served as pasture during the last centuries of the empire the growth of forests was retarded, if not checked altogether, because pasturage on a large scale, as carried on in many parts of Italy, made it impossible for the forest to re-establish itself. The forests of beech and oak which probably covered the land about Rome in early historic times never returned.

The Original Composition of the Forest Changed by Man

There is another important influence which man has exerted upon the forest. The colonization of forest regions not only reduces the forest area but radically changes the entire structure and composition of the remaining forest. In analyzing the names of places, towns, and cities which are made up of words designating forest trees of one kind or another, one is at once impressed by the large number made up of the names of hardwood trees and the very small number designating pines, spruces, or even fir. Of the geographic names of central Europe which indicate the origin of the settlements in forested regions, nearly 90 per cent point to the existence of broad-leaved forests. One can find any number of names indicating an origin in a locality where linden was prevalent: Lindewiese, Lindenfels, Lindenau, Linden, Lindenhoff. With oak there is even a larger number, of which it is enough to mention Eichendorf, Eichorst, Eichrodt, Eichenfeld, Eichstat, Eichwald. Birch also takes a prominent part in. giving names to many places; as, for instance, Birkenfeld, Birkenhain. Beech is also prominently represented, such names as Buchholz and Buchhorn being very numerous. Ash also contributed to the names of many towns; as, for instance, Eschenbach, Eschweiler. Even alder enters into the formation of geographic names, as, for instance, Erlau. One looks almost in vain, however, for towns or places whose names signify pine or spruce. Once in a while one finds such a name as Tannhausen.

From this it is natural to infer that in the past the conifers had not the same wide distribution that they now have. As far as Germany is concerned, the preponderance of coniferous over broad-leaved trees has undoubtedly been brought about artificially by planting pine and spruce as the most profitable species. It is also possible that the land first cleared was that occupied by broad-leaved forests because of the more fertile soil naturally found under such growth, while the poorer sandy soils occupied by the conifers remained uncleared and unsettled. In Michigan the repeated fires have undoubtedly helped the spread of jack pine and Norway pine at the expense of the hardwoods, just as in the South the scrub pine, loblolly pine, and slash pine extended their range at the expense of other species also as a result of fires accompanying settlement. In the central Rockies fire has changed many a Douglas fir stand into a lodgepole pine forest. This change in the composition of the original forest is evidenced throughout the entire world. Thus in Sweden, pine successfully competes with fir only in the presence of frequent fires, since on burns it comes up and grows faster than fir. In

Europe it is an interesting fact that the pine extends its range parallel
with the advance of towns and villages.

Civilization Dominating Forests

Over a large part of the world the forest is now conquered. It is not
only conquered, it is exterminated beyond any possible chance of natural recovery. It has now become important to civilization to preserve
and restore the forest instead of struggling against it. Out of a land area
of some 32½ billion acres there is little more than 5 billion acres remaining in forest—exclusive of brush land—or only one-sixth of the
land area. The greatest change of course has taken place in Europe,
where of a total land area of nearly 2½ billion acres there remain now
barely 750 million acres in forest. Even of this, two-thirds are found
in European Russian and Finland and about 250 million acres in the
rest of Europe. In some countries—Great Britain, for instance—nearly
95 per cent of all the original forest is gone. In France, Spain, Belgium,
Rumania, and Greece, from 80 to 90 per cent of the original forest has
been destroyed; in Bulgaria, Serbia, and European Russia exclusive
of Finland, from 60 to 70 per cent; and in North America the original
forest has shrunk from some 822 million acres to 463 million acres in
the course of three centuries.

The Increasing Need of Wood

The disappearance of the forest, however, has not done away with the
use of wood by the present civilization; on the contrary, it has only
intensified it. Although steel, brick, and concrete are now more and
more taking the place of wood for structural purposes, industries are
arising every day which are dependent upon wood as raw material.
As a striking illustration may be mentioned the pulpwood industry
which within a few decades has assumed enormous proportions. In 1880
the consumption of pulpwood in our own country was barely 300,000
cords; twenty years later the consumption had grown to 2,000,000 cords;
in ten years more this had more than doubled, and at present it has
grown to around 6,000,000 cords. In Great Britain the total consumption
of lumber during the period 1851–1911 increased fivefold, and the per
capita consumption has also steadily increased, being in 1911 more than
three times what it was 60 years before. In spite of the fact that production from German forests has doubled in volume within the past
century, the imports from other countries have steadily increased in
amount. While there are factors, such as the preservative treatment of
wood and the substitution of other materials for construction purposes,
which may tend to check the consumption of timber, it is a feature of
modern commercial progress that, in spite of this consumption per
capita is steadily increasing.

Not only are the densely populated countries of Europe making heavy importations of lumber and other forest products. In our own country large sections like the Northeast and the Lake states, which not long ago had enormous forest areas and supplied the needs not only of the country but of other countries, are dependent upon wood from other regions, such as the Southeastern Pine Belt and the Pacific coast. This wood has to be brought from distances even greater than those over which some of the European countries are now importing. Backward countries in various parts of the world are now being called upon more and more to meet the growing deficit of wood in the world. Armed with powerful logging machinery and highly developed means of transportation the timber trader invades the remaining primeval forests and re-enacts there the same process which the European countries had gone through centuries ago—only at a more accelerated rate.

Social and Economic Evils of Forest Devastation

The clearing of the forest, aside from depriving the thickly settled and highly civilized countries of timber needed for their industries, has produced other bad economic and social effects. The stripping of the mountain forests resulted in the occurrence of torrents, in erosion, in floods, and in a general change in the régime of streams. The disappearance of the forest has also affected the climate and with the growth of industrialism has resulted in the physical deterioration of a large part of the population. Much of the forest land that has been cleared on mountain slopes, sandy plains, or rocky hills has proved unsuitable for agriculture and has failed to provide room for permanent settlement. Just as in the past the primeval forests proved a barrier to human settlement, today it is the vast stretches of cut-over and burned-over forest lands, unsuited to agriculture, which are an economic barrier to permanent settlement in many parts of the United States, Canada, and other new countries. In the United States alone there are over 80,000,000 acres of such idle waste land. The soil too poor to maintain purely agricultural communities and the lumber industry gone with the disappearance of the forest and therefore no longer a source of livelihood to the local population—there is nothing left to keep the settler on the land. The dreary wastes, dismantled sawmills, deserted towns, so common throughout the Lake states, Pennsylvania, and other sections of the East, are depressing reminders of the day when these regions were the centers of lumber production for the entire country and sustained prosperous communities.

The products of the forest have now become altogether too valuable, and no civilized nation can afford forest devastation on a large scale without regard to the future possibilities of the land. The demand for forest products is now so great that the cutting away of the forest, even on fairly good agricultural land, is far in advance of the possibility of actual land settlement. If the cutting is not followed by another forest growth or the land is not taken up by settlers for cultivation, the result is an economic waste and reduced production of the primary necessities of life.

Practically all of the civilized countries of the world have now come to realize that there is a point beyond which further clearing of the forest, no matter what the density of the population may be, proves detrimental to progress itself. Europe reached that point several centuries ago.

In central Europe the period of the greatest clearing of forest land for settlement was practically completed by the end of the thirteenth century, although considerable clearing has taken place since then in the more remote districts and particularly in the Alps. In the Canton of Zurich it is very definitely established that for the last 250 years the forest area has been reduced only 2.85 per cent. Better agricultural methods which made it possible to produce larger crops on smaller areas, and the apparent evils resulting from the destruction of forests on mountain slopes led to adoption of legislative measures for the purpose of checking further clearing of forest on non-agricultural land.

The lesson of the older countries found a reaction also in countries still having abundant forests. In practically the entire civilized world a new economic force has now been born—a general appreciation of the value of forests and a movement toward the introduction of rational forest management. There is no doubt whatever that in civilized countries there is enough accessible actual and potential forest land not suitable for agriculture to produce under proper management timber enough to supply indefinitely the world's great demand.

The New Movement toward Rational Management

Nearly every civilized country at the present time has adopted or is considering measures for the perpetuation of the existing forests, or even for extending their present area. Thus England which, because of her insular position and proximity to countries still possessing vast forest areas and because of her cheap water transportation, could best of all get along with a small forest area has now, as a result of bitter experience during the war, worked out a plan for planting some 1,700,000 acres and providing a forest area sufficient to sustain her domestic needs in case of emergency for three years. France, which for over a century has been carefully husbanding her forests, is further elaborating plans for their careful management and is enlarging her forest nurseries for extensive planting. Germany, Switzerland, Italy, Norway, Sweden, and New Zealand are also considering means of increasing forest products. Even in our own country the maintenance and protection of existing forests has become a pressing question of the day.

Nearly all of the forests now found in western Europe are man-made.

With increase in population more intensive use of all resources became necessary, especially of those resources which through more intensive application of labor, knowledge, and skill could be made to produce more fully. Forests being a poor-land crop prove more profitable than agricultural crops on non-agricultural lands. The day of the forester—the timber farmer—has now arrived in practically all densely populated countries of the world, and his work is to secure forest crops by human skill just as food crops are now being secured. Nor is the less material rôle of the forest being overlooked. In order to offset deterioration in the physical and ethical well-being of the people crowded in industrial centers with poor housing facilities, state and municipal forests are being established as a source of healthy recreation for the densely populated countries of Europe.

The new forest may be different from the original forest which once occupied the ground. It certainly bears a more utilitarian aspect. The trees that are being grown are not always of the kind that nature would prefer to produce under given conditions of climate and soil, but are those which man needs most. Just as intensive farming has increased the production of the land, so the forester is now producing five to ten times as much useful material as nature unaided produced before. Although the man-made forest may not have the beauty and grandeur of the wild woods which were the result of the free play of natural forces, it has a new beauty—the beauty of orderliness and usefulness. It is no less an important factor in civilization from the ethical and geographical point of view, because at present the economic principle is applied to it, as it is now being applied to the raising of agricultural crops.

20. Environment of Natural Grassland

C. P. Barnes

A fundamental question confronting both botanist and geographer is the uneven distribution of grass and forest—what are the natural environmental conditions, the ecology, that give rise to vegetation differences from place to place on the surface of the earth? In this selection, Barnes examines thoroughly the necessary natural conditions for growth of the three major types of grasses.

SOURCE: *Grass, the 1948 Year Book of Agriculture.* (Washington, D.C.: U. S. Department of Agriculture, 1948), pp. 45–49. The author is chief analyst in the Division of Soil Survey, Bureau of Plant Industry, Soils and Agricultural Engineering, Beltsville, Maryland.

The four great plant formations of the land surface of the earth are forest, grassland, desert shrub, and tundra. Grasslands are believed to include about a fourth of the area occupied by these types of vegetation and about a fifth of the land surface of the globe.

These four formations reflect chiefly climate. Generally speaking, humid lands are woodlands and dry lands are desert shrub or waste; the grasslands lie between these climatic extremes in zones of intermediate moisture supply. There are many important exceptions to this generalization: lack of moisture does not explain the marshlands, and some kinds of trees grow even in desert climates, like the Joshua tree of the Mohave Desert. Actually, grasslands will stand greater extremes of environment than forest—not only greater aridity but also greater cold—and will grow in wetter places.

Grass is usually first to invade shallow water, and the marshlands thus created may exist for centuries until the accumulating organic remains of the grasses and the sediment lodging in them create an environment where trees can live. Grassland extends into the frigid zones above the timber line on high mountains, forming alpine meadows. Grass will stand soils with more soluble salts than forest, even though the mangrove tree can grow with its roots in sea water at high tide.

Near the transition zones between the major plant formations, soils may offset the effect of climate and tip the scales in favor of forest, grass, or desert shrub, although the climate might lead us to expect a different formation. In some places we find natural grassland not because forest would not grow there but because the forest has not had time enough or opportunity to invade and occupy them. In Manitoba and Saskatchewan and on Kodiak Island, for example, forest has advanced considerably into grassland during the past century.

Once the land is covered with vigorous turf grasses, it is hard for forest to gain an entry; the tiny tree seedling must compete with the grass for moisture and light. Conversely, grass advances with great difficulty into dense forest, even though it might grow perfectly well were the forest cleared away. Quite often a plant formation dominates in the transition zones until some accident or slight change in environment gives the competing formation opportunity to invade.

The grassland formation tends to dominate when the upper layers of the soil are moist during a considerable part of the year, but the deeper layers are too dry for such doop-rooted plants as trees. The soil moisture, therefore, rather than total rainfall, governs the distribution of grasslands. Deep sandy soils that allow moisture to penetrate deeply may support trees in a region that is generally grassland, while adjoining fine-textured soils that allow water to run off or evaporate from the surface before it can penetrate will be grass-covered.

Three broad kinds of grassed lands are recognized: The short-grass land, sometimes called steppe; the tall-grass land, or prairie; and savanna. Each has many variations. The first and third make up the great bulk of the earth's grasslands.

Short-grass lands characterize a large part of the subhumid lands of the Temperate Zone. The largest and best known are the Great Plains of North America and the steppes of Eurasia. The rainfall of the short-grass lands keeps the upper soil layers moist during the warm season in most years, sufficient to support the shallow-rooted short grasses.

The rainfall is not enough to moisten the soil down to the ground water; hence, a permanent dry layer lies beneath the moist layer. The depth of the moist surface layer varies with the rainfall and the soil. Near the humid border of the short-grass land, several years of above-normal rainfall may encourage tall grasses and convert the short-grass land to tall. Sandy soils that permit water to penetrate and moisten a deeper layer of soil will often bear tall grasses in a short-grass region. The western part of the Nebraska sand hills is a good example.

Rainfall in the short-grass lands fluctuates enormously from year to year. Years occur when the rainfall is no greater than might be expected in the desert, and so do years when it equals that in the humid forested regions. Evaporation is rapid in the warm season because of much wind and high temperatures. Farming must be adjusted to these conditions. Land is kept fallow in alternate years to accumulate enough soil moisture for good crops.

Some of the feed produced in the moist years must be stored for use in dry ones to come. Incomes must likewise be husbanded. The soils of the short-grass areas tend to be fertile, but the rainfall in most years is not enough to allow the full potentialities of the fertile soils to be realized. Fertilizers, as a rule, do not produce substantial increases in crop yield because moisture rather than fertility usually limits production. Limestone is seldom needed, since the short-grass lands exist under climates where lime accumulates in the soil, instead of leaching out.

Prairie

Tall-grass land, or prairie, is found where soil moisture is deeper than in short-grass lands. Prairies are found mainly in three parts of the world—in Central North America, the Argentine Pampa and nearby Uruguay and Brazil, and European Russia. In each, the prairies lie along the moister edge of the short-grass lands. A great many small bodies of prairie exist, but altogether prairies cover far less of the earth than the short-grass lands or savannas.

Toward its drier margin, prairie occupies soils where a dry layer intervenes between moist surface and ground water. Toward its moister margin it extends into the region of soils that are moist down to the ground water. In fact, in the United States and in Argentina, prairies extend onto soils where the water table reaches the surface. Thus prairies occupy both humid and subhumid lands. In the United States particularly, prairies extend into the humid region where trees grow perfectly well when planted.

Why prairies should be found in such a climate has long been a matter of speculation. Given prairie to start with, it is not hard to imagine that the dense, vigorous grass, with the help of fire, could have kept trees from invading. A good prairie fire would destroy any tree seedlings that might have come up, with no permanent injury to the grass. There is some evidence that the central prairie region has somewhat more dry years and perhaps less actual moisture than the forested regions adjoining it.

But this fact obviously cannot explain the absence of trees in the wet swales that, before they were drained, covered a great acreage in northern Illinois and northern Iowa. These wet places in the prairies were grass-covered, while in the forested parts of Indiana and Ohio some of the correspondingly wet places had become timbered. It seems possible, then, that forest might in time have occupied the humid prairie, if the white man had not intervened.

Some prairies are found in humid climates where soils have developed from chalk, marl, or other highly calcareous material. The Black Prairies of Texas and Alabama are examples. Most trees seem to be less tolerant of salts, including calcium carbonate, than grasses are. This may explain these humid, calcareous prairies, the soils of which are known as Rendzinas.

Some tall-grass prairies are marshlands. Some of these wet prairies, as I have noted, occur within general prairie regions; others occur in forested or in desert regions. Some, like the Everglades, occur in fresh water; others, like the tidal marshes, grow in salt water. Marshlands generally occur in environments too wet for most trees—yet mangrove woodlands grow with roots submerged by sea water. The most we can say by way of general explanation of marshland is that tree species tolerant enough of the soil and moisture conditions of the particular marshland to compete with grasses have not existed near enough to invade the marsh. This can be said about any grassland near the transition zone between woodland and grassland.

The humid prairies combine high soil fertility with adequate moisture for high yields of crops. They have contributed a great deal to the impressive agricultural productivity of the United States and Argentina.

Savannas are the great grasslands of the Tropics. In extent they greatly exceed the tall-grass prairies of the Temperate Zone and nearly, if not fully, equal the short-grass areas. They cover more of Africa than any other plant formation and occupy a great area in the interior of Brazil.

Measured by total annual rainfall, the climate of the savannas might seem to be humid, but little rain falls in 3 to 8 months in winter. That dry period, plus the high temperature and evaporation typical of the Tropics, hinders the development of forests.

Characteristic of the savannas are scattered trees that usually are small and scrubby and grow singly or in groups. The vegetation is dominantly grass, however. Where the rainfall is greater or where the soils collect and hold more moisture, the trees grow close enough to form woodland. In some areas the grasses are tall, in others short, corresponding to zones of greater or less moisture. They generally do not form sods as in the prairies and short grasslands. During the dry period they become dormant and dry out, and the scattered trees lose their leaves. Fires burn over much of the grassland in this period and hinder the spread of woodland.

Soils of the savannas are generally far less fertile than those of the prairies and short grasslands. A very small part has been put into cultivation. Under good husbandry, with adequate fertilization, an enormous area of this grassland can be brought into production when food needs of the world require it. Crops must be adjusted to the dry period—but that, of course, is no longer than the winter dormant period in much of the Temperate Zone. Much research will be needed before modern methods of farming suited to this region can be widely practiced.

21. The Evolution of a Wild Landscape and Its Persistence in Southern California

Homer Aschmann

Human habitation, especially that of the last several hundred years in North America, greatly alters and often completely destroys the natural vegetation cover. But even where urbanization has been the most rapid in recent decades, as in Southern California, some of the natural vegetation, a "wild landscape" as Aschmann phrases it, struggles successfully to persist. In examining these developments for the various kinds of natural vegetation complexes, he also considers early aboriginal settlement patterns and their close relationship to the essentially "wild landscape." Twelve vegetation types are established, and seven early Indian settlement patterns can be discerned. In the more

> *primitive social systems, correlations with natural landscapes*
> *are usual, and even in the present-day complex of Southern*
> *California, man's activities are related to the wild landscapes.*

Despite efforts on the part of archeologists to work out a system of post-glacial climatic fluctuations in the Southwestern United States, the bulk of the evidence suggests that for the past 10,000 years the climates of Southern California have been as they are now. As in the historic period, wet and dry cycles lasting a decade or two probably alternated in rather irregular fashion throughout this long time. Since so much of Southern California is arid, semiarid, or subhumid, even these minor climatic fluctuations would have had a substantial effect on the environment as far as its ability to support a non-agricultural human population is concerned.

Prior to 8000 B.C., however, climatic fluctuations of far greater amplitude had occurred; specifically, the last major glacial advance (Tioga or Wisconsin) was a time of more southerly storm tracks and greater winter precipitation, although temperatures in the lowlands need not have been substantially lower. The now dry lake basins of the interior deserts and the oversize stream valleys of the coast provide incontestable evidence that more humid climates existed not too long ago. During such times plant communities involving forests, now largely restricted to highland areas, were more widespread; since then there has been an increase in the more xerophytic plant communities as the forest retreated to higher, wetter localities. In Southern California most of the forests are relics of a wetter age, hanging on but often incapable of reestablishing themselves if seriously disturbed.

Throughout this 10,000-year period of modern climatic conditions, the so-called natural vegetation of many marginal districts has been moving toward a new equilibrium adjusted to drier climates. But in this shift human activities have played a continuing part, and man still affects a substantial part of even those plant environments that he does not completely dominate as lawns or cultivated fields.

What the natural vegetation of Southern California would be like if it were completely free of human influence is a question that is just as subject to an observationally supported answer as the famous "How many angels can dance on the head of a pin?" Whether or not we choose to accept the full time span for human occupation of western North American that Dr. Carter has suggested, it is generally agreed that man has been present the whole time since the local climates attained their present character. Archeologically demonstrated hearths show that he controlled fire. I shall attempt to show that the native

SOURCE: *Annals Association of American Geographers*, XL (1959), 34–56. The author is on the staff of the Department of Geography, University of California, Riverside.

population was numerous, almost ubiquitous, and that it deliberately burned, though it probably could not and did not put the fires out once they were set. The wild landscapes are products of plants and animals adjusting to reasonably stable physical environments and each other. But deliberate, extensive burning has been a continuing feature of most of the environments. Though forest and brush fires make newspaper headlines every summer and fall they may be less abundant now than they were before 1769.

The Natural Vegetation of Southern California

Although a few introduced species of plants, particularly certain grasses, have naturalized themselves in Southern California and have become extremely abundant during the last two centuries, the accounts of early explorers seem to describe accurately the same vegetative associations that we know today in the uncultivated parts of the region. The explorers' notes, however, are too fragmentary to permit an assessment of the extent of each association which might be compared with present or late nineteenth-century distributions.

Working from the seacoast eastward, the following are the principal plant communities found today in Southern California (Fig. 1). All are

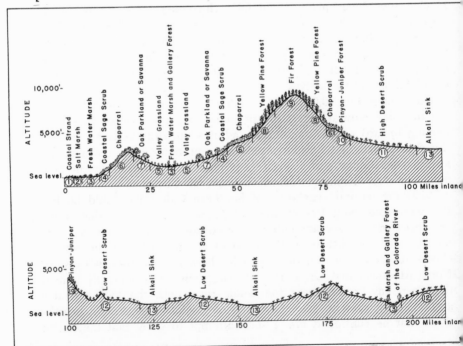

FIGURE 1: Plant communities of Southern California. This hypothetical transect broken into two sections in order to show both a high desert and a low desert se

mentioned in the earliest explorers' accounts in the same ecologic settings. The classification of plant communities used here is adapted from that of Munz and Keck,[1] and is an especially attractive one in that both the floristic composition and the vegetative aspects of the communities are considered.

1. *The Coastal Strand* occurs on coastal dunes and sandy beaches. This community occupied only a limited area, but its composition is quite specific to the peculiar ecologic situation of relatively low rainfall but high humidity and a great deal of fog. Many of the plants are succulents. The naturalized *Mesembryanthemum,* or iceplant, distinguishes the modern flora, but the general aspect of the plant community probably has not changed too much from aboriginal times. The Indian population was dense in this zone and the nitrogen-enriched soils of campsites correspond to the heavy feeding Chenopodiaceae and similar plants in the zone. Modern picnickers, if not too abundant, may almost match the aborigines in maintaining spots attractive to weedy, heavy-feeding plants.

2. *Coastal Salt Marsh* still fills the numerous tidal lagoons behind barrier beaches that have not been "developed" by modern subdividers, and these lands are costly to make suitable for residences. In fact, with the saltwater infiltration associated with falling ground water tables, this ecologic situation, appropriate to a limited number of halophytic species, may be becoming more prevalent in the Ventura and Orange County lowlands.

3. *Fresh Water Marsh* with its reeds and rushes does not have the extensive distribution it had, and to some extent still has, in the Great Valley of California farther north. Areas regularly flooded by fresh water never were large in this dry land, and modern drainage control and water-storage projects have reduced them. This plant community is widely scattered throughout Southern California, and is dependent on local topographic and drainage conditions. A notable gallery forest often borders the reeds, rushes, and marsh grasses, frequently presenting the only native trees in an extensive lowland area. These are willows, sycamores, and poplars along the streams that drain toward the sea and willows, mesquite, and screwbean on the desert side.

4. *Coastal Sage Scrub* might be described as an impoverished chaparral. The semi-shrub plants are smaller and more widely spaced, but many of the same species are represented as in the chaparral. Coastal sage scrub may occur within a mile of the sea (as on Kearney Mesa north of San Diego and the seaward slopes of the Santa Monica Mountains), or as far inland as western Riverside County. It is appropriate to relatively gentle but well-drained slopes. Old, dissected marine or riverine terraces, the decomposed granite soils of the Peninsular

[1] Philip A. Munz and David D. Keck, "California Plant Communities," *El Aliso,* Vol. 2 (1949), pp. 87–105.

batholith, and the areas of active alluviation at the heads of alluvial fans provide such an environment; even rather steep, south-facing slopes are likely to have a sage scrub cover. This plant association occurs primarily in situations that are climatically or edaphically dry. Sometimes the soil is notably porous, or it may have a shallow hardpan. This was a widespread but not a productive plant community for the Indians, and archeological sites are few.

5. *Valley Grassland* is alluded to frequently by the earliest explorers, who noted that near various watercourses there was extensive excellent pasture. While the stream courses were bordered by gallery forests, and great valley oaks were scattered through the lowlands, fairly solid stands of grass and herbs seem to have covered the heavy alluvial soils of the floors of the valleys in moderately humid localities. Such localities include much of the coastal lowlands and also some valleys at and above 4,000 feet in and east of the mountains. These grassland districts characteristically included the land most attractive for agricultural and urban development. Little of this wild landscape remains today. Furthermore, in the limited areas that are still uncultivated, introduced grasses and herbs such as wild oats, foxtails, and mustard have come to cover most of the surface; the native bunch grasses (*Stipa*, etc.) are notably scarce. Students of range management commonly attribute the growing dominance of the introduced grasses to the effects of grazing and overgrazing.

6. *Chaparral* is generally considered the most characteristic plant association for all but the desert areas of Southern California. The evergreen shrubs and scrubby trees, forming a complete, smooth ground cover when seen from above, and developing a brownish-gray color as the dry summer progresses, still mantle extensive areas. The chaparral covers, and apparently has long covered, the steeper coastal hills, grading into coastal sage scrub on the smoother surfaces and on the edaphically drier south-facing slopes. It constitutes the typical vegetation on the lower slopes of the higher mountain ranges of the interior, especially the steeper ones. On the rainier coastal side it ranges from 1,000 to 4,000 feet above sea level, while occupying a narrower belt (3,000 to 5,000 feet) on the interior sides of the various ranges. The lower margins of the chaparral on south-facing slopes are so degraded as to be more like the coastal scrub. Gentler slopes in moist localities often are covered with a park landscape of grasses and scattered live oaks. Toward the upper edge of the chaparral scattered clumps of bigcone spruce and yellow pine first take over shady, relatively moist spots and then form the dominant vegetation. The plant community possesses an extraordinary diversity of species, though chamise (*Adenostema fasciculatum*) is almost everywhere the most abundant plant.

The chaparral is intimately related to fire, both that set by lightning and that caused by man. The brushy vegetation is resinous and highly inflammable toward the end of the long dry summer. The component plants in the association have either or both of these characteristics: they sprout heavily and quickly from thickened root bases after even severe burning, or they produce a heavy crop of fire resistant seeds of long viability. Many of these seeds seem to germinate only after being scorched or having the soil surface cleared of organic matter. Regular burning then does not eliminate the chaparral, and may cause it to spread into other plant formations. One bit of evidence developed at the San Dimas Experimental Forest on the south slopes of the San Gabriel Mountains suggests that this widespread plant community can only persist where there are recurring fires. The extent of the many fires in the San Gabriel Mountains during the last century has been plotted on large-scale maps. At elevations within the chaparral range only a few small spots, characteristically the outer points of spur ridges, have not been burned. These specific spots have an oak–grass plant association quite distinctive from the surrounding typical chaparral.

Though a barrier to travel, and perhaps a little dangerous because of its bear population, the chaparral carried a large game population. Scrub oaks, an important element in the association, provided substantial vegetable foods to the Indians. Conversely, the chaparral offers little of direct economic worth to the modern population. It survives in substantial measure because the steep slopes it occupies are not easy to use for other purposes. In Italy they would probably be planted to olives and grapes, but labor is too expensive in California to make low producing, dry-farmed orchards profitable. Also, chaparral resists, if it does not thrive under, repeated burning.

7. *Oak Parkland or Savanna* involves a parklike landscape which for most of the year displays live oaks and other small evergreen trees, such as sumacs, scattered sparsely or densely on bright yellow fields of dry grass. In late winter and spring the grass is pale green, and the darker leaved oaks stand out against it. In the northwest corner of Southern California as here defined—northern Ventura and Santa Barbara counties—gray-needled Coulter pines are scattered among the oaks in roughly equal abundance. This plant asociation occurs on the leveller surfaces in the same general areas as the chaparral. It is found in the high flat valleys of the Peninsular Range, as near Warner Hot Springs, Santa Ysabel, and Vandeventer Flat, in lower valleys as at Calabasas in the Santa Monica Mountains, and formerly occupied the upper alluvial-fan surfaces along the southern edge of the San Gabriel Mountains. Most of these areas receive winter rains amounting to 20 inches or more, but all have a long, hot, dry summer. The existence of gentler slopes seems to favor the oak park as opposed to a chaparral vegetation.

Today the predominant grasses and herbs—wild oats, fescue, foxtails, and mustard—are recently naturalized introductions, and the lands are heavily and efficiently grazed. This is an economically attractive plant community, and the ranchers struggle to expand it against the chaparral or at least prevent the latter's encroachment. Something like it, however, with native grasses and herbs, may go back to Indian times. The earliest accounts of localities now covered by this plant community mention good pasture, and the standing oak trees are often centuries old. Oak-park localities were economically attractive to the Indians, for, with their acorns and grass seeds, they supported large Indian villages. Annual fires running through the light grasses will scorch but not kill the oak trees. The grasses or their seeds sprout with the next winter's rain and, save for the problem of establishing new oak trees, an event which requires a series of years without fires, the association maintains itself.

8. *Yellow Pine Forest* occupies the lands immediately above the chaparral on the higher mountains. On north-facing slopes Ponderosa pine and big-cone spruce may grow in favorable canyons below 4,000 feet; on south-facing ones a complete chaparral cover may extend above 5,000 feet; from 6,000 to 8,000 feet the yellow pines and incense cedar, mixed with the deciduous black oak, form a dense cover. Many chaparral shrubs, such as manzanita and *Ceanothus,* penetrate the lower, more open parts of the forest.

The visitor to these forests cannot escape the feeling that they are retreating upslope and being replaced by chaparral, a movement accelerated by modern logging operations. While the Indians did not cut the forests, they did start fires in the chaparral, and it is reasonable to assume that the lower edge of the forest has been rising slowly but more or less continuously during the last 10,000 years.

The yellow pine forest was not too attractive to the Indians except as hunting grounds, but the high meadows on poorly drained flats furnished vegetable foodstuffs. Here there are numerous remains of campsites, probably visited by bands from the surrounding lowlands for a few months every summer.

9. *Fir Forests* occur above the pines, occasionally as low as 6,500 feet but characteristically above 8,000 feet. This is a dense forest except near the wind-swept peaks. The relatively small areas at these great elevations were rarely visited by the Indians, and in general are little affected by the modern summer grazing and recreational visits they experience.

10. *Pinyon-Juniper Woodland* occurs below the yellow pine forests on the interior side of the major mountain ranges, occupying elevations roughly the same as the eastern chaparral belt, i.e., 3,500 to 5,000 feet. North and east of Southern California it is found near the crests of many desert ranges. The pinyon-juniper country has little economic attraction today. It is at best poor pasture or resort land. But it was worth much to the Indians, who came up from the deserts every fall to harvest the pinyon nuts and juniper berries. This association seems

to be vulnerable to fire, and after burning is likely to be replaced by chaparral. My impression is that this subarboreal vegetation now occupies the steepest and rockiest districts and the lower growing chaparral the smoother areas with deeper, more continuous soil cover. A reasonable interpretation of this distribution is that the pinyon-juniper only survives where, because of lack of soil, the plant cover is too thin to support extensive fires. Such a differentiation of plant associations in this zone of relatively uniform climate most likely long antedates the historic period.

11. *High Desert Woodland and Scrub* characterizes the western and northern Mohave Desert, particularly the long alluvial slopes north of the San Gabriel and San Bernardino Mountains. Typical elevations are from 4,000 down to 2,500 feet; annual rainfall is around 10 inches with high temperatures and low humidity in summer and relatively severe cold in winter. The striking Joshua tree and juniper forest is prevalent in the higher and wetter areas, though a greater fraction of the surface is covered by more truly desert plants such as sagebrush, *Encelia,* and unusually tall creosote bushes (*Larrea*). Following rainy winters an understory of flowering herbs and grasses will provide excellent but ephemeral pasture. Only after an unusually wet series of years is the plant cover dense enough to maintain an extensive brush fire. Though not without edible seeds and small game, this region was of low attractiveness for the Indians. The scarcity of permanent water sources undoubtedly reduced their ability to exploit the region. Similarly, it is generally too dry to farm without irrigation, and is not much affected by the sporadic grazing on the ephemerals which sprout after rainy winters. Thus the association probably continues essentially unaltered from the distant past.

12. *Low Desert Scrub* perhaps covers more square miles than any other plant community in Southern California, occupying most of the eastern Mohave Desert and the Colorado lowlands. Creosote bush and burroweed (*Franseria*) are clearly the dominant plants, and over hundreds of square miles their widely spaced low bushes form almost the entire vegetation. Succulents, particularly *Opuntia* cacti, are locally abundant and in a few places there is a remarkably diverse though sparse xerophytic flora. That these deserts could support any non-farming Indians is surprising, but they did. The desert plants in general spend more of their energy on reproduction and so provide far more concentrated nutrients suitable for animal consumption than would the same amount of vegetative matter grown in more favored regions. An Indian band occupied almost every permanent water source at least seasonally, ranging out from these to seek game and edible seeds and roots. The edible *Agaves* may even have been seriously depleted near the waterholes by native exploitation. Today the Indians no longer seek wild plant foods, and this land is either completely untouched or com-

pletely modified as are the extensive irrigated lands of Imperial and Coachella Valleys.

13. *Alkali Sink* vegetation occurs on and close to the playas of the numerous undrained basins of the Mohave Desert. This community is composed mainly of salt tolerant species of the family Chenopodiaceae, especially of the genus *Atriplex*. Potable water is likely to be absent from these salty flats, and the historic Indians scarcely used them; nor does the modern population. During the Pleistocene, when there were permanent and overflowing lakes, however, this region was densely populated, as is attested by the many archeological sites around the extinct lake shores. In those times, of course, a completely different plant community was present, probably fresh water marsh and gallery forest.

The Indian Occupance of Southern California

While from archeological sources we have some knowledge of the size, distribution, and activities of the human populations that have occupied Southern California since glacial times, our data from these sources are thin. The protohistoric sites are the most abundant and productive and contain the greatest variety of cultural materials. These materials effectively supplement the contact ethnographic information provided by explorers, missionaries, and early settlers. By the time modern professional ethnographers (Kroeber and his associates) began to study the Southern California Indians, the native cultures had been seriously deformed if not destroyed, though clever reconstructions have been able to expose ancient aspects of these cultures that the earlier observers had missed completely. The Lower Colorado River and the West Coast were visited by the European explorers Ulloa, Alarcon, and Cabrillo as early as 1539–43, but, until the founding of the Franciscan mission at San Diego in 1769, exploration was sporadic and accounts of the Indians most elliptic. Such accounts as exist indicate that no major cultural changes occurred among the Indians in the two hundred years preceding the beginnings of the missions, a conclusion supported by all the available archeological evidence. In the more distant past there were substantial cultural changes, but, as Dr. Carter has suggested, Southern California has been characterized by a remarkably stable and persistent material culture. It therefore seems appropriate to examine the human geography of the region as it was at the advent of the missionaries in 1769, postulating that the ancestral patterns of life and land use since the end of the Wisconsin glaciation were generally the same.

Though its climates have remained stable, Southern California, in addition to the relatively minor coastal erosion and the construction of bay-mouth bars and the filling of coastal lagoons, has repeatedly experienced one enormous topographic change, namely the filling and drying-up of the Blake Sea (Lake Cahuilla) in Imperial and Coachella Valleys.

When the Colorado River takes a northerly course across its delta, an
area about five times as great as the present Salton Sea fills with fresh
water, which then spills south to the Gulf of California. When the
river flows directly into the Gulf, the lake dries up, its condition during
the eighteenth and nineteenth centuries. The old shore line is plainly
visible along a contour just above sea level. Along the old shore there
is an almost continuous line of Indian campsites, each thin midden
filled with the bones of fresh-water fish. Radiocarbon dates indicate
that the last filling and drying of the Blake Sea occurred entirely within
the last millennium. Older open sites exist, but unfortunately they are
not so readily dated. The structure of the Colorado River Delta assures
us that the same sequence of events has occurred many times; a filling
and drying of the lake during each millennium for the last fifty would
not be impossible.

That the great fresh-water lake was an enormously attractive living
site for the Indians is attested by the tremendous number of essentially
contemporary campsites along its shore. Except where the old shore
line cuts through the recently irrigated lands of Imperial and Coachella
Valleys, the sites lie in one of the most barren wastes in North America.
Estimates of the Indian population when the prehistoric lake was full
range from 20,000 to 100,000. Until modern irrigation systems were
established, the lakeless region of historic times did not support 1,000
people. As the Blake Sea ceased to overflow its salinity increased, and
at some point all the fresh-water fish died. This enormous human population had to leave or starve. The last great emigration probably occurred between 1000 A.D. and 1500 A.D. The Indians could move to
the Colorado River, where flood farming was practiced, or to the more
humid lands west of the mountains where acorns were the major food
source.

The social and economic organization of the Indian tribes in the areas
of immigration must have been strongly affected. Curiously, in the
Colorado River Valley, where farming could have been extended to
support a vastly greater population, an extraordinarily vicious war
pattern which effectively killed, kept out, or drove out newcomers was
in existence from 1540 to 1850. In the coastal areas the Indians who depended on gathering, hunting, and fishing were notably peaceful at
the time of European contact, and each village recognized sharply
delimited territories. Some sort of peaceful accommodation of an enormous influx of former desert dwellers must have been accomplished.

Three diverse linguistic families—Yuman, Shoshonean and Chumash
—were represented in Southern California, with the fourth, the Penu-
tian Yokuts, extending south from the San Joaquin Valley almost to its
watershed (Fig. 2). It is probable that the lake-shore dwellers around
the former Blake Sea involved both Shoshonean- and Yuman-speaking

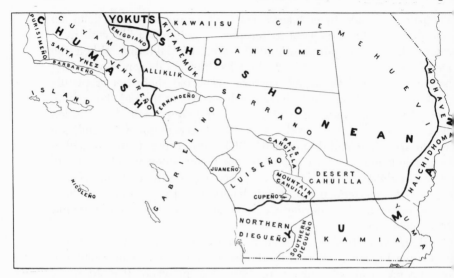

FIGURE 2: Aboriginal linguistic families of Southern California (after Kroeber).

villages, and that when the sea dried up emigration was to the coastal lands of their respective linguistic congeners.

The Yuman and Chumash families are both included in the Hokan stock, but their linguistic relationship is more distant than that between English and Russian. Otherwise the several families bear no detectable relationships with one another. Within the linguistic families there is further a tremendous separation of languages and dialects. In the extreme instance, Cupeño was spoken by the inhabitants of two villages occupying no more than fifty square miles around Warner Hot Springs. Cupeño differs from its Shoshonean neighbors by about as much as does English from German and is completely alien to Diegueño, spoken to the south. In the desert areas where something approaching nomadism was economically necessary, single languages such as Chemehuevi had far more extensive distribution, though they were spoken only by small populations.

This linguistic situation affords strong support to certain inferences concerning Indian history and the economic and political organization of the region in aboriginal times. First, the distribution and diversification of languages suggests that the three major linguistic families had been in the region for many millennia and that they had diversified into dialects and languages *in situ*. Some thousands of years ago the Shoshoneans may have intruded to the coast between the two Hokan groups, moving from their desert homeland in the northeast; since then they have not expanded but have lived in socially semi-isolated and localized communities which permitted distinctive dialects to develop. Secondly, the basic political unit, except along the Colorado

River, was the village or at most a few nearby villages. Social contacts were closely restricted to one's home and neighbor villages, and linguistic variations between villages could establish and intensify until they created separate languages. Generally speaking, the more productive the territory, the smaller would be the extent of a village's lands, and the smaller would be the area over which a single language or dialect was spoken. Finally, there was essentially no tribal loyalty. Each village attempted to maintain its rights on the lands that supported it, but there was no pattern of a group of villages uniting to dispossess their neighbors of land.

Except for the Yuman tribes along the Colorado River, the only people within the state for whom farming was an important economic activity, the foregoing statements apply to all of California and to much of the Pacific Northwest. Along the Colorado real tribes such as the Mohave and Yuman existed, and people moved freely from one small village to another, keeping their main loyalty to the whole linguistic unit and its lands. These tribes could and did unite for ceremonies and to wage aggressive or defensive warfare. Their failure to expand their small territories is related to the complete unattractiveness of the adjacent lands.

Aboriginal Population Density

Before considering the Indian economy and ecology, it is vital to learn how many Indians occupied Southern California in pre-contact times. A consideration of the total size of the Indian population must begin with Kroeber's estimates. He gives an aboriginal population figure of 133,000 for the state of California as a whole, of which between 35,000 and 40,000 lived in Southern California, about 31,000 if we exclude the farming tribes of the Colorado River. The prestige of Kroeber's scholarship is not easily shaken, but a number of more recent studies in adjacent areas make it likely that this figure should be at least doubled, and almost the entire increase will be placed in the coastal areas. The crux of the problem is that Kroeber explicitly refuses to accept the mission population figures and estimates; by the time censuses he could accept were available in the heavily missionized coastal regions, the native populations had almost vanished.

Meigs's excellently documented study in the northwest corner of Baja California, and Cook's and my work farther south on the peninsula demonstrate that mission data can be used to make thoroughly consistent population estimates, and these are twice as large as Kroeber's for similar areas. Meighan and Eberhart surveyed archeologically the tiny, unattractive offshore island of San Nicolas; their estimate of the population of this 32-square-mile section of Southern California is 600 to 1,200. Extrapolated to the other islands and coasts of Southern California occupied by fishing people with similar economies, figures of a higher order of magnitude than Kroeber's are obtained. In 1943 Cook more or less accepted Kroeber's figures for California's aboriginal population, raising them about 7 per cent, but more recently he has begun reworking the aboriginal population data from various parts of the state other than Southern California, and his population estimates at least double Kroeber's for those areas. A total population for Southern California of 75,000 in 1769, then, seems like a conservative estimate. This figure, or even Kroeber's lower one, is striking when we note that the total pre-Columbian Indian population of the United States is generally estimated at less than 1,000,000. In pre-contact times Southern California held at least 7.5 per cent of the total population of the territory that became the United States; its burgeoning population today amounts to only 4.5 per cent of the country's total!

The Indian Economy

The bulk of the California Indians did not farm, but they did exploit the wild flora and fauna with remarkable thoroughness. The critical factor in California's Indian population being so large in comparison with that of the remainder of the United States seems to be the remarkable peacefulness of the people and the stability of their communities. Each group stayed in its home territory and learned of its resources and how to exploit them for food until the group substantially filled the area. Furthermore, since all sorts of land and sea resources were exploited, the sorts of famine that might result from the failure of a single staple crop did not occur.

The technology of the California Indians never has received a very good press from the white man, perhaps because the implements that might be used for war were undeveloped. For hunting they used a relatively weak bow, a good throwing stick, and various sorts of snares. In the game-rich districts, however, they did get a small steady take of rabbits and other rodents, deer, and birds, apparently without depleting the breeding stock even in densely populated localities. Land animals provided a small but fairly dependable fraction of the food of all groups. On ceremonial occasions when much food was needed, productive local fire drives for small game would be undertaken.

Much more attention was given to the gathering and preparation of wild vegetable foods, and the gathering of insects, grubs, and small reptiles is best included in this kind of economic activity. Excellent basketry was made for this purpose (an art in which these Indians excelled by any standards), as well as crude seed beaters and digging sticks. More critical was their comprehensive knowledge of the potential utility of each plant in the local floras and how to render it edible or otherwise useful. The acorn was the most important single plant food, and its abundance was the principal factor in determining population densities in the valleys and hill lands back of the coasts. It was pounded to a flour in deep stone mortars, leached of its bitter tannin with warm water, and boiled into gruel or *pinole* or baked as a flat bread. The seeds of many grasses and such herbs as amaranths and chia (sage) were ground on flat stone slabs or metates and similarly cooked. On the desert the seeds or whole pods of mesquite, screwbean, and palo verde (*Cercidium*) served as substitutes for acorns. Various wild roots were dug and boiled or roasted, as were *Agave* and *Yucca* hearts and buds. Berries, nuts, especially pinyon and other pine seeds, and fruits were collected as available, and the pits of the wild prune, manzanita, and other fruits were pounded to flour and leached to make them edible. On the desert the fruits of all sorts of cactus were eaten. Except for the coastal and island villages, gathering vegetable foods and making such utensils as baskets from wild plants to use in gathering were the principal economic activities, both in terms of investment of time and energy and in terms of rewards obtained.

Such intense exploitation of the wild flora could not help but alter it. In the process of collection, seeds were continually being dispersed into new habitats. The refuse of campsites brought into existence concentrations of nitrogen-rich soil, on which, of occasion at least, tobacco was grown. Above all, the Indians would burn the landscape to promote the growth of desired grasses and herbs in the following season. Modern authorities are still uncertain of the long-range effects of repeated burning in specific situations. Did it cause the degradation of a complex chaparral to the less useful chamise or coastal sage association, or did it expand the oak-grassland parks? Most likely shifts in both directions occurred in different climatic and ecologic situations. In any event the wild landscape the European explorers found was a product of millennia of such disturbances.

The coastal and island peoples fished, collected shellfish, and hunted sea mammals with technologically more refined equipment. A result of the concentration of available food resources along the shore is the large Chumash villages with populations of more than 600 persons reported by Fages and Crespi on the coasts of Ventura and Santa Barbara counties. These Chumash, with their sewn-plank, asphalt-caulked canoes, their fine shell fishhooks, and three-pronged harpoons seem to have been most successful in developing a technology for the efficient exploitation of marine resources. All peoples also hunted and gathered and prepared plant foods, but the marine resources provided additional food security and permitted far greater population concentrations.

Style and Focus of the Indian Cultures

The Indian cultures of Southern California, as those of all human groups, merit some consideration in their own terms. What were these people seeking in life, and how successful were they in finding it?

An assessment of the "style" of their civilization may come closest to answering this basic question, and clearly there were two distinctive styles represented in Southern California, that of the Colorado River farmers, and that of all the other groups.

Our widely held, "folklore-like" opinions about the differences in attitudes toward the world held by farmers and by nomads are almost perfectly contradicted by the California data. The Mohave and Yuman farmers are reported, both by early explorers and modern ethnographers, to have been outgoing, inquisitive, individualistic people. Shyness and reserve did not mark their personalities. Their loyalties were to a small nuclear family and to the tribe as a whole, not to villages or local communities. Dream experiences were important to them as individuals, not as part of a community ritual process. On the river and with the tribes to the east they waged a kind of national warfare which involved close fighting with potato masher clubs, resulting in numerous fatalities. Individual Mohaves would journey as far west as the Santa Barbara coast, apparently impelled only by curiosity, and the foreign villages through which a man passed deferred to him as a thirteenth-century Russian village would defer to a representative of the Mongol Khan. In their sexual behavior, both sexes displayed a freedom and virtuosity that can be compared only with that of classical Greece. Finally, they worked at planting and harvesting crops, at hunting, fishing, and fighting in intense spurts of great activity interspersed with long periods of nearly complete indolence.

The gathering societies to the west present an almost opposite impression. These were quiet, reserved, and intellectually conservative peoples. Their loyalties were to their village and its immediate territory. People seldom travelled beyond the villages of their adjacent neighbors. The procurement of sustenance involved long and patient, but not violent, effort in gathering tiny grass seeds and grinding them or in pounding and leaching the acorn meal, and such activity went on incessantly. Making a coiled basket, perhaps their most developed craft, involves easy work but scores of hours for each product. The peaceful life was sought, and codes of laws were really concerned with manners that would permit all members of a village or band to get along in close and continuing association with a minimum of friction. The intoxicating Jimson weed and tobacco were taken in order to bring the recipient into touch with the supernatural, but he did so in connection with ceremonies and rituals concerned with the welfare of the group rather than with the exaltation of the individual. There must be substantial correlation between these attitudes and the population concentrations in California which were so much greater than those in other parts of the United States.

Some regional variation in "style of civilization" did exist within this area. In the first place the poorer lands of the interior uplands and deserts had both smaller bands and more extensive territories to be exploited by each. More time and energy was devoted to gleaning subsistence and less to non-economic group activities than in the larger, richer, and more closely spaced villages on the coast and in the rich alluvial valleys. In the latter areas large, permanently resident populations encouraged the elaborations of rituals. Further, there were distinctions between representatives of the three major linguistic groups, even where all lived in closely comparable environments. Some of the apparent diversity, however, may stem from the uneven quality of the records: the Chumash had no Father Boscana. The Chumash were better craftsmen and, because of their boats and effective fishing gear, were richer. They could afford more effort on fine ornaments as well as fine tools. The Shoshoneans seem to have put their creative energy into spiritual questions and observances and literary invention. The clear evidence of borrowing by the Diegueño of Gabrielino songs, stories, and religious ceremonies marks the Gabrielino land as a center of invention and diffusion for this aspect of culture. The Diegueño may have held a poorer land, wherein getting a living occupied more of their effort, but their enthusiastic borrowing of stories, religious concepts, and ceremonies from the Shoshonean peoples is striking. Relatively speaking, these were culturally backward pioneers who gratefully received from the sophisticates north of them.

The differential reaction to missionization of the three linquistic groups gets us into a later time period, but may further our understanding of basic cultural attributes. The relatively rich, technologically progressive Chumash seemingly welcomed the missionaries; they became extinct culturally within a century. The more backward Diegueño resisted Christianity and survive in substantial numbers, even though they were the first group to be contacted. The various Shoshonean groups had an intermediate history of cultural survival; their survival was aided by the fact that some groups such as the Cahuilla, Luiseño and Serrano lived east of the area of strong mission influence.

In terms of the subsequent development of the Southern California landscape it is pertinent to note that the Indians were concentrated on the same lands that the Europeans found attractive. Though the resources sought by the two civilizations differed, their distributions were similar. Where the Indians had been most numerous and prosperous, they could not resist the flood of Europeans and were substantially obliterated by the time California became part of the United States. Indian communities survive as such only in the interior uplands and on the edge of the desert, areas that until very recently were not sought by Europeans for intensive agricultural, residential, or industrial development.

Distinctive Zones of Indian Settlements

From the Indian standpoint Southern California might be divided into seven ecological zones (Fig. 3), with some villages or communities exploiting two of them at different seasons, others only one. It may be noted that there is almost no correspondence between a zone and any of the major linguistic families present in Southern California. From the coast to the interior these zones are:

1. *The Coastal Zone* involved a strip extending about one-half day's journey inland, and included all the offshore islands. People this close to the shore depended heavily on marine and estuarine animals. These were an almost inexhaustible food source, although a week of very stormy weather might make them inaccessible and produce severe hunger. The size and proximity of villages reported both by explorers and by modern archeologists make it clear that this was the zone of densest settlement. Almost every permanent water source close to the

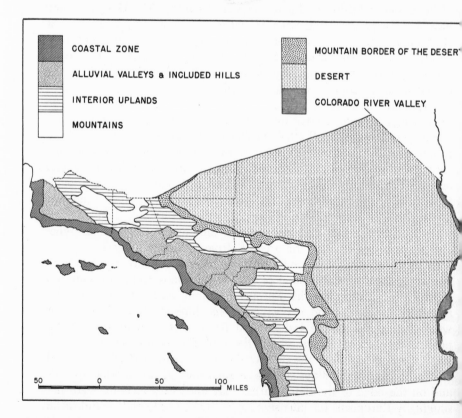

FIGURE 3: Ecologic Zones in Southern California. The zones are outlined in term: the distinctive opportunities which each afforded to the Indian economies.

beach has a large campsite nearby; some have several, though probably not all were occupied concurrently. They represent large and apparently permanent settlements, and many, such as at Point Sal, Malaga Cove, and the La Jolla Beach and Tennis Club, show substantial stratigraphic depth.

2. *The Alluvial Valleys and Included Hills* included both the extensive coastal lowlands, such as those around Los Angeles or Oxnard, and narrower valleys, such as that of the Santa Margarita River. The immediately adjacent and included hills were exploited by Indians from this zone. These districts also were notably populous; the gallery forests and the marshy vegetation along the streams, with its edible roots, stems, and seeds, and the animal life attracted to such localities were important resources. The combination of valley grasses and herbs and valley oaks growing on alluvial soils was similarly sustaining. Where the stream valleys cut through more broken country the chaparral and sage scrub on the hills could be exploited from more or less permanent village sites near the stream courses. Villages were fairly large, ranging in population from 150 to 400 persons, and rather closely spaced wherever pemanent water was present.

3. *The Interior Uplands.* Within the coastal drainage of the Peninsular and Transverse Ranges there are extensive denudational surfaces, some rough and some quite smooth. The lower and drier of the smooth surfaces are likely to be covered with sage scrub, the higher ones by an oak-grass parkland. The rougher surfaces have a chaparral cover, often with a substantial scrub oak component. This country was more sparsely populated, and, if accessible, likely to be exploited from villages in the alluvial lowlands. But there were also a substantial number of bands or villages who had their home bases at the scattered springs within the interior upland zone. For example, the entire Cupeño and Mountain Cahuilla tribes were based here. Gathering the wild plant foods was their main occupation, but they hunted as they could. Firing the grass or brush was a standard practice, and in late summer a fire might burn long and far. Villages were relatively small and ordinarily occupied only seasonally. Typical bands involved 100 individuals, and in summer and fall they would regularly camp in the higher mountains collecting pine seeds of all sorts as well as the acorns of the deciduous black oak (*Quercus Kelloggii*). Clearly, population densities in this ecologic zone were lower than in the ones previously considered, but as this area was less affected by the Missions far more of the natives survive, especially the Eastern Diegueño, Luiseño, and Cahuilla groups. Modern ethnographers know of more native villages in the interior uplands than in the richer lowlands.

4. *The Mountains.* There do not seem to have been any permanent Indian residents in the high forested mountains. These areas are singularly cold in winter, and both ethnographic accounts and archeo-

logical evidence indicate that the ill-clothed Indians invariably moved down to lower, warmer camps after the fall pine-nut harvest.

The enormous bear population (primarily the great California grizzlies) seems to be another reason why the Indians did not establish permanent settlements high in the mountains. Men and bears place remarkably similar demands for sustenance on their environment. The intense competition which this provokes is likely to result in somewhat mutually exclusive distributions for the two species. The Indian technology was such that a lone hunter was nearly helpless against a grizzly, but groups of men or villages, protected by fire, were fairly secure. Effectively, the bear was the better adapted creature in the mountains, the Indians in the lowlands. During the short "fat" season of the pinyon harvest an Indian band could camp together and protect itself, but the individual hunting or gleaning that would have been necessary to maintain a human population in the mountains permanently was too dangerous. The relative positions of the two species changed abruptly when Mexican and American ranchers with horses and firearms entered the area, and the bears were deliberately and promptly exterminated.

5. *The Mountain Border of the Desert.* The bulk of the desert-dwelling Indians actually lived in a narrow zone close to the foot of the mountains that form the western border of the Southern California deserts. Villages of from 100 to 200 persons were located at the permanent springs at the bases of various canyons, as at Palm Springs, Borrego, the middle course of the Mohave River, and many others. The Cahuilla even dug wells for drinking water to depths as great as sixteen feet in the washes at the base of the San Jacinto and San Bernardino Mountains. From their canyon headquarters bands would range out over the adjacent open desert and lower mountain slopes in winter and spring, hunting and gathering vegetable foods. In summer and fall the Indians would move up into the mountains to get the harvest of pinyon nuts and other seeds and perhaps to enjoy the cooler weather. Despite the apparent barrenness of the landscape, this narrow zone in the edge of the desert supported an aboriginal population density comparable to that on the seaward sides of the mountains.

Barrows long ago pointed out the notable concentration of nutrients in the buds and seeds of desert plants, which makes a relatively small vegetative mass capable of supplying a large amount of food for men. The pods of the mesquite, screwbean, and palo verde, which grow in great thickets where the water table is high, were the most important foodstuff, but palm seeds, cactus fruits, agave buds, and the flowers and seeds of many other desert shrubs also were utilized.

6. *The Desert.* On the open desert away from the mountain canyons, springs are few and widely scattered, and in this vast region a single spring would rarely have sufficient food resources in its neighborhood to support a permanently resident band. Such groups, typically involving

50 persons or less, ranged from water source to water source, though generally within a defined territory, exploiting the thin supply of plant foods. The animal foods available to the desert dwellers were scarce and, in this area especially, reptiles, insects, and the smallest rodents supplied the bulk of the animal foods. It may be added that the extra-desert residents in Southern California also did not hesitate to consume these forms of animal life. The sparseness of the human population on the open deserts of California is less surprising than that anyone could learn enough about the potential food resources to eke out a living in this barren and inhospitable land.

7. *The Colorado River Valley.* Here a completely un-Californian economy prevailed. The Yuma and Mohave planted maize, tepary beans, and squash on the mud banks left when the river receded after its late spring floods. Heavy yields were obtained from the fertile soil, and these were supplemented by mesquite pods from great forests along the river and by roots and seeds of rushes, marsh grasses, and other riverine plants. There is no question but that the agricultural potential of this areally small region was not fully exploited; here, almost uniquely in California, the Indian population was kept down by a pervasive and lethal war pattern comparable to the war patterns in the Eastern Woodlands of the United States. Fish taken from the river and game from the bordering thickets probably gave a smaller proportion of animal food to the diet than elsewhere in Southern California, but substantial surpluses of vegetable foods were normal. On the other hand, when spring floods failed to occur or late ones washed out the plantings, acute famine is known to have afflicted these flood farmers. Such famines did not affect the gatherers of other parts of Southern California, who might be chronically hungry, but who drew on such diverse resources that not all could fail at once.

The Persistence of the Wild Landscape

An interesting, though not definitively answerable, question concerns how much of the wild landscape remains in Southern California. That is, how much of the region would look like home if an Indian resident of the mid-eighteenth century could see it now? A reasonable answer is: much more than the contemporary visitor or many permanent residents might suspect. Our road-bound travels show us freeways with their great road-cuts and clearings along the right of ways, ribbon commercial and residential developments along roads, and the great spread of suburbs and intensive agriculture in the lowlands which the roads tend to follow. But away from these roads much broken country is utilized only as extensive grazing land, or it is protected as a National Forest and closed to visitors from May to December. The intent of this closing is to protect the natural vegetative cover from fire, in the belief that its destruction by burning would increase runoff damage during severe winter floods.

In considering this survival of the wild landscape we may take as a basis the ecologic zones recognized by the Indians, with some reference to the plant communities which characterize each zone.

In the coastal zone proper the large native population died early, but it was not immediately replaced by comparably intensive white exploitation of the land. On the islands it has not yet been replaced. Ports did develop at the few good natural harbors, and within this century beach resorts have gradually been filling up all the strands that are proximate to the larger cities. Two decades from now there may be no wild beach in Southern California, but at present there is a nearly wild strand vegetation along two-thirds of the sandy beach, though commonly the Coast Highway cuts it off from its normal plant neighbors. The Mission Bay salt marsh north of San Diego has just been converted into a completely artificial playground with lawns, bare sand, and dredged channels, but perhaps half of the thirty or so coastal lagoons are still essentially wild salt marshes. The rising popularity of small boat harbors may result in their disappearance within a decade. With the exception of the scrub-covered Otay and Kearney Mesas south and north of San Diego, which possess unusually unattractive soils, most of the marine terraces have been farmed or subdivided or both. Even if not readily irrigable, their relatively level surfaces invite mechanized farming. Where steeper slopes approach the sea, however, the coastal sage scrub or, in the case of the Santa Monica Mountains, chaparral prevails until a pretentious house is built and an approach road cut.

The alluvial valleys, of course, have been affected most completely. They were attractive to agriculture and commonly readily irrigable. So little of the wild landscape of this zone survives that only historical documents can suggest the appearance of these valleys in 1769. Interestingly enough, the tremendous residential-tract construction of the last fifteen years has concentrated on just the areas that had been cultivated during the preceding century, so that it is principally the cultivated landscape that is being further altered, not the wild one.

The steeper hills, however, still retain much of their chaparral cover, even near the heart of the Los Angeles metropolitan area. Unfarmable, these hills are also expensive to develop as residential sites. Homes tend to be pretentious and estates large. A growing number of their owners are coming to prefer a wild vegetative cover on the land upon which they do not build rather than the formal gardens they might afford, and the storied palaces of the Hollywood Hills and along the Arroyo Seco in Pasadena are often half-hidden in chamise, sumac, and scrub oaks. The survival of the mammalian fauna is particularly suggestive. Rabbits play nightly on the small lawns and gardens, and householders within a mile of Hollywood and Sunset Boulevards complain that the deer eat their rose bushes. The chaparral-covered steep slopes of the more distant hills and mountains are even more untouched, the accidental fires caused by passing motorists perhaps having almost exactly the same effect as the deliberately set fires of the Indians in maintaining the chaparral association.

Within the general coastal lowlands there is another sort of terrain which has not supported a chaparral cover in recent times. This involves hills composed of soft shales and characterized by gently rounded contours. Baldwin Hills, the Puente Hills, Signal Hill, and Palos Verdes are typical examples, all of course rapidy being subdivided for residences. Before that, they were grass-covered on the south slopes, with a park landscape on the north ones, as the name Palos Verdes might suggest. Their original cover may have been similar, but coastal sage scrub or even chaparral may have been present before the hills were occasionally dry farmed in small grains, thus permanently altering the normal vegetative cover.

The park landscapes of the interior uplands have in some places been plowed for wheat and barley; elsewhere they are grazed and often accidentally or deliberately burned. The oaks are the same, but introduced grasses have generally replaced the natives ones. In the grazed areas the vegetational aspect, if not the floristic composition, probably varies little from what it was in aboriginal times.

There is little doubt but that there has been a decrease in the area covered by coniferous forest in the mountains. In the Peninsular Range, the San Bernardino Mountains, the San Gabriel Mountains, and the Transverse Ranges to the northwest, logging and the burning of slash have exerted a more intense pressure on the lower margins of the yellow pine forest than did fires set by the Indians. On south-facing slopes there are scores of localities where chaparral covers charred pine stumps, but no seedling pines are present. This recent upward retreat of the forest is only an acceleration of a process that began with the end of the Pleistocene. Unfortunately the process seems to be tragically irreversible. At higher elevations and in less sunny sites, however, seedling pines quickly recover logged areas. The roads and clusters of resort cabins in the mountains affect only a tiny, though growing, fraction of the forested areas. Furthermore, the owners of resort cabins have preferred to set them into the forested landscape rather than cutting the trees indiscriminately and creating completely artificial landscapes.

As far as surface area is concerned, the bulk of all the desert landscape and vegetation types scarcely have been altered during the last two centuries. The exceptions are striking. Irrigated agriculture has completely re-created the flora and aspect of Imperial and Coachella Valleys and smaller oases along the Colorado and Mohave Rivers.

Resort and residential communities at the eastern and northern bases of the mountains that mark the desert's western edge, such as Palm Springs and Lancaster-Palmdale, show that the urban sprawl which has taken over the coastal lowlands threatens to leap the mountains. Ragged "jackrabbit homesteads" intrude over more extensive areas, though almost all the surface of the typical two and one-half acre plot remains in desert scrub. In Antelope Valley substantial areas of high desert are being dry farmed, or sprinkler irrigated if adequate ground water supplies can be tapped. Other than this, only along transportation routes is the desert affected. The gas-station oasis and the elongated beer-can midden along the highway is with us, but the desert highway also creates a strip of slightly more verdant land along its edge. The runoff after a light summer shower from the highway's impervious surface will often promote the growth of summer annuals when there is insufficient moisture in an open spot to produce germination.

Though they undoubtedly would support some domestic grazing animals, the deserts of Southern California are rarely if ever used as pastures. With the high costs for labor, it has never been profitable to herd the small flocks of sheep or goats which this poor and sparse pasture can normally maintain. Mining activties have been widespread in the past, but on the California deserts the pattern of uprooting every nearby bush for fuel, so characteristic in Mexico, was never established; only the actual locus of mining has been seriously disturbed by man. Thus, nearly half of Southern California is still covered by a wild desert landscape.

A very substantial part of this almost uninhabited land has been, and continues to be, used for military air fields, air gunnery and missile ranges, and desert training centers. Aside from truck tracks, air strips in valley bottoms, and the occasional unexploded shell or discarded casing, this activity has affected the great expanse of the desert's surface only moderately, but the effects on the fauna have been more severe. It is reported that wells and springs were filled during World War II in order to prevent soldiers in training from supplementing their sharply restricted water rations. Local extinction of the less mobile of those species that have to drink is almost certain. The military personnel have guns and are bored. The last pronghorn antelope herd in the Mohave Desert has not been reported since World War II, and mountain sheep have disappeared from many desert ranges they once occupied. Even humbler forms of animal life, such as chuckwallas, have suffered. We do not yet understand just what part each element of the fauna plays in maintaining the ecologic balance in the desert, but we are progressively more certain that the balance is a delicate one. Subtle but cumulative changes in the flora of these extensive military reservations may even now be occurring.

TABLE 1. Extent and Utilization of the Ecological Zones in Southern California.

Zone	Per cent of the total surface in aboriginal wild landscape	Indian population density per sq. mile	Per cent of total surface at present in wild state	Modern population density per sq. mile
Coastal zone[2]	4	13	1	1000
Alluvial valleys and adjacent and included hills	18	3	3	600
Interior uplands	14	2	8[3]	40
Mountains[4]	6	—[5]	5	9
Desert slopes of major mt. ranges[6]	5	2	4.5	18
Desert[7]	51	.1	48	3.5
Colorado River. valley[8]	2	5.5	.5	30

WILD LANDSCAPE = 100
SURVIVING TO THE PRESENT = 70

[1] No distinction has been made between urban and rural residents; obviously the high density figures refer primarily to urban settlement.

[2] Includes all islands and the strip of land immediately accessible to the coastal Indian villages.

[3] Almost all of this area is grazed at present, but unless it has been plowed or deliberately seeded for pasture it is assumed that the character of the wild landscape has not been altered significantly.

[4] The generally forested areas in the major mountain ranges. This involves areas more than 4,000 feet above sea level, but does not include the barren desert ranges which exceed this elevation.

[5] This area had practically no permanent Indian villages, but it was exploited in summer and fall by Indians from the interior uplands and the desert slopes of the mountain ranges. Its productivity accounts in part for the relatively high aboriginal population density in the two adjacent zones.

[6] The eastern and northern slopes of the Peninsular Range, San Bernardinos, San Gabriels, and Tehachapis. From pinyon country down to and including the canyon bottom oases.

[7] Includes the scrub land in both the low and the high deserts.

[8] An area of roughly equal extent and equal aboriginal and modern population density lies across the river in Arizona.

Table 1 is an attempt to represent numerically the extent of the various sorts of landscape discussed in this paper. It is offered only as a series of estimates in the belief that it presents at least the right orders of magnitude, and in the hope that through the internal cancellation of errors of ignorance and misinformation it may project a substantially correct picture. Southern California is interpreted as having an extent of some 45,000 square miles, with its northern boundary being that of Santa Barbara County, the Tehachapi Mountains, and the Garlock Fault across Kern and San Bernardino counties. I assume a total Indian population of 75,000 persons for that area in 1769.

Conclusion

One final consideration is suggested by a comparision of population densities in Southern California and in the United States as a whole during pre-Columbian times with those of the present. Then and now the coastal areas of Southern California stand among the most densely peopled districts in the continent north of Central Mexico, and in the earlier period this region did not enjoy the economic advantages of farming, present in much of the rest of North America. Two sorts of conditions can be used to explain this phenomenon: the extraordinarily favorable environment and peculiar local developments in human history. It is my belief that both explanations are appropriate, but I should like to examine briefly the environmental one.

It is well known that the mass of the vegetative cover bears only a slight relation to the mass of the animal life that can be supported in a given area. The faunal poverty of tropical rainforests contrasted with faunal abundance of certain grasslands is an obvious illustration. Two somewhat interrelated factors seem to be involved: the proportion of the vegetative matter that is in the form of nutritious starches, sugars, and proteins as opposed to less edible cellulose, and the mineral content of the soil and its parent rock which will support a nutritious or a less nutritious plant cover. The pronounced seasonality of vegetative growth, which in Southern California depends largely on winter and early spring rains, seems to favor those plants which invest much of their vital energy in storing concentrated food in their reproductive parts, and these plants maintain a rich fauna, with many species included therein. Furthermore, the complex rock types in Southern California's crystalline mountains, and the depositional shales and alluvial soils derived therefrom, provide to the plants an adequate supply of the scarce and rare minerals needed to keep this life pattern circulating at a high level.

An examination of the wild landscape then suggests that Southern California is truly a favored land for the higher types of animal life, of which man and the once abundant but now extinct bears are good examples. Two hundred years ago it supported lots of both. Today many more men live here. At the same time we should recognize that in paving the best part of this surface with roads and ranchtype houses we are making inaccessible one of the choicest spots on earth.

22. A Geographic System of Vegetation

A. W. Küchler

*In this attempt to develop a rational and useful classification
system for the various kinds and complexes of natural
vegetation, Küchler indicates one of the difficulties of
describing meaningfully—an essential in good geographic
writing and mapping—the great variations found in vegetation
types. In the preceding section, twelve different natural
vegetation sequences were established for southern California,
which underscores the difficulty of Küchler's problem.
Even so, it is possible to take the notation system developed
below and apply it to the California or any other vegetation
complex. The differences between Aschmann's paragraphs
and Küchler's two- to six-letter notations are obvious,
and for most phases of geographical analysis and description,
the letter system has many advantages. Küchler also points
out the importance of vegetation as a valuable indicator
of so many less-evident things in the landscape.*

One of the great handicaps to the development of the science of
phytogeography is the confusion that exists in the minds of both
botanists and geographers with regard to terminology. A number of
terms have evolved during the past two generations. These terms are
given different meanings by different authors. An author may use two
different terms for the same type of vegetation, or different types of
vegetation may be designated by the same term by different authors or
even by the same author.

To illustrate this confusion in the nomenclature of vegetation types,
a few examples may be cited. In his book on Asia, Stamp uses the term
"deciduous forests" on one map and "monsoon forests" on another map
for the same type of vegetation. The variation is not employed to lend a
certain elegance of style or to avoid repeition but is used on vegetation
maps, where such a procedure is unacceptable. This is a minor trans-
gression, however, as compared with what we find on White and
Foscue's vegetation map of "Anglo-America." On this map the barren
desert of the lower Colorado and the lush Iowa prairies are under the
same designation—an inexcusable grouping even in view of the small
scale of the map. On the same map, "northern" forests, named from the

SOURCE: *Geographical Review*, XLVII (1947), 233–40. The author is a member
of the staff of the Department of Geography, University of Kansas.

latitude, are set off against "spruce-ponderosa" forest, which is a poor name combining a genus in the English language with a species of another genus in Latin. De Terra leans in the same direction with his peculiar usage of "semi-deciduous forest" and "mixed forest." According to Phillips the most important plant community of central Tanganyika is one that he calls the *"Berlinia-Brachystegia*-Other Species Woodland communities." He cites other investigators and the names they have given to this one vegetation type—no fewer than nineteen! A large assortment of such confusions could be instanced. I must emphasize that I am not criticizing either the authors or their work, but I do wish to show the pitfalls with which our path is strewn when we make investigations in the field of phytogeography. In certain cases more discretion might have been advisable, but in general the culprits must be excused on the ground that an accepted phytogeographic classification is nonexistent. From the point of view of a critical terminology many terms are of local value only; for example, Central Forest, Southern Forest, Coast Forest. Such expressions can be applied almost anywhere, each time with a new meaning and conveying nothing to the reader unfamiliar with the area under discussion. They are useless in analyzing vegetation and should not appear on a vegetation map.

The lack of an accepted terminology makes it difficult to join vegetation maps of contiguous areas when the maps are by different authors; compilation of a world map of vegetation becomes an exasperating if not hopeless task.

The science of plant geography has remained largely in the hands of botanists, who have failed to adopt a uniform nomenclature. The extent of the confusion in botanical circles was made clear by Du Rietz when addressing the Sixth International Botanical Congress on the classification and nomenclature of vegetation units.

At the Fifth International Botanical Congress (Cambridge, 1930) the author presented an attempt to parallelize some of the most prominent terminological systems of phytosociology, demonstrating the chaos prevailing even in the application of such fundamental terms as "association" and "formation" . . . . Unfortunately there does not seem to be much hope at present of arriving at a general agreement in this respect. The leading phytosociological schools of the present day are not willing to sacrifice any essential part of their traditional terminology for the purpose of an international agreement.

At the same congress another prominent leader in the field, Braun-Blanquet, spoke of "the need for establishing order in the ever increasing chaos in the description of vegetational groupings."

Even the best-known botanical scheme have not found much support among geographers. Raunkiær's system of life forms is unsuitable for a geographic approach. So are systems based on floristics with terms like "Salicornietum radicantis," "Salicornion," and "Salicornietalia." Du Rietz uses "socion," "sociation," "consociation," "association." This is not the place to criticize the relative merits of the botanists' systems. The fact remains, however, that none of them has been found acceptable by a majority, even among botanists.

In describing any type of vegetation, the forms actually existing must be considered before references to habitat are made. Only after the vegetation has been fully described can climate, soil, bios, and culture find a place in the discussion. The point of view exhibited in the following quotation deserves full support.

> Vegetation should be primarily characterized *by its own features,* not by habitat, indispensable as is the study of habitat for the understanding of its nature and distribution. It is the *structure* and *composition* of a plant community that we must first ascertain and record as the secure basis of all subsequent knowledge.[1]

One of the primary tasks confronting geographers is to formulate a classification of vegetation for their own specific use.

> Native vegetation is an expression of the composite physical environment. It is the integration of all physical factors, past as well as present, and as a consequence often provides a better basis for classifying and judging the potentialities of environments than any other one single factor or set of factors.[2]

> Vegetation types are the visible reflection of the climates . . . . Even the rhythm of the seasons finds expression in the changing aspect of the vegetation cover.[3]

> The plant-cover of an area forms the best key to the sum-total of the climatic conditions.[4]

Most geographers hold the same or similar points of view, and it seems strange, therefore, that more attention has not been devoted to the study of vegetation in American geographical circles—at least until one actually beholds the green garment of our globe. Life manifests itself in a perplexing variety of forms, and the earth's vegetation is no exception. But life also obeys the great laws of the universe, and it is at this point that the work of the phytogeographer begins. Were there no law, his efforts would be futile. The fact that the vegetation is grouped and distributed all over the world in a definite pattern permits him to make reasonable investigations and to draw logical conclusions. It permits him also to devise a classification and a nomenclature that will be his most important tool.

[1] P. W. Richards, A. G. Tansley, and A. S. Watt: The Recording of Structure, Life Form and Flora of Tropical Forest Communities as a Basis for Their Classification, *Journ. of Ecology,* Vol. 28, 1940, pp. 224–239; reference on p. 229.
[2] V. C. Finch and G. T. Trewartha: Elements of Geography: Physical and Cultural, 2nd edit., New York and London, 1942, p. 483.
[3] P. E. James: An Outline of Geography, Boston, New York, etc., 1943, p. 6.
[4] M. I. Newbigin: A New Regional Geography of the World, New York, 1929, p. xvii.

The best statement the author has been able to find on the nature of an ideal terminology was made by Dr. Barnhart:

The rules of terminology ought to be simple and based on reasons clear enough and strong enough that everyone understands them and is disposed to accept them.[4]

This precise statement is entirely acceptable, but if it is adopted as a basic formula, it becomes at once one of the most formidable barriers on the road to our goal! Terms that are "simple" and "clear" seem a matter of course in a terminology, but with regard to vegetation types nothing is simple or clear.

Among the factors that complicate the formulation of satisfactory terms may be listed the variety of vegetation types, the transitions between types, and the terms themselves.

The vegetation of the continents presents an intricate pattern of different types. Even though a given type may recur several times, it is by no means always the same. This results in the application of one term for all occurrences by some observers and a separate term for each occurrence by other observers. Just how much a type must differ from another before a new term is justified is a difficult question to answer.

What has been said of vegetation types applies also to their divisions and subdivisions. If the process of dividing is continued logically, the considered area becomes so small that one passes from geography into ecology   and had better resort to the quadrat method, which is not geography. It is quite impossible to say where to draw the line between geography and ecology, since circumstances vary from one case to the next. We are here confronted with one of the major questions of phyto*geographic* methodology and hence also of terminology: how much detail is permissible in a study of vegetation that is to stay within the boundaries of geographic research?

The second, and perhaps the most perplexing, problem is caused by the fact that types of vegetation do not generally possess clear boundaries. One type merges into the next, and between the areas of distinct types there appears a belt of varying width the vegetation of which belongs to neither one of the distinct types. Transitions are difficult to analyze. One needs only to remember Forrest Shreve's repeated efforts to define the edge of the desert. If there is no agreement on the definition of a major term, how can one establish boundaries?

A transition between two very different life forms—for example, trees and grasses—is less troublesome than one that lacks contrast. For instance, there are innumerable places where it is almost impossible to distinguish between trees and shrubs, and any boundary line shown on a map is largely abitrary. Transitions are very frequent indeed. Of an Alaskan region Griggs said: "Transitions, in fact, occupy more ground

[4] *Proc. Fifth Internatl. Botan. Congr., Cambridge, 1930,* p. 559.

than areas which could be called typical." To make matters worse, transitions usually proceed irregularly, so that the transition between two distinct types of vegetation may adopt different, yet characteristic, forms.

A third great problem lies in the terms themselves. A given term conveys a different meaning to different authors. Some students of vegetation attempt to avoid this danger by coining new terms. Others use foreign terms or foreign terms translated into English—a dangerous method unless an unequivocal definition is given every time.

The question arises whether a clear and simple classification of the world's vegetation is possible, and in his correspondence with colleagues and in numerous discussions the author has often met with a negative attitude. This pessimism he considers unfounded, and if he ventures to propose a method that he hopes may prove acceptable to geographers, he does so because he is convinced that a systematic approach to the geographic study of vegetation is both necessary and possible.

There are, of course, a considerable number of terms that are well established in phytogeography. Every geographer is familiar with *paramo, prairie, health, taiga, tundra, savanna, maquis, steppe,* and numerous others. Many of these terms are variously defined. *Tundra, taiga, steppe,* and a few others are used in several continents, but the great majority of terms refer one to a definite area. These names should be used as in the past, though perhaps they should be more clearly defined wherever that is possible or desirable. But they have not been found adaptable to a general, unified system that can be expressed on maps. The author likes and frequently uses these terms and proposes to continue to do so. Their use is not exclusive of the phytogeographic classification presented in this paper.

A New Classification Proposed

The new classification proposed herein endeavors to follow Dr. Barnhart's behest. The author hopes that its rules are clear and simple, that they are intelligible and acceptable to every geographer. The approach is physiognomic, which has a triple advantage for geographers: (1) direct observations can be used as a basis of classification; (2) floristic terms are avoided; (3) cartographic representation is simplified.

The author is happy to acknowledge his inspirational debt to Köppen. Climates, no less than vegetational types, are difficult to express in formulas, and it is to Köppen's lasting credit that he succeeded in devising a system that is used by geographers all over the globe and has been a stimulus to further efforts at classification. In developing his system Köppen was greatly influenced by considerations concerning the distribution of vegetation, and it is therefore not difficult to see that a classification of vegetation may be developed along parallel lines. The principles are essentially the same in both systems: a few basic groups, designated with capital letters, and a larger number of qualifications, designated with small letters. Combinations of capital letters appear primarily in transitions from one type to another, though this is not a necessary implication. Another feature common to the two systems is the arbitrary nature of some of the boundaries. It does not seem possible to do away entirely with arbitrary choice, and such choice is, of course, open to criticism. But the author feels that the arbitrary boundaries are too few in number, and not of sufficient significance, to threaten the value of the classification as a whole. The Köppen classification describes the climate of any region with satisfactory detail. It does not state what weather one may expect there on a given day, though the climate of a place is ultimately the sum total of individual weather conditions. Likewise the classification presented in this paper describes the vegetation of any region with satisfactory detail. It does not give the species that make up this vegetation.

The fundamental geographic division of the plant kingdom is that between the woody plants and the nonwoody or herbaceous ones. The appearance of the latter in the landscape is relatively uniform; they are therefore all combined under the one capital letter G. The appearance of woody plants varies much more, both as regards height and as regards general characteristics. There are four primary groups: B, broadleaf evergreen; D, broadleaf deciduous; E, needleleaf evergreen; and N, needleleaf deciduous. "Needleleaf" includes scalelike leaves such as those of some cypresses. The term is usually but not always synonymous with "coniferous." To these are added the capitals M for mixed growth of D and E, and S for semideciduous vegetation, composed of B and D.

These capitals stand for trees unless they are qualified by s or z. It is not always necessary or even desirable to refer to the height of trees (l, m, t), but it is imperative that one of these small letters be added if both trees and shrubs occur on the same ground, with trees dominant.

The capitals may be qualified by appropriate small letters. On maps of small scale this is often not necessary, and a·capital letter may well stand alone. The following list gives the capital letters and four groups of small letters. These qualifying letters should always be arranged in the order of the groups from which they are taken.

CAPITALS: B   broadleaf evergreen woody vegetation
            D   "   deciduous   "   "
            E   needleleaf evergreen   "   "
            N   "   deciduous   "   "
            M   mixed (D and E)   "   "
            S   semideciduous (B and D) "   "
            G   grasses and other herbaceous plants

SMALL LETTERS:

GROUP I: l   low; with trees: maximum height: 10 meters
               " grasses: "   "   ½ meter

           m   medium; with trees: height 10–25 meters
                " grasses: "   ½– 2   "

           t   tall; with trees: minimum height 25   "
                " grasses: "   2   "

GROUP II: h   herbaceous plants other than grasses

           s   shrubs with a minimum height of 1 meter

           z   "   "   " maximum   "   " 1   "   (dwarf shrubs)

GROUP III: a   arid. Vegetation distinctly xerophytic or completing its life cycle within a few weeks. Bare ground between plants is conspicuous.

           b   barren. Vegetation largely or entirely absent.

           c   continuous dense growth. With G it signifies continuous sod.

           d   dominant. Attached only to a feature that is considerably more prominent than others in the same group.

           g   galeria forms and any vegetation limited to the vicinity of bodies of water (e.g. mangroves).

           i   interrupted. Trees and shrubs stand so far apart that their crowns frequently do not touch. With G it signifies bunch grass.

           p   growth singly or in groves (of trees and shrubs; parks, etc.) or in disconnected patches (of G).

           r   rare. The feature is not frequent yet is conspicuous.

GROUP IV: e   epiphytes occur in abundance.

           j   lianas are conspicuous.

           k   succulents are conspicuous.

           w   aquatic vegetation, whether submerged, as *Sargassum,* or floating entirely or in part on the surface, as water lilies (*Nymphaea alba*) or duckweed (*Lemma minor*). Plants that root under water but carry important parts above the surface (e.g. mangroves) are not included in w.

Evidently not all four groups are needed every time. If there is more than one capital, each one will have its own set of small letters. The qualifying letter always follows the feature it qualifies, so that the small letters always stand on the right side of the capital letter to which they belong. Any group of qualifying letters containing the letter d should be placed before any other qualifications or groups thereof, so that the group containing the d is separated by the d from the features to which the d does not apply. All qualifying letters refer to features on their left. If more than one capital letter is required, the feature most prominent in the landscape is placed first. A few examples will illustrate this.

A moss or lichen tundra: Gh
An area thinly covered with sagebrush: Bzi
Taiga: E

Elfin or tropical high-altitude forest: Ble
Selva: Btej
Chaparral scrub: Bs
"   "   with scattered live oaks: BsBi
Savanna: GDp
"   (low grasses, occasional shrubs): GlDsr
"   (tall   " , galeria forests): GtDpBg
Broadleaf deciduous forest: D
Pine forest with ground layer of blueberry bushes: EmDz

The examples indicate that considerable detail can be shown whenever wanted. One of the advantages of this system is its adaptability to
maps on a wide variety of scales. Large-scale maps will show more
formulas per unit area, and possibly longer ones, than small-scale maps.

VI. SOILS

Soils are a complex of both organic and inorganic surface materials, and not only constitute the essential base for most natural vegetation, but also are fundamental for agriculture. Although tradtionally geographer have classified soils as elements of the lithosphere—that is, as a surface material of landforms—the primary function of soils is to support the growth of vegetation; hence, functionally they can be considered a part of the biosphere. Qualitatively, soils are one index of agricultural potential, and though soils can be improved through careful management and the use of fertilizer, it is almost axiomatic that successful farming begins with fertile soil. "Because they are there," soils often are abused and misused and millions of acres rendered unproductive through failure to recognize and follow simple principles of conservation. This recognition becomes critical when we realize that perhaps no more than 10 percent of the land surface of the world has soils that can be classified as really productive.

23. Grass and the Soil

Charles E. Kellogg

Soil is the basic ingredient of both agriculture and grazing; the latter is dependent on the natural or cultivated vegetation of an area. Interrelationship between soils and plants is of great significance to man, and his understanding of the nature of soils, their physical characteristics and productive capabilities is essential. Maintenance of the soil, vital to continued productivity, is a problem of increasing importance, as soils are becoming more and more exhausted through constant cropping or grazing. Kellogg indicates the important facts concerning soils, as well as the significance of the relationships between different soil types and vegetation.

The great variety and complexity of the country scene appeals to most people whether they are professional naturalists or not. Each rural landscape has its own set of characteristics. Any one may be just a little

Source: *Grass, Yearbook of Agriculture* (Washington, D.C.: U.S. Department of Agriculture, 1948), pp. 49–55. The author is Chief of the Division of Soil Survey of the United States Department of Agriculture.

different from the thousands of others, or very unlike any of them. Through science modern man tries to understand these landscapes—to unravel their many interlocking relationships—in order to discover principles that can be used to guide the great producing powers of nature to his own ends.

But the job is so big that scientists have had to divide it among them. Thus botanists, geologists, foresters, climatologists, horticulturists, agronomists, soil scientists, farmers, and others are each concerned with some part of the whole. Yet at some stages in scientific work the facts and principles discovered in these specific lines of inquiry must be brought together if principles of prediction value in the real world are to be developed. That is, plants growing in even the simplest farm, or garden, or forest are subject to all the influences of the environment acting together and they contribute to this environment as well.

Nothing illustrates this complexity better than grass. In some landscapes tall, luxuriant grasses grow naturally and help make black soils that are naturally productive for cultivated plants. The invasion of such landscapes by forest degrades these soils—they lose part of their great producing potential for crops. And this may happen quickly—not in terms of a man's lifetime perhaps, but in 200 years or so.

Yet in other places more productive soils are found under forest than under grass. Here invasion of the soil by grasses degrades it rapidly, within the period of one man's life or much less.

These are two extremes. But often it is by looking at the extremes that we discover principles of great importance to the soils between them, where differences are not so easily seen.

The Soil

Suppose we look at the soil itself. What is it? First of all, it is the natural medium in which plants grow. It is a mixture of mineral matter and organic matter, some of which is living. Things are being added to it and taken away from it. The soil on the very surface is not like that just beneath it; in fact, the soils in most places consist of a series of unlike layers, one over the other, each from a few inches to several feet in depth.

Then, too, the surface is gradually changing. Some soils are slowly being eroded, bit by bit, so that all the layers move down. To each layer a bit of the one beneath is being changed and added to its lower side as it loses its upper part by erosion or to another layer above it. Finally, new fresh minerals from the rock beneath are incorporated into the lower part of the lowest layer of the soil.

Other soils, of course, receive additions to the top instead of the bottom. Along great rivers silty alluvium settles out of the water over the soil. Dust settles from the air—perhaps just a little; often a great deal.

Volcanoes add ash or cinders to soils, sometimes lowering their productivity for crop plants but more often increasing it.

When water enters the soil, air is forced out of the pore spaces. Then as the soil dries, air returns. In this process gasses like carbon dioxide escape and others like ammonia enter the soil to be absorbed.

The entering water, either as rain or irrigation water, brings soluble materials with it too—usually just a little, but sometimes a great deal. The excess water beyond what the soil can hold seeps out into deep drainage and carries soluble materials away.

Then, of course, plants are growing on the soil, extracting nutrients, and producing organic matter from these soil nutrients and those from the air and water. Depending on the kind of vegetation, the total organic matter may be a ton or so per acre up to several hundred tons. Thus, in the living organic matter the soil has a great storehouse of nutrients. When the plants and animals die, the remains serve as food for micro-organisms. As it decomposes, the nutrients in it are made available to new plants.

Thus a soil changes between day and night, from season to season, and over long periods of geological time.

Yet soils are not quite so difficult to understand as this recital might suggest, because many of the processes go together. Ignoring for the moment man's interference, a soil—an individual set of soil characteristics that we call a soil type—results from a particular combination of five genetic factors: climate, vegetation, parent rock, relief, and time. Thus soils are not distributed promiscuously over the earth, but in an orderly discoverable geographic pattern. A given set of the five genetic factors everywhere produces the same set of soil characteristics—the same soil type.

But to these natural types of soil must be added the changes caused by use—often drastic changes for better or for worse, in terms of crop production. That is, many soils developed originally under forest in the humid temperate regions have been made ever so much more productive by careful husbandry, including the growing of grasses, the use of lime and manures, and improved drainage for hundreds of years. Other soils have been deprived of their essential cover of grass or trees and exposed directly to the sun, wind, and water, with serious degradation by erosion, blowing, burning of organic matter, and loss of structure.

Soil scientists have been and are now attempting to discover precisely what types of soil exist in the world, where they are, and how they respond to that whole group of practices we call "husbandry."

One cannot understand a soil by looking simply at one or two of its characteristics. Slope, depth, texture, color, structure, chemical composition, and many more must be seen in combination. Not only that, a soil must be seen in relation to those around it. A soil is three-dimensional. It occupies discrete areas of the earth. Around each area are boundary lines that separate it from the other soil types with different sets of soil characteristics. These boundary lines come in places where there is a change in one or more of the five genetic factors.

So a soil is a solid, the upper surface of which is the surface of the land. The lower surface is defined by the lower limits of biological forces, and the sides are the boundaries with other soil types. One cannot take a soil into the laboratory any more than he can a mountain or a river; but one may take samples of rock, water, or soil into the laboratory for important investigations to determine some of the characteristics of mountains, rivers, or soils.

Even further, a soil is a landscape with a characteristic climate and vegetation. Thus plants and soils are essential parts of one whole, each influencing the other and both reacting to the climate.

Soil Productivity

A central problem of inquiry in soil science is soil productivity for various crops, grasses, and trees and how to increase it or maintain it efficiently. The two principal aspects of soil productivity are its structure, or tilth, and its fertility, or content and balance of available plant nutrients.

Let us consider the fertility. Commonly, soil scientists attempt to express the amounts of nutrients available to plants in terms of "pounds per acre" of available phosphorus, potassium, calcium, and so on. These figures permit the comparison of soils only in the narrow sense, not as landscapes.

Suppose, for example, that we compare the black grassland soils (Chernozem) of eastern North Dakota with the light-colored forested soils of northern Michigan (Podzol). We shall see at once that the content of available plant nutrients is considerably higher in the Chernozem than in the Podzol. But to compare the total nutrients in, and available to, the biological cycles of the natural untouched landscapes, we shall need to add to the amount in the acre of soil that in the living matter— in the trunks, branches, and leaves of the trees, in the animals, and in the other plants and micro-organisms. This additional amount will be large for the forest and relatively low for the grasses. Of course, the nutrients tied up in living matter are not subject to much leaching— not until the material dies and begins to decompose. It is mainly the material in the soil that is subject to leaching. Thus, of this total, more will be subject to leaching under grass than under forest.

Generally, the percentage of mineral plant nutrients in the organic remains from grass is higher than in those from forest. Thus more organic acids result from the decomposition of forest litter, even though the total of minerals supplied is somewhat greater. Per ton of dry matter produced, grasses return to the soil more bases, like calcium, potassium, and so on, than trees, other conditions being comparable; and with nearly equivalent synthesis of organic matter, grasses produce more humus—black, stable organic matter—because of their chemical nature and their dense, fibrous root systems.

Then because of the relatively drier climate, the Chernozem soil is much less subject to leaching than the Podzol. Grass, side by side with forest in the moist Podzol region, holds less against leaching than the forest; grass side by side with forest at the boundary between the Chernozem and Podzol zones gives a darker soil, higher in organic matter and plant nutrients, than forest. The dark, fertile, granular surface soil is deeper under the grass and more suitable for crop plants than that under forest from the same rock material.

Thus, the figures selected for a comparison of an acre of Chernozem with an acre of Podzol vary greatly, depending upon whether we think only of the soil in a narrow sense or of the total landscape, including soils and plants together. In both scientific and practical work, both sets of comparisons are needed.

If the light-colored Podzols are fertilized, it is possible to have soil fertile for grass, despite the leaching. If this grass cover is maintained, the cultivated soil itself then takes on some of the physical and biological characteristics of the Chernozem of the black grasslands. But if we do not make up for the greater leaching in the Podzol landscape by the proper use of lime and fertilizers, the pastures and meadows are likely to be poor—indeed, not only poor, but the soil may actually become less fertile under the grass than under the forest. (Young alluvial soils or others too young to have received normal leaching are exceptions.)

In practice a farmer on the Podzol soils, let us say in New England, will produce pasture more efficiently by using lime and fertilizer on a small area to develop a soil approaching the less-leached Chernozem in fertility than to use a far larger area for untreated pasture. That is, a hundred acres of untreated pasture will, ordinarily, give less return in the Podzol landscape than the same area with 20 acres of well-treated pasture and 80 acres of forest, to say nothing of the fact that the long-time productivity of the soil will be better.

In this comparison both landscapes have a cold season when the ground is frozen. Let us look at the contrasting relationships between grass (savanna) and soil, and forest and soil in the humid Tropics with only a short dry season. In these comparisons it must be clear that reference to "grass" or "forest" includes all the plants, animals, and micro-organisms associated with them, not simply the trees and grasses themselves.

First of all, leaching under the heavy rainfall in equatorial regions is very severe. At high temperatures all chemical reactions are accelerated. (Generally the speed of chemical reactions doubles with each rise of

18° F.) Thus at any moment the (unfertilized) soil is low in all available plant nutrients (again except for very young soils like those on fresh alluvium or volcanic ejecta). The deep-rooted trees of the tropical rain forest draw nutrients from a great volume of soil. A large amount of these nutrients is collected and stored in the great tree trunks, in the branches and leaves of trees and other plants, and in micro-organisms and animals. At equilibrium, a small amount continually returns to the soil surface as the plants drop their leaves, and some is returned on or near the surface as the other living matter dies. And the amount lost by leaching balances the gains from new minerals and from the atmosphere. But the total amount of nutrients collected in the savanna is relatively small.

Thus, if we compare equal areas of the two landscapes under the same climate, one with a cover of tropical rain forest and the other with a cover of savanna, we shall find an enormous amount of material held by the living plants and not subject to leaching under the forest, and only a small amount held by the plants in the savanna with the rest subject to leaching. And, of course, that which is subject to leaching is leached out of the soil. Matters are made worse by fire. Whereas the tropical forest does not burn unless it is cut and made to burn, the savanna burns like gasoline-soaked rags when dry and so usually burns in the dry season. Moreover, tropical soils are relatively low in their capacity to absorb plant nutrients. Thus, a large part of the ash from burning the savanna is lost with the first heavy rains.

In such landscapes, then, we find the most productive soils, other things being equal, under the forest—the reverse of our comparison at the boundary between Chernozem and Podzol. In the Chernozem region where leaching is low and temperatures are relatively low, grass acts as a great soil builder and conserver of plant nutrients. In the hot humid Tropics, grass has the reverse effect and becomes a degrader of soil.

After cutting the luxuriant forest, crops may be grown in rotations and mixtures for periods of 2 to 7 years—sometimes even longer—depending upon local soil conditions. But it is necessary for forest to return to this soil again before the nutrient supply built up under the forest has been seriously depleted. Otherwise, the savanna will come into the cleared land and injure the soil for both trees and crops. After 10 to 15 years of forest growth, the land may again be devoted to a rotation of crops.

Soil Structure

Soils productive for crops are permeable to roots, water, and air. The productive soil has the individual grains grouped into aggregates so there are pore spaces for passage. Generally speaking, tillage by itself tends to destroy structure, tends to break up the soil crumbs and granules, and causes the clay particles to "run together" into masses. This effect of tillage varies enormously with different soil types and within one soil type, according to moisture conditions at the time of tillage and other cultural practices. In fact, a few soils become too granular with tillage, so that contacts between roots and soil particles are too few for the proper transfer of water and the nutrients.

Even though tillage has the effect of injuring soil structure—scarcely at all with some soil types and a great deal with others—it often cannot be eliminated. Soil structure must be good in the lower layers as well as in the upper ones. Since an active population of micro-organisms is essential for good structure in most soils, organic materials and fertilizers must be added to many soils to make them productive for crops and grasses, and added not only to the surface, but also to the sub-soils. This may require deep plowing or chiseling to get the materials into the lower layers, so that roots may go deeply.

The exposure of many soils to the hot sun injures structure by decreasing the micro-population, hastening the decomposition of organic matter, and causing a hard crust at the surface. Excess erosion, beyond that normal for the soil, may remove surface layers with good crumb structure and expose lower layers with poor structure. In fact, this type of injury by erosion is, generally, far more important than the nutrient losses from erosion.

Vigorous, close-growing, deep-rooted vegetation is the best builder of soil structure. Generally, the deep-rooted legumes and grasses are best for cultivated soil, provided, and only provided, that proper varieties are grown with adequate fertilization or manuring as needed on the individual soil type. But a well-growing forest produces better soil structure than poorly growing grasses. The best structure of all is produced under tall grasses in subhumid regions, as in Chernozem. Where leaching is low, organic matter and nutrients are conserved, and a deep fibrous root system develops. In areas of high leaching, like the humid Tropics, where the forest grows much better than grasses and conserves the nutrients, forest is superior to grass in developing and maintaining good soil structure.

In temperate regions, like most of the United States and Europe, the growing of vigorous stands of the deep-rooted grasses and legumes is generally the most effective way to develop soil structure, provided the soil is properly fertilized, as needed, in depth as well as in the surface. Of course, in the humid parts of the country soil structure can be maintained under a stand of forest also. But it is usually more efficient in the United States to work out a cropping system that does not require the periodic use of forest for the regeneration of soils for cropping.

The Place of Grass

Grass is the natural cover of many soil types throughout the world. It is the natural cover of the Chernozem—the famous black soils of subhumid temperate regions. But we must not conclude that grass is everywhere a conserving cover or that it always improves the soil. In moist regions where there is a great deal of leaching, the forest is generally a more conserving natural cover because it gathers a large body of plant nutrients, holds them in living forms, and gradually returns them to the soil.

In hot humid regions it is especially difficult to have good grass and productive soil together—one must make up through practice the great ability of the forest to shade the soil and keep it cool, to maintain structure, and to conserve plant nutrients against the strong forces of leaching. Unless management practices can offset these changes in environment, grasses will not grow well and the soils will deteriorate.

The same principle holds in all humid regions, like the eastern part of the United States, where the natural cover is forest, except for young soils that have not been leached importantly, even though the contrast may not appear to be so great as in the Tropics. Grass can often be established and maintained in naturally forested regions simply by seeding and by fire, mowing, or cutting to keep out the young shrubs and trees. But under such conditions, without fertilizers or manures, most pastures and meadows will be poor and the soils will deteriorate, perhaps rapidly, perhaps slowly.

Farmers really should make a clear decision between grass or forest. Although wild grass is a good soil-building cover in semiarid and subhumid regions if protected against overgrazing, it usually is not in humid regions except for relatively unleached soils. Wild, uncared for, frequently burned grassland in humid regions produces little. The soil is made more productive and yeilds more if forested.

Thus grass cannot be classified definitely as "soil-conserving" or "soil-depleting"; it may be one or the other on the same farm, on the same soil type, depending on cultural practices.

Except for young alluvial soils, most soils in the United States must be periodically devoted to the grasses and grasslike plants to remain productive for crop plants. Thus proper liming and fertilization for deep-rooted legumes, alone or in mixtures with grass, are the first steps for either production or soil conservation on millions of American farms. The amount of lime and the kinds of fertilizers vary from soil to soil but emphasis needs to be given phosphates, potash, and boron, roughly in that order, although each field has its individual needs for these and other nutrients according to the soil type and previous management.

For the efficient production of grasses—efficient in terms of equality, yield, and good effects on the long-time productivity of the soil—practices must be used to maintain within the soil conditions similar to those in the natural Chernozem. This means abundant plant nutrients and good structure for considerable depth. Such a deep layer of fertile soil with good structure often needs to be made by the farmer from the natural soil. An individual set of practices to this end will be required in each individual landscape.

With the proper practices, grasses can be grown efficiently in most parts of the world, but not everywhere. One of the great problems of agricultural science is to learn how to make these practices more efficient and especially how to adapt them more precisely to the individual soil types. Then too, we need to discover practices for growing good grass efficiently on those soils for which we have as yet no satisfactory methods.

24. The Basis of Fertility

Sterling B. Hendricks and Lytle T. Alexander

Our primary concern with soils is for their fertility—all other characteristics are quite secondary. Fertility, as this selection shows, is not a simple matter, nor can it be readily measured. The development and present knowledge of soil fertility characteristics are reviewed and summarized, but as yet many unknowns about the relationship between fertility and plant growth remain.

The old and new meet in soil management. From ancient days man has plowed, drained, terraced, and irrigated land. He has manured his crops and has used rotations, either blindly or by plan.

Early man was limited by not knowing how things happened. When a background of knowledge had developed to the point where the question of *how?* could be approached, further progress was possible. That progress was late, even in the period of recorded history—between 1800 and 1850.

Humphry Davy, an English chemist and a professor of the Royal Institution in London, made one of the first steps toward explaining the value of manure and ashes. He wrote in 1813:

"If land be unproductive, and a system of ameliorating it is to be attempted, the sure method of obtaining the object is to determine the

SOURCE: *Soil, Yearbook of Agriculture* (Washington, D.C.: U.S. Department of Agriculture, 1957), pp. 11–16. The authors are soil scientists with the U.S. Department of Agriculture.

cause of its sterility, which must necessarily depend upon some defect in the constitution of the soil, which may be easily discovered by chemical analysis."

Twenty-seven years later, in 1840, Davy's ideas were still being debated and had not been put to wide use on farms. At that time the German, Justus von Liebig, the foremost organic chemist of his day, was turning his attention to the problems of soil fertility. In his book, *Organic Chemistry in its Applications to Agriculture and Physiology*, he pointed out that the chemical elements in plants must have come from the soil and air. If fertility is to be maintained, the loss from the soil must be replaced.

Even before Liebig had so emphatically pointed out the essential basis of fertility, others were conducting tests.

Prominent among them was John Bennet Lawes, who was devoting his estate at Rothamsted, north of London, to the purpose. In 1840 Lawes was trying out the effectiveness of crushed bones as a source of phosphate for plants. He found the bones to be quite ineffective, contrary to Liebig's teachings. Lawes reasoned that a more soluble type of phosphate compound was needed. To prepare such a material, he and his associate, J. H. Gilbert, in 1842 treated bones with sulfuric acid. The resulting fertilizer came to be known as superphosphate and is the basis of much of our present fertilizer industry.

The concern of Liebig, Lawes, Gilbert, and other agricultural chemists between 1840 and 1860 centered on the elements required in large amounts for plant growth. These include nitrogen, potassium, and calcium as well as phosphorus. The success of superphosphate (P) as a fertilizer quickly led to the wide use of soluble potassium (K) salts and compounds of nitrogen (N) in complete fertilizers. Thus, N–P–K as components of a complete fertilizer, or rather N–P_2O_5–K_2O, as we know them on our fertilizer tags, came into being.

The principles involved in nitrogen supply to plants and in the production of nitrogenous fertilizers have developed since 1850. Liebig thought that plants derived their nitrogen from ammonia in the air. The French agricultural chemist and farmer, J. B. Boussingault, however, in 1838 on his estate at Bechelbronn in Alsace showed that legumes can obtain nitrogen from the air only when the soil or medium in which they are growing has not been heated. Boussingault argued that the free nitrogen of the air is changed into compounds suitable for plant growth by something that is alive in the soil. Heat killed the living organisms. The time, 1838, however, was too long before the development of bacteriology as a science to allow the organisms to be found.

Fifty years after Boussingault's experiments, a Dutch scientist, M. W. Beijerinck, isolated bacteria from nodules on legume roots. He showed that the bacteria, which came to be known as *Rhizobia*, or root living, had to be present for nitrogen to be taken up by the legume. It was the rhizobia that were killed by Boussingault's heating of the soil. But the 50 years between Boussingault and Beijerinck had seen the development of bacteriology by the German physician, Robert Koch, and by one of the greatest benefactors of mankind, Louis Pasteur.

This was discovery. It served to explain the importance of legumes in land use, but it did not give the principles for changing the nitrogen of the air into soluble compounds.

The way in which nitrogen can be caused to react with other elements is basic to its fixation from the air. The principles of this fixation process are needed, both for an understanding of the part played by the legume bacteria as well as for the creation of a fertilizer industry. Both depend on catalysts, which are materials for speeding up reactions that otherwise are too slow to be effective.

Metallic iron is the most effective catalyst for promoting the combination of nitrogen and hydrogen to form ammonia, NH_3. This catalyst was developed by the German chemist, Fritz Haber, in the early years of the First World War.

Haber knew from the principles of chemistry that the catalyst could only increase the rate of combination of the nitrogen and hydrogen without changing the degree of their combination—that is, the equilibrium between nitrogen, hydrogen, and ammonia. To obtain the greatest degree of combination required pressures of many hundreds of atmospheres and temperatures of about 800° F. But even under those conditions, the combination did not take place unless the catalyst was present, and iron was the best catalyst.

Haber's successful synthesis of ammonia answered the most serious problem of soil management and of world food production, a supply of nitrogenous fertilizers. More than 3 million tons of ammonia are now produced yearly in this way in the United States from the elemental nitrogen of the air and hydrogen, obtained chiefly from natural gas or petroleum refining.

The catalysts that promote nitrogen fixation by rhizobia growing on legume roots are still unknown. The German bacteriologist, H. Bortels, in 1930 showed, however, that free-living forms of nitrogen-fixing bacteria will grow in the absence of nitrogen compounds only if they have a supply of molybdenum. Bortels reasoned that some molybdenum compound must be the catalyst in bacteria for nitrogen fixation. On the basis of this idea, he showed in 1937 that nitrogen fixation by clover, beans, and peas was greatly enhanced by an adequate supply of molybdenum.

The practical application of Bortels' findings first came in Australia, where large areas were known to be unsuited for pastures containing clover. The agronomist, A. J. Anderson, showed in 1942 that this condition could be corrected by use of a few pounds an acre of molybdenum compounds mixed with superphosphate, for the soils were deficient also in phosphate.

Another discovery about the association of nitrogen-fixing bacteria and legumes was made by a Japanese scientist, H. Kubo, in 1939. He learned that the nodules containing the bacteria are effective only when a red pigment is present. He demonstrated that this pigment is a hemoglobin much like that of blood, which has never been observed under other conditions in plants. Herein is a suggestion to explain the uniqueness of legumes among plants for nitrogen fixation, but much more must be found to explain the process.

The importance of a rather rare element such as molybdenum as essential for establishing legumes introduces the minor nutrient elements. A group of these elements are known to be essential for plant growth.

The first to be recognized was iron, the absence of which leads to a general yellowing, or chlorosis, of leaves. A French scientist, A. Gris, in 1844 described how chlorosis of some plants can be corrected by sprays of iron salts. Progress, however, was slow, and it was not until after 1900 that the importance of other minor-nutrient elements such as boron, copper, manganese, and zinc was appreciated.

The principle of essentiality of these elements has been stated by D. I. Arnon, of the University of California, in this form:

"An element is not considered essential unless a deficiency of it makes it impossible for the plant to complete . . . its life cycle; such deficiency is specific to the element in question and can be prevented or corrected only by supplying this element; and the element is directly involved in the nutrition of the plant quite apart from possible effects in correcting some unfavorable microbial or chemical condition of the soil or other culture medium."

Most minor—or "trace"—nutrients act as required parts of enzyme systems, the catalysts of living things, that speed up the reaction necessary for growth, although many of these enzymes are still to be discovered.

Thus molybdenum acts in nitrogen fixation as a part of some enzyme system; it also is required for the reduction of nitrates in plants, the enzyme required being nitrate reductase. The element is also required in animals for the oxidation of xanthine, a material similar to uric acid, which must be oxidized before it can be eliminated adequately.

A principle intimately involved in fertility, but with broader implications as well with regard to physical features of soils, is that of base or cation exchange. Today this is often a first factor to consider in management, as it involves liming of acid soils and amelioration of alkali soils.

The principle is that soils act to hold base elements such as calcium, sodium, potassium, and magnesium and the acid element hydrogen.

Generally, one element can only be replaced by another. Thus, as calcium is removed from soil by plant growth, or by leaching with water, its place might be taken by hydrogen until the soil is too acidic for use. This is the tendency in most soils of the Eastern and Southern States.

The principle of base exchange was discovered just a little over a century ago by the Englishman, J. T. Way, an associate of Lawes at Rothamsted.

Way was concerned with the possible loss of water-soluble fertilizers from soil by leaching. He established instead that the soluble material was held and displaced an equal amount of material present in the soil. This was a fundamental principle. It foreshadowed by three decades the development of a part of modern chemistry, namely, the law of mass action, later (1867) stated by the Scandinavian scientists, C. M. Guldberg and Peter Waage.

The law of mass action formulated the idea that in a chemical reaction such as $A+B \rightleftharpoons C+D$, in general, or $Na^+ + H$ soil $\rightleftharpoons H^+ + Na$ soil, in particular, an equilibrium is attained. If, then, A is increased, the reaction will be driven toward the right; if D, toward the left. Thus acid, H^+, increase displaces sodium, Na, so that it can be washed from soils. This is the basis for the use of sulfur as an acid-forming element in the recovery of alkali soils.

The principle of base exchange and that of mass action expressed in the reaction $Na^+ + H$ soil $\rightleftharpoons H^+ + Na$ soil is in a very general form, in that inquiry is not made into the nature of H soil and Na soil.

This serves some of the requirements of management, but it does not explain, for instance, why Na soils often have very poor drainage and why one soil differs markedly from another when both have high sodium contents. The ends of management both for use of many soils under irrigation in the Western States or for recovery of land from the sea, as in the Netherlands, require a more detailed knowledge of Na soil.

Way, in the period near 1850, established that the base exchange was due chiefly to the very finely divided materials in the soil. Prominent among these materials were the clays, and Way made synthetic materials by precipitating aluminum and silicon compounds that somewhat resembled the clays and possessed base-exchange properties. But these synthetic materials, which have long been exceedingly important for softening water, differed markedly from clays in many of their properties, such as the capacity to remain suspended in water without change. An understanding of base exchange, then, became largely an effort to understand the nature of clays. This search was successful after 1925.

We can separate soils into fractions of various particle sizes by shaking them through sieves and by suspending them in water. The coarse fractions are sands. The intermediate ones down to the limits of microscopic magnification are silt. Those below these limits are the clays, which settle very solwly in water.

If a soil after separation into fractions is reconstituted with omission of the clay, its cohesive properties will be greatly diminished, particularly if the soil is a loam or heavier in clay content. The clay, then, apparently is the fraction involved not only in base exchange but also in interaction with water in soil. In management, as an example, the clay interaction with water is determinative for many properties, such as those underlying the tendency of soil to erode and its features of internal drainage.

The basic principles about clays are to be found on an atomic scale. You might think it strange that this is the case for such gross features of a field as its lime requirement, its tendency to erode, the draft requirement for plowing, or the required spacing of drains. These properties of the whole field, though, are only reflections of the most minute parts. While the four features are quite different in external appearance, they might depend on the same (or on only a few) minute features.

Knowledge about clays on the atomic scale advanced only after a long period of development in the basic physics of atomic structure. In principle, to work with phenomena on a particular scale, the measuring instruments must have features on that scale. Thus, for measuring a mile to the nearest foot, a measuring tape need only be divided into feet, which would make it unsuited for measurement of thickness for a plastic film.

The desired basic information about clays was the arrangement of the atoms. The measuring method that proved useful in finding the arrangement was the diffraction of X-rays.

X-rays are like visible light in that they can be resolved into different wavelengths by diffraction and refraction. In visible white light, the resolution into the different component wavelengths or colors by refraction is shown in a rainbow. This resolution can also be done with an ordinary window screen and a light by diffraction, as can be seen by looking at a distant light through the screen. The degree to which the various colors are separated depends on the fineness of the screen—the smaller the separation of the wires, the greater the color separation. The diffraction then can be used to measure the wire separation in the screen.

X-rays have wavelengths, equivalent to color in visible light, of about the same value as the separation of atoms in clays. The atoms in the clays, as in all crystals, irrespective of size, are arranged in an orderly and repeated manner much like the men in an army passing in review. This arrangement corresponds to the wires of the screen for visible light. Accordingly, the diffraction of the X-rays by the atomic arrangement in the clays can serve to measure the arrangement.

The kinds of atoms present in the clays are chiefly silicon, aluminum, and oxygen, with small amounts of the basic elements such as calcium, magnesium, sodium, and potassium, and the acid element hydrogen. They are the ones taking part in base exchange. This knowledge of composition came from the analysis by chemists of many pure clays collected from mineral deposits by geologists and mineralogists.

The diffraction of X-rays by a clay shows that the silicon atoms, which are relatively small, are each surrounded at the corners of a tetrahedron by larger oxygen atoms and that each oxygen atom is between two silicon atoms, which thus serve to link tetrahedrons together. The aluminum atoms, which are similar in size to silicon, are substituted, in part, in place of the silicon atoms. The tetrahedrons upon linking are formed into sheets, and two of these atomic sheets are joined by aluminum atoms between them.

This arrangement of the atoms in the clays has three features, which are the basic ones underlying many properties of soils. These features are: The atoms are arranged in sheets; the surfaces of the sheets are largely the surfaces of oxygen atoms; and the attraction between atoms in the sheets depends on the relative number of oxygen, silicon, and aluminum atoms.

As a result of the atomic arrangement in sheets, the clays can be split between the sheets and thus reduced to particles that are exceedingly thin. The clays therefore are finely divided; that is one of the necessary features for formation of a mud.

Oxygen atoms on the surface result in attraction of water molecules through binding with the hydrogen atoms of the water. In other words, the sheets have a high tendency to be wetted with water. In one type of clay, as a matter of fact, water molecules on the sheet surfaces separate the sheets and cause the clays to swell. It is for this reason that many of the alkali soils have such poor drainage. It is the basic reason for the cracking of many soils during prolonged droughts.

If the attraction of the atoms is not balanced on the scale of atomic dimensions, other atoms must be present for the balance. These atoms can only be present on the surfaces of the sheets. On the surfaces they can readily be separated in the water layers that are also there. Accordingly, they are the atoms that can be exchanged with others—the atoms of base exchange—the atoms involved in the acid reactions of soils and the liming requirements.

As knowledge of clays developed, it was found that there are several ways of making the atomic arrangements in sheets and that clays with different arrangements differ considerably in such properties as the amount of their base exchange and their tendencies to swell in water.

A first question about most soils is, "What is the clay type?"

This question is accompanied by, "What is the soil texture; how much clay is present?" Finally, "What is the base-exchange capacity?"

A guiding method for learning more about clays in soils was to work on pure clays and from their properties to assess their degree of contribution to the general properties of the soil. Other soil components also affect these properties, and the part played by organic matter or humus can be great. Can the principles basic to the action of organic matter also serve as a guide through some of the complexities of soil?

Until the time of Liebig, the idea was held that humus was directly used by plants and as such contributed to soil fertility. Liebig showed that plant growth instead depends upon inorganic compounds. Organic matter is useful for fertility only as it is broken down with release of the constituent nitrogen and phosphorus into inorganic forms. Even today, though, some nonagricultural persons maintain that humus has direct attributes in fertility.

With the advance near the end of the last century in knowledge of bacteriology and the requirements of micro-organisms for growth, it became evident that humus was, in part, a product of the action of micro-organisms and, in part, their sustaining food. The release of the nutrient elements required the destruction by micro-organisms of the organic matter from past crops or that of the native soil. From this point of view alone, the best practice would utilize the organic matter as rapidly as possible.

The organic matter has other properties. One is base exchange, or the capacity to hold nutrient elements, such as potassium, calcium, and magnesium, in saltlike combination much as do clays. Destruction of organic matter naturally reduces this exchange capacity of the soil.

The desirable effects of organic matter on the structure and, through these effects, on the physical properties of soil are of greatest importance. This is the discovery of no particular person but it is readily observed by all who are familiar with soils. It has to do with mellowness and friability, with the maintenance of a good tilth, and the preservation of a loose and uncompacted soil.

The question of principle would be to establish how organic matter contributes to desirable structure in soil.

The answer has not been found even by repeated inquiries into the nature of organic matter. Rather, it seems that something still is to be established about the interaction between organic matter and surfaces of clay minerals.

The most progress in this regard was the finding that some of the polymeric compounds related to the materials of plastics but containing more acid groups when added to clays or to soils have the desired action on structure. The principle, as vaguely formed, involves, in part, the presence of a number of acidic organic groups held together in one molecule that is resistant to attack by micro-organisms.

These acidic groups interact with the surfaces of the clay minerals. The natural materials possessing these properties, in part, are gums formed by bacteria. They are not very stable against further attack by bacteria, however, and have to be constantly renewed by supplying fresh organic matter for the bacteria to consume.

Fertility, the properties of clay, and the functioning of organic matter are examples of factors in soils for which basic principles have been sought.

. . . . .

In the end, the search for principle is the only way by which we can gain information from one soil that is useful for farming another soil. Information about properties of the individual soils become an orderly and consistent part of knowledge about all soils.

25. Land-Capability Classification
A. A. Klingebiel and P. H. Montgomery

The major (indeed, almost the only) function of soils so far as man is concerned is as a base for growing crops—those plants that produce the seeds, flowers, leaves, stalks, roots, or other parts for which man has a particular need or use. Soils may be classified in many ways, often as substances with characteristics that have intrinsic properties themselves. For the geographer, however, it is the soil as land—usually cropland—that is of primary interest. As land, soil has, in connection with other factors such as slope and drainage, a particular productive capability. This study, done by experts in the U.S. Department of Agriculture, classifies soil as an element of land having a discernible and measurable capability for growing the crops man desires.

The standard soil-survey map shows the different kinds of soil that are significant and their location in relation to other features of the landscape. These maps are intended to meet the needs of users with widely different problems and, therefore, contain considerable detail to show important basic soil differences.

The information on the soil map must be explained in a way that has meaning to the user. These explanations are called interpretations. Soil maps can be interpreted by (1) the individual kinds of soil on the map, and (2) the grouping of soils that behave similarly in responses

SOURCE: *Agriculture Handbook No. 210* (Washington, D.C.: U.S. Department of Agriculture, Soil Conservation Service, 1962). The authors are soil scientists with the Soil Conservation Service.

to management and treatment. Because there are many kinds of soil, there are many individual soil interpretations. Such interpretations, however, provide the user with all the information that can be obtained from a soil map. Many users of soil maps want more general information than that of the individual soil-mapping unit. Soils are grouped in different ways according to the specific needs of the map user. The kinds of soil grouped and the variation permitted within each group differ according to the use to be made of the grouping.

The capability classification is one of a number of interpretive groupings made primarily for agricultural purposes. As with all interpretive groupings the capability classification begins with the individual soil-mapping units, which are building stones of the system. In this classification the arable soils are grouped according to their potentialities and limitations for sustained production of the common cultivated crops that do not require specialized site conditioning or site treatment. Nonarable soils (soils unsuitable for longtime sustained use for cultivated crops) are grouped according to their potentialities and limitations for the production of permanent vegetation and according to their risks of soil damage if mismanaged.

The individual mapping units on soil maps show the location and extent of the different kinds of soil. One can make the greatest number of precise statements and predictions about the use and management of the individual mapping units shown on the soil map. The capability grouping of soils is designed (1) to held landowners and others use and interpret the soil maps, (2) to introduce users to the detail of the soil map itself, and (3) to make possible broad generalizations based on soil potentialities, limitations in use, and management problems.

The capability classification provides three major categories of soil groupings: (1) Capability unit, (2) capability subclass, and (3) capability class. The first category, capability unit, is a grouping of soils that have about the same responses to systems of management of common cultivated crops and pasture plants. Soils in any one capability unit are adapted to the same kinds of common cultivated and pasture plants and require similar alternative systems of management for these crops. Longtime estimated yields of adapted crops for individual soils within the unit under comparable management do not vary more than about 25 percent.

The second category, the subclass, is a grouping of capability units having similar kinds of limitations and hazards. Four general kinds of limitations or hazards are recognized: (1) Erosion hazard, (2) wetness, (3) rooting-zone limitations, and (4) climate.

The third and broadest category in the capability classification places all the soils in eight capability classes. The risks of soil damage or limitations in use become progressively greater from class I to class VIII. Soils in the first four classes under good management are capable of producing adapted plants, such as forest trees or range plants, and the common cultivated field crops and pasture plants. Soils in classes V, VI, and VII are suited to the use of adapted native plants. Some soils in classes V and VI are also capable of producing specialized crops, such as certain fruits and ornamentals, and even field and vegetable crops under highly intensive management involving elaborate practices for soil and water conservation. Soils in class VIII do not return on-site benefits for inputs of management for crops, grasses, or trees without major reclamation.

The grouping of soils into capability units, subclasses, and classes is done primarily on the basis of their capability to produce common cultivated crops and pasture plants without deterioration over a long period of time. To express suitability of the soils for range and woodland use, the soil-mapping units are grouped into range sites and woodland-suitability groups.

Capability Classes

Land Suited to Cultivation and Other Uses

CLASS I / *Soils in class I have few limitations that restrict their use.* Soils in this class are suited to a wide range of plants and may be used safely for cultivated crops, pasture, range, woodland, and wildlife. The soils are nearly level[1] and erosion hazard (wind or water) is low. They are deep, generally well drained, and easily worked. They hold water well and are either fairly well supplied with plant nutrients or highly responsive to inputs of fertilizer.

The soils in class I are not subject to damaging overflow. They are productive and suited to intensive cropping. The local climate must be favorable for growing many of the common field crops.

In irrigated areas, soils may be placed in class I if the limitation of the arid climate has been removed by relatively permanent irrigation works. Such irrigated soils (or soils potentially useful under irrigation) are nearly level, have deep rooting zones, have favorable permeability and water-holding capacity, and are easily maintained in good tilth. Some of the soils may require initial conditioning including leveling to the desired grade, leaching of a slight accumulation of soluble salts, or lowering of the seasonal water table. Where limitations due to salts, water table, overflow, or erosion are likely to recur, the soils are regarded as subject to permanent natural limitations and are not included in class I.

Soils that are wet and have slowly permeable subsoils are not placed in class I. Some kinds of soil in class I may be drained as an improvement measure for increased production and ease of operation.

[1] Some rapidly permeable soils in class I may have gentle slopes.

Soils in class I that are used for crops need ordinary management practices to maintain productivity—both soil fertility and soil structure. Such practices may include the use of one or more of the following: Fertilizers and lime, cover and green-manure crops, conservation of crop residues and animal manures, and sequences of adapted crops.

CLASS II / *Soils in class II have some limitations that reduce the choice of plants or require moderate conservation practices.* Soils in class II require careful soil management, including conservation practices, to prevent deterioration or to improve air and water relations when the soils are cultivated. The limitations are few and the practices are easy to apply. The soils may be used for cultivated crops, pasture, range, woodland, or wildlife food and cover.

Limitations of soils in class II may include singly or in combination the effects of (1) gentle slopes, (2) moderate susceptibility to wind or water erosion or moderate adverse effects of past erosion, (3) less than ideal soil depth, (4) somewhat unfavorable soil structure and workability, (5) slight to moderate salinity or sodium easily corrected but likely to recur, (6) occasional damaging overflow, (7) wetness correctable by drainage but existing permanently as a moderate limitation, and (8) slight climatic limitations on soil use and management.

The soils in this class provide the farm operator less latitude in the choice of either crops or management practices than soils in class I. They may also require special soil-conserving cropping systems, soil conservation practices, water-control devices, or tillage methods when used for cultivated crops. For example, deep soils of this class with gentle slopes subject to moderate erosion when cultivated may need one of the following practices or some combination of two or more: Terracing, stripcropping, contour tillage, crop rotations that include grasses and legumes, vegetated water-disposal areas, cover or green-manure crops, stubble mulching, fertilizers, manure, and lime. The exact combinations of practices vary from place to place, depending on the characteristics of the soil, the local climate, and the farming system.

CLASS III / *Soils in class III have severe limitations that reduce the choice of plants or require special conservation practices, or both.* Soils in class III have more restrictions than those in class II and when used for cultivated crops the conservation practices are usually more difficult to apply and to maintain. They may used for cultivated crops, pasture, woodland, range, or wildlife food and cover.

Limitations of soils in class III restrict the amount of clean cultivation; timing of planting, tillage, and harvesting; choice of crops; or some combination of these limitations. The limitations may result from the effects of one or more of the following: (1) Moderately steep slopes; (2) high susceptibility to water or wind erosion or severe adverse effects of past erosion; (3) frequent overflow accompanied by some crop damage; (4) very slow permeability of the subsoil; (5) wetness or some continuing waterlogging after drainage; (6) shallow depths to bedrock, hardpan, fragipan, or claypan that limit the rooting zone and the water storage; (7) low moisture-holding capacity; (8) low fertility not easily corrected; (9) moderate salinity or sodium; or (10) moderate climatic limitations.

When cultivated, many of the wet, slowly permeable but nearly level soils in class III require drainage and a cropping system that maintains or improves the structure and tilth of the soil. To prevent puddling and to improve permeability it is commonly necessary to supply organic material to such soils and to avoid working them when they are wet. In some irrigated areas, part of the soils in class III have limited use because of high water table, slow permeability, and the hazard of salt or sodic accumulation. Each distinctive kind of soil in class III has one or more alternative combinations of use and practices required for safe use, but the number of practical alternatives for average farmers is less than that for soils in class II.

CLASS IV / *Soils in class IV have very severe limitations that restrict the choice of plants, require very careful management, or both.* The restrictions in use for soils in class IV are greater than those in class III and the choice of plants is more limited. When these soils are cultivated, more careful management is required and conservation practices are more difficult to apply and maintain. Soils in class IV may be used for crops, pasture, woodland, range, or wildlife food and cover.

Soils in class IV may be well suited to only two or three of the common crops or the harvest produced may be low in relation to inputs over a long period of time. Use for cultivated crops is limited as a result of the effects of one or more permanent features such as (1) steep slopes, (2) severe susceptibility to water or wind erosion, (3) severe effects of past erosion, (4) shallow soils, (5) low moisture-holding capacity, (6) frequent overflows accompanied by severe crop damage, (7) excessive wetness with continuing hazard of waterlogging after drainage, (8) severe salinity or sodium, or (9) moderately adverse climate.

Many sloping soils in class IV in humid areas are suited to occasional but not regular cultivation. Some of the poorly drained, nearly level soils placed in class IV are not subject to erosion but are poorly suited to intertilled crops because of the time required for the soil to dry out in the spring and because of low productivity for cultivated crops. Some soils in class IV are well suited to one or more of the special crops, such as fruits and ornamental trees and shrubs, but this suitability itself is not sufficient to place a soil in class IV.

In subhumid and semiarid areas, soils in class IV may produce good yields of adapted cultivated crops during years of above average rainfall; low yields during years of average rainfall; and failures during years of below average rainfall. During the low rainfall years the soil must be protected even though there can be little or no expectancy of a marketable crop. Special treatments and practices to prevent soil blowing, conserve moisture, and maintain soil productivity are required. Sometimes crops must be planted or emergency tillage used for the primary purpose of maintaining the soil during years of low rainfall. These treatments must be applied more frequently or more intensively than on soils in class III.

Land Limited in Use—Generally Not Suited to Cultivation[2]

CLASS V / *Soils in class V have little or no erosion hazard but have other limitations impractical to remove that limit their use largely to pasture, range, woodland, or wildlife food and cover.* Soils in class V have limitations that restrict the kind of plants that can be grown and that prevent normal tillage of cultivated crops. They are nearly level but some are wet, are frequently overflowed by streams, are stony, have climatic limitations, or have some combination of these limitations. Examples of class V are (1) soils of the bottom lands subject to frequent overflow that prevents the normal production of cultivated crops, (2) nearly level soils with a growing season that prevents the normal production of cultivated crops, (3) level or nearly level stony or rocky soils, and (4) ponded areas where drainage for cultivated crops is not feasible but where soils are suitable for grasses or trees. Because of these limitations cultivation of the common crops is not feasible but pastures can be improved and benefits from proper management can be expected.

CLASS VI / *Soils in class VI have severe limitations that make them generally unsuited to cultivation and limit their use largely to pasture or range, woodland, or wildlife food and cover.* Physical conditions of soils placed in class VI are such that it is practical to apply range or pasture improvements, if needed, such as seeding, liming, fertilizing, and water control with contour furrows, drainage ditches, diversions, or water spreaders. Soils in class VI have continuing limitations that cannot be corrected, such as (1) steep slope, (2) severe erosion hazard, (3) effects of past erosion, (4) stoniness, (5) shallow rooting zone, (6) excessive wetness or overflow, (7) low-moisture capacity, (8) salinity or sodium, or (9) severe climate. Because of one or more of these limitations these soils are not generally suited to cultivated crops. But they may be used for pasture, range, woodland, or wildlife cover or for some combination of these.

Some soils in class VI can be safely used for the common crops pro-

[2] Certain soils grouped into classes V, VI, VII, and VIII may be made fit for use for crops with major earthmoving or other costly reclamation.

vided unusually intensive management is used. Some of the soils in this class are also adapted to special crops such as sodded orchards, blueberries, or the like, requiring soil conditions unlike those demanded by the common crops. Depending upon soil features and local climate the soils may be well or poorly suited to woodlands.

CLASS VII / *Soils in class VII have very severe limitations that make them unsuited to cultivation and that restrict their use largely to grazing, woodland, or wildlife.* Physical conditions of soils in class VII are such that it is impractical to apply such pasture or range improvements as seeding, liming, fertilizing, and water control with contour furrows, ditches, divisions, or water spreaders. Soil restrictions are more severe than those in class VI because of one or more continuing limitations that cannot be corrected, such as (1) very steep slopes, (2) erosion, (3) shallow soil, (4) stones, (5) wet soil, (6) salts or sodium, (7) unfavorable climate, or (8) other limitations that make them unsuited to common cultivated crops. They can be used safely for grazing or woodland or wildlife food and cover or for some combination of these under proper management.

Depending upon the soil characteristics and local climate, soils in this class may be well or poorly suited to woodland. They are not suited to any of the common cultivated crops; in unusual instances, some soils in this class may be used for special crops under unusual management practices. Some areas of class VII may need seeding or planting to protect the soil and to prevent damage to adjoining areas.

CLASS VIII / *Soils and landforms in class VIII have limitations that preclude their use for commercial plant production and restrict their use to recreation, wildlife, or water supply or to esthetic purposes.* Soils and landforms in class VIII cannot be expected to return significant on-site benefits from management for crops, grasses, or trees, although benefits from wildlife use, watershed protection, or recreation may be possible.

Limitations that cannot be corrected may result from the effects of one or more of the following: (1) Erosion or erosion hazard, (2) severe climate, (3) wet soil, (4) stones, (5) low-moisture capacity, and (6) salinity or sodium.

Badlands, rock outcrop, sandy beaches, river wash, mine tailings, and other nearly barren lands are included in class VIII. It may be necessary to give protection and management for plant growth to soils and landforms in class VIII in order to protect other more valuable soils, to control water, or for wildlife or esthetic reasons.

Capability Subclasses

Subclasses are groups of capability units within classes that have the same kinds of dominant limitations for agricultural use as a result of soil and climate. Some soils are subject to erosion if they are not protected, while others are naturally wet and must be drained if crops are to be grown. Some soils are shallow or droughty or have other soil deficiencies. Still other soils occur in areas where climate limits their use. The four kinds of limitations recognized at the subclass level are: Risks of erosion, designated by the symbol (e); wetness, drainage, or overflow (w); rooting-zone limitations (s); and climatic limitations (c). The subclass provides the map user information about both the degree and kind of limitation. Capability class I has no subclasses.

Subclass (e) *erosion* is made up of soils where the susceptibility to erosion is the dominant problem or hazard in their use. Erosion susceptibility and past erosion damage are the major soil factors for placing soils in this subclass.

Subclass (w) *excess water* is made up of soils where excess water is the dominant hazard or limitation in their use. Poor soil drainage, wetness, high water table, and overflow are the criteria for determining which soils belong in this subclass.

Subclass (s) *soil limitations within the rooting zone* includes, as the name implies, soils that have such limitations as shallowness of rooting zones, stones, low moisture-holding capacity, low fertility difficult to correct, and salinity or sodium.

Subclass (c) *climatic limitation* is made up of soils where the climate (temperature or lack of moisture) is the only major hazard or limitation in their use.[3]

Limitations imposed by erosion, excess water, shallow soils, stones, low moisture-holding capacity, salinity, or sodium can be modified or partially overcome and take precedence over climate in determining subclasses. The dominant kind of limitation or hazard to the use of the land determines the assignment of capability units to the (e), (w), and (s) subclasses. Capability units that have no limitation other than climate are assigned to the (c) subclass.

Where two kinds of limitations that can be modified or corrected are essentially equal, the subclasses have the following priority: e, w, s. For example, we need to group a few soils of humid areas that have both an erosion hazard and an excess water hazard; with them the e takes precedence over the w. In grouping soils having both an excess water limitation and a rooting-zone limitation the w takes precedence over the s. In grouping soils of subhumid and semiarid areas that have both an erosion hazard and a climatic limitation the e takes precedence over the c, and in grouping soils with both rooting-zone limitations and climatic limitations the s takes precedence over the c.

[3] Especially among young soils such as alluvial soils, although not limited to them, climatic phases of soil series must be established for proper grouping into capability units and into other interpretive groupings. Since the effects result from interactions between soil and climate, such climatic phases are not defined the same in terms of precipitation, temperature, and so on, for contrasting kinds of soil.

Where soils have two kinds of limitations, both can be indicated if needed for local use; the dominant one is shown first. Where two kinds of problems are shown for a soil group, the dominant one is used for summarizing data by subclasses.

Capability Units

The capability units provide more specific and detailed information than the subclass for application to specific fields on a farm or ranch. A capability unit is a grouping of soils that are nearly alike in suitability for plant growth and responses to the same kinds of soil management. That is, a reasonably uniform set of alternatives can be presented for the soil, water, and plant management of the soils in a capability unit, not considering effects of past management that do not have a more or less permanent effect on the soil. Where soils have been so changed by management that permanent characteristics have been altered, they are placed in different soil series. Soils grouped into capability units respond in a similar way and require similar management, although they may have soil characteristics that put them in different soil series.

Soils grouped into a capability unit should be sufficiently uniform in the combinations of soil characteristics that influence their qualities to have similar potentialities and continuing limitations or harzards. Thus the soils in a capability unit should be sufficiently uniform to (a) produce similar kinds of cultivated crops and pasture plants with similar management practices, (b) require similar conservation treatment and management under the same kind and condition of vegetative cover, and (c) have comparable potential productivity. (Estimated average yields under similar management systems should not vary more than about 25 percent among the kinds of soil included within the unit.)

Other Kinds of Soil Groupings

Other kinds of interpretive soil groupings are necessary to meet specific needs. Among these are groupings for range use, woodland use, special crops, and engineering interpretation.

The range site is a grouping of soils with a potential for producing the same kinds and amounts of native forage. The range site for rangeland is comparable to the capability unit for cultivated land. The purpose of such a grouping is to show the potential for range use and to provide the basis for which the criteria for determining range condition can be established. The soils grouped into a single range site may be expected to produce similar longtime yields and respond similarly to alternative systems of management and to such practices as seeding, pitting, and water spreading.

Soils suitable for range but not for common cultivated crops may be placed in capability classes V and VI if they are capable of returning inputs from such management practices as seeding, fertilizing, or irrigating and in class VII if they are not. If these soils do not give economic returns under any kind of management when used for cultivated crops, pasture, woodland or range, they fall in class VIII.

Soil-woodland site index correlations are essential for interpreting the potential wood production of the individual soil units that are mapped. Woodland-site indices are comonly developed for individual kinds of soils. Soil-mapping units can be placed in woodland groupings according to site indices for adapted species and other responses and limitations significant to woodland conservation. Such groupings do not necessarily parallel those for capability units or range sites; however, in some areas capability units may be grouped into range sites and woodland-suitability groups.

Rice has soil requirements unlike those of the common cultivated crops requiring well-aerated soils. Some fruits and ornamentals do not require clean cultivation. Therefore, these crops are not given weight in the capability grouping. Instead, special groupings of the soils for each of these crops are made in the areas where they are significant.

With a good basic table of yields and practices the soils can be placed in any number of suitability groups. Commonly, five groups—unsuited, fairly suited, moderately suited, well suited and very well suited—are sufficient.

Kinds of soil shown on the soil map are also grouped according to need for applying engineering measures including drainage, irrigation, land leveling, land grading; determining suitability as subgrade for roads; and constructing ponds and small dams. Such groupings may be unlike those made for other purposes.

Criteria for Placing Soils in Capability Classes

Soil and climatic limitations in relation to the use, management, and productivity of soils are the bases for differentiating capability classes. Classes are based on both degree and number of limitations affecting kind of use, risks of soil damage if mismanaged, needs for soil management, and risks of crop failure. To assist in making capability groupings, specific criteria for placing soils in units, subclasses, and classes are presented here. Because the effects of soil characteristics and qualities vary widely with climate, these criteria must be for broad soil areas that have similar climate.

Capability groupings are based on specific information when available—information about the responses of the individual kinds of soil to management and the combined effect of climate and soil on the crops grown. It comes from research findings, field trials, and experiences of farmers and other agricultural workers. Among the more common kinds of information obtained are soil and water losses, kinds and amounts of plants that can be grown, weather conditions as they affect plants, and the effect of different kinds and levels of management on plant response. This information is studied along with laboratory data on soil profiles. Careful analysis of this information proves useful not only in determining the capability of these individual kinds of soil but also in making predictions about the use and management of related kinds of soil.

Basic yield estimates of the adapted crops under alternative, defined systems of management are assembled in a table. Where data are few, the estimates should be reasonable when tested against available farm records and studies of the combinations of soil properties.

Where information on response of soils to management is lacking, the estimates of yields and the grouping of soils into capability units, subclasses, and classes are based on an evaluation of combinations of the following:

1. Ability of the soil to give plant response to use and management as evidenced by organic-matter content, ease of maintaining a supply of plant nutrients, percentage base saturation, cation-exchange capacity, kind of clay mineral, kind of parent material, available water-holding capacity, response to added plant nutrients, or other soil characteristics and qualities.
2. Texture and structure of the soil to the depth that influences the environment of roots and the movement of air and water.
3. Susceptibility to erosion as influenced by kind of soil (and slope) and the effect of erosion on use and management.
4. Continuous or periodic waterlogging in the soil caused by slow permeability of the underlying material, a high water table, or flooding.
5. Depth of soil material to layers inhibiting root penetration.
6. Salts toxic to plant growth.
7. Physical obstacles such as rocks, deep gullies, etc.
8. Climate (temperature and effective moisture).

This list is not intended to be complete. Although the soils of any area may differ from one another in only a few dozen characteristics, none can be taken for granted. Extreme deficiencies or excesses of trace elements, for example, can be vital. Commonly, the underlying geological strata are significant to water infiltration, water yield, and erosion hazard.

Any unfavorable fixed or recurring soil or landscape features may limit the safe and productive use of the soil. One unfavorable feature in the soil may so limit its use that extensive treatment would be required. Several minor unfavorable features collectively may become a major problem and thus limit the use of the soil. The combined effect of these in relation to the use, management, and productivity of soils is the criterion for different capability units.

Some of the criteria used to differentiate between capability classes are discussed on the following pages. The criteria and ranges in characteristics suggested assume that the effects of other soil characteristics and qualities are favorable and are not limiting factors in placing soils in capability classes.

Arid and Semiarid, Stony, Wet, Saline-Sodic, and Overflow Soils

The capability-class designations assigned to soils subject to flooding, poorly or imperfectly drained soils, stony soils, dry soils needing supplemental water, and soils having excess soluble salts or exchangeable sodium are made on the basis of continuing limitations and hazards after removal of excess water, stones, salts, and exchangeable sodium.

When assessing the capability class of any soil the feasibility of any necessary land improvements must be considered. Feasible as used here means (1) that the characteristics and qualities of the soil are such that it is possible to remove the limitation, and (2) that over broad areas it is within the realm of economic possibility to remove the limitation. The capability designation of these areas is determined by those practices that are practical now and in the immediate future.

The following kinds of soil are classified on the basis of their present continuing limitations and hazards: (1) Dry soils (arid and semiarid areas) now irrigated, (2) soils from which stones have been removed, (3) wet soils that have been drained, (4) soils from which excess quantities of soluble salts or exchangeable sodium have been removed, and (5) soils that have been protected from overflow.

The following kinds of soil are classified on the basis of their continuing limitations and hazards as if the correctable limitations had been removed or reduced: (1) Dry soils not now irrigated but for which irrigation is feasible and water is available, (2) stony soils for which stone removal is feasible, (3) wet soils not now drained but for which drainage is feasible, (4) soils .that contain excess quantities of soluble salts or exchangeable sodium feasible to remove, and (5) soils subject to overflow but for which protection from overflow is feasible. Where desirable or helpful, the present limitation due to wetness, stoniness, etc., may be indicated.

The following kinds of soil are classified on the basis of their present continuing limitations and hazards if the limitations cannot feasibly be corrected or removed: (1) Dry soils, (2) stony soils, (3) soils with excess quantities of saline and sodic salts, (4) wet soils, or (5) soils subject to overflow.

Climatic Limitations

Climatic limitations (temperature and moisture) affect capability. Extremely low temperatures and short growing seasons are limitations, especially in the very northern part of continental United States and at high altitudes.

Limited natural moisture supply affects capability in subhumid, semiarid, and arid climates. As the classification in any locality is derived in part from observed performance of crop plants, the effects of the interaction of climate with soil characteristics must be considered. In a subhumid climate, for example, certain sandy soils may be classified as class VI or class VII, whereas soils with similar water-holding capacity in a more humid climate are classified as class III or IV. The moisture factor must be directly considered in the classification in most semiarid and arid climates. The capability of comparable soils decreases as effective rainfall decreases.

In an arid climate the moisture from rain and snow is not enough to support crops. Arid land can be classed as suited to cultivation (class I, II, III, or IV) only if the moisture limitation is removed by irrigation. Wherever the moisture limitation is removed in this way, the soil is classified according to the effects of other permanent features and hazards that limit its use and permanence, without losing sight of the practical requirements of irrigation farming.

Wetness Limitations

Water on the soil or excess water in the soil presents a hazard to or limits its use. Such water may be a result of poor soil drainage, high water table, overflow (includes stream overflow, ponding, and runoff water from higher areas), and seepage. Usually soil needing drainage has some permanent limitation that precludes placing it in class I even after drainage.

Wet soils are classified according to their continuing soil limitations and hazards after drainage. In determining the capability of wet areas emphasis is placed on practices considered practical now or in the foreseeable future. The vast areas of marshland along the seacoast or high-cost reclamation projects not now being planned or constructed are not classified as class I, II, or III. If reclamation projects are investigated and found to be feasible, the soils of the area are reclassified based on the continuing limitations and hazards after drainage. This places the classification of wet soils on a basis similar to that of the classification of irrigated, stony, saline, or overflow soils. Some large areas of bottom land subject to overflow are reclassified when protected by dikes or other major reclamation work. There are examples of these along streams where levees have been constructed. Land already drained is classified according to the continuing limitations and hazards that affect its use.

Needs for initial conditioning, such as for clearing of trees or swamp vegetation, are not considered in the capability classification. They may be of great importance, however, in making some of the land-management decisions. Costs of drainage, likewise, are not considered directly in the capability classification, although they are important to the land manager.

Toxic Salts

Presence of soluble salts or exchangeable sodium in amounts toxic to most plants can be a serious limiting factor in land use. Where toxic salts are the limiting factor, the following ranges are general guides until more specific criteria are available:

Class II—Crops slightly affected. In irrigated areas, even after salt removal, slight salinity or small amounts of sodium remains or is likely to recur.

Class III—Crops moderately affected. In irrigated areas, even after salt removal, moderate salinity or moderate amounts of sodium remains or is likely to recur.

Classes IV-VI—Crops seriously affected on cultivated land. Usually only salt-tolerant plants will grow on noncultivated land. In irrigated areas, even after leaching, severe salinity or large amounts of sodium remains or is likely to recur.

Class VII—Satisfactory growth of useful vegetation impossible, except possible for some of the most salt-tolerant forms, such as some Atriplexes that have limited use for grazing.

Slope and Hazard of Erosion

Soil damage from erosion is significant in the use, management, and response of soil for the following reasons:

1. An adequate soil depth must be maintained for moderate to high crop production. Soil depth is critical on shallow soils over nonrenewable substrata such as hard rock. These soils tolerate less damage from erosion than soils of similar depth with a renewable substrata such as the raw loess or soft shale that can be improved through the use of special tillage, fertilizer, and beneficial cropping practices.

2. Soil loss influences crop yields. The reduction in yield following the loss of each inch of surface soil varies widely for different kinds of soil. The reduction is least on soils having little difference in texture, con-

sistence, and fertility between the various horizons of the soil. It is greatest where there is a marked difference between surface layers and subsoils, such as among soils with claypans. For example, corn yields on soils with dense, very slowly permeable subsoils may be reduced 3 to 4 bushels per acre per year for each inch of surface soil lost. Yield reduction is normally small on deep, moderately permeable soils having similar textured surface and subsurface layers and no great accumulation of organic matter in the surface soil.

3. Nutrient loss through erosion on sloping soils is important not only because of its influence on crop yield but also because of cost of replacement to maintain crop yields. The loss of plant nutrients can be high, even with slight erosion.

4. Loss of surface soil changes the physical condition of the plow layer in soils having finer textured layers below the surface soil. Infiltration rate is reduced; erosion and runoff rates are increased; tilth is difficult to maintain; and tillage operations and seedbed preparation are more difficult.

5. Loss of surface soil by water erosion, soil blowing, or land leveling may expose highly calcareous lower strata that are difficult to make into suitable surface soil.

6. Water-control structures are damaged by sediments due to erosion. Maintenance of open drains and ponds becomes a problem and their capacity is reduced as sediment accumulates.

7. Gullies form as a result of soil loss. This kind of soil damage causes reduced yields, increased sediment damage, and physical difficulties in farming between the gullies.

The steepness of slope, length of slope, and shape of slope (convex or concave) all influence directly the soil and water losses from a field. Steepness of slope is recorded on soil maps. Length and shape of slopes are not recorded on soil maps; however, they are often characteristic of certain kinds of soil, and their effects on use and management can be evaluated as a part of the mapping unit.

Where available, research data on tons of soil loss per acre per year under given levels of management are used on sloping soils to differentiate between capability classes.

Soil Depth

Effective depth includes the total depth of the soil profile favorable for root development. In some soils this includes the C horizon; in a few only the A horizon is included. Where the effect of depth is the limiting factor, the following ranges are comonly used: Class I, 36 inches or more; class II, 20–36 inches; class III, 10–20 inches; and class IV, less than 10 inches. These ranges in soil depth between classes vary from one section of the country to another depending on the climate. In arid and semiarid areas, irrigated soils in class I are 60 or more inches in depth. Where other unfavorable factors occur in combination with depth, the capability decreases.

Previous Erosion

On some kinds of soil previous erosion reduces crop yields and the choice of crops materially; on others the effect is not great. The effect of past erosion limits the use of soils (1) where subsoil characteristics are unfavorable, or (2) where soil material favorable for plant growth is shallow to bedrock or material similar to bedrock. In some soils, therefore, the degree of erosion influences the capability grouping.

Available Moisture-Holding Capacity

Water-holding capacity is an important quality of soil. Soils that have limited moisture-holding capacity are likely to be droughty and have limitations in kinds and amounts of crops that can be grown; they also present fertility and other management problems. The ranges in water-holding capacity for the soils in the capability classes vary to a limited degree with the amount and distribution of effective precipitation during the growing season. Within a capability class, the range in available moisture-holding capacity varies from one climatic region to another.

26. Wastebasket of the Earth

William A. Albrecht

The notion of "wastebasket" presents a different view of soils —as a continual processor and consumer of what is essentially the waste of the biotic elements on the earth. Albrecht suggests that man in his primarily "predator" role is either unwilling or unable to reach a rational adjustment to the productive elements of the earth, especially soils. He makes a rather neat point by suggesting that when we speak of soil as "dirt," or dirty, actually the converse is more accurate, in that we contaminate the soil and are in general a biological liability not only for and to ourselves, but to all other life forms that sustain us on the earth.

Contamination in the food we eat, the water we drink, and the air we breathe suggests close connection with the soil. Usage such as "your

SOURCE: *Bulletin of the Atomic Scientists,* October, 1961, pp. 335–40. Copyright 1961 by the Educational Foundation for Nuclear Science. Reprinted by permission

hands are dirty," serves as a reminder that the thin surface layer of the soil is the wastebasket of the earth, the collector for the disposal of all matter that has once lived and moved.

Role of the Soil

The thin layer of the earth's surface is an intensive transformer of all the waste it collects. In that shallow stratum, elements are separated out of combinations and reunited into other compounds, effecting vast changes in every kind of matter. These activities include transformations of energy by such processes as oxidation, reduction, hydration, hydrolysis, and molecular rearrangement. Oxidation, like combustion, dissipates energy in the form of heat, which escapes from the earth. Reduction concentrates it in compounds of high heat and fuel values. This is illustrated most significantly by the plant's reduction of carbon dioxide by water, storing the sun's energy in the resulting carbohydrates.

These transformations of matter and energy create, nourish, protect, and maintain all living creatures. These creatures vary in physiological complexity from the simplest microbial cell to man, whose high state of evolution has equipped him with a mind to comprehend—and to modify—his environment, even as far as unwittingly contaminating it.

The term *contamination* has many meanings. The wastes of one population may be either the poison or the life-support of another. We consider populations of different forms of life to see whether their coexistence is cooperative or competitive, and whether their respective wastes may be of benefit or harm to each other.

A high degree of cooperation through evolution and adaptation characterizes nature's management of environment. But when man manages environment, competition stands out—with frequent examples of contamination. As managers, we are biased toward aims and benefits for man alone. We have concerned ourselves little with how, in modifying the environment for ourselves, we may be disrupting it for all the other populations of the biotic pyramid—microbes, plants, animals, and man—all supported by the one creative foundation—the soil.

Instead of speaking of the soil as "dirt" to emphasize its contamination of ourselves, the converse might be more appropriate. Man is upsetting much of the natural environment by his contamination of the air, the water, and particularly the soil, reducing its ability to dispose of wastes safely and to nourish healthy populations of men and all other living things. It is a dangerous boldness to believe that we can manage environments completely by technologies designed for our economic advantage.

The True Agrarian

Given to a belief in the homocentric purpose of the earth, we have come to take our soil for granted. This view is quite the opposite of that of the pioneer—living mainly by agriculture—who respected and studied his environment and struggled to be naturally fit for his evolutionary survival there. He considered the seasons, the annual amount and distribution of the rainfall, the degrees of heat and cold, the winds and storms. He did not consider land as a commodity. The pioneer appreciated the fact that the soil had been built by nature during the ages pre-dating him, brought about by the climatic forces breaking down the rocks, growing the microbes, the plants, the many other kinds of life. For him, those were the natural forces of soil construction, and he knew he must maintain soil productivity if he were to survive. The pioneers were truly agrarian people. For them the soil was holy ground. Too, it was living soil.

Because of the scientific organization of our recently increased knowledge about the soil, we forget that the decomposition of rocks, the growth of vegetation, and the complete return of that organic matter in place—all under nature's management—are what brought about productive soils. At first, these soils were not contaminated against the healthy coexistence of a specific, but limited, set of species. The early balance represented an evolutionary set, each form unique in relation to the others, to the soil's particular geologic-climatic setting, and its degree of development in a given area. Examples of this limited balance would include the particular plant and wildlife forms of virgin forests, or the American plains or prairies. All of these conditions were major determinants of the coexistent species; the survival of each was dependent on the survival of the others.

Man's management of agricultural crops and livestock has not been directed by knowledge of the limitations of soil fertility, nor by knowledge of the required climatic-geologic setting for crops and livestock with each in its natural ecological climax. Instead, we have been given to transplanting any species from anywhere to everywhere for economic gain, ignoring biological benefits or dangers to the species involved. We have brought in higher (or lower) species while depleting the very soil fertility support required to grow them in health.

We have thrown natural evolution into reverse. We struggle to nurture species we have made unfit for the environment because creative forces there cannot offer the required quality of food and energy support. We now need to view the pampered species as contamination against all other lower species which would otherwise arrive at their natural climax. We must accept the fact that the soil, with its dynamics of producing and accumulating organic substances through plants with the support of climatic forces, is still the only energy supply on which all kinds of life depend. Transformation is the major role played by the soil.

Granting that the entire biosphere is dependent on the inflow of that bit of the sun's energy fixed in organic substances by photosynthesis, it is helpful to note that as Nelson G. Harston, Frederick E. Smith, and Lawrence B. Slobodkin said in their article "Community Structure, Population Control and Composition" in *The American Naturalist* last year, populations divide themselves appropriately into three trophic levels: the decomposers, the producers, and the predators.

The Decomposers

The decomposers are represented by the varied kinds of microbial life which live by degrading organic debris through processes giving the microbes their energy and growth substances. The slow accumulation (at great depths below the earth's surface) of these remnants as fossil fuels of organic origin and a high degree of oxygen removal indicates that this heterotrophic group did not have much in the way of energy-giving "leftovers." Nor can these remains be considered contamination when they are far beneath the soil surface. But when they are brought into the atmosphere, and into the highly aerobic surface soils, after laboratory work has turned them into products such as antiseptics, pesticides, and herbicides, they are the most extensive and powerful biochemical contaminations we have yet known. Their range of disturbances covers the entire biotic pyramid.

Hydrocarbons, which can disrupt the transformations in the soil's surface zone, were buried by nature at great soil depths. These high concentrations of energy are now our industrial fuels. But even such deep burial of the wastes resulting from the use of atomic fuels will not serve as safe removal. Atomic fuels, with their lingering rays for a lingering death of all living cells, are not respecters of the beneficial portions of the soil's microbial flora.

Nutritional requirements of microbial decomposers are met by the contents of the debris and the soil. The essential elements remain very much in the cycle of use and reuse, since sulfur, phosphorus, nitrogen, and carbon occur as major elements in the leftovers. Oxygen is almost absent there, but carbon, linked to hydrogen, occurs in high concentration.

Ever since the work of Pasteur, our fear of microbes has singled them out as our environment's major contamination. We have made them the victims of vengeance and we boil them under steam pressure at every opportunity. Their disrepute has been shared recently by dusts, fungus spores, pollen grains of trees, grasses, weeds, and other particles. Today the professional allergist devotes his attention to atmospheric contaminants and to other substances disturbing the mucous membranes and similar tissues of the human body. But when microbes are viewed as disposers and transformers they become major benefactors for other populations. Microbes in surface soil serve as wrecking crews and salvage agencies. Simplifying the residue of past population for energy release and reuse, these decomposers make the upper stratum of soil the real living foundation of the entire biotic pyramid. They keep open the sewage disposal systems of all the population levels.

Microbes are uniquely equipped to maintain their own populations. They reproduce at the rate of one generation per hour or even faster. They synthesize their own extra- and intra-cellular compounds—some of which we term antibiotics—for protection against competitors for their environment. The antibiotic quality may be merely an evolutionary accident that served to bring death to competitor cells. Nature's conservation practices use wastes from some life forms to make the environment serve its own survival more completely.

Benzene rings characterize the chemical structure of the antibiotic terramycin, for example. Modified ring structures with substitutions of nitrogen and sulfur for some of the carbon are found in penicillin, aureothrycin and other microbial products developed for their bacteriocidal effects on the human body. That ring structure represents highly reduced organic compounds such as those found in crude oil and coal. The chemical structures and biochemical energy potential represents the opposite of that of natural organic wastes dumped on the surface soil. While natural organic wastes offer much as energy through microbial oxidations, crude oil and coal are too stable for biochemical transformation and energy release, even though they rank high as industrial fuels. They are seldom broken down by digestion. They overload the liver, the chemical censor of the human body. They are leftovers from an aerobic microbial populations and are well removed as serious contaminants by their natural placement far below the surface soil and by disposal well beyond the entire biotic pyramid.

The benzene ring, in a simpler compound distilled from coal tar—carbolic acid—was an early antiseptic. But now, long-chain compounds and ring structures of carbon, sulfur, or nitrogen substitutions, or in chlorinated, nitrated, and sulfonated forms as synthetics from the industrial chemistry laboratory, are being distributed extensively, acting as deadly poisons against the populations in the biotic pyramid. They come into the atmosphere in "smog" and carbon monoxide, and in herbicides, pesticides, and the like. Those microbial wastes welling upward from the depths of the earth, in their natural forms and in our more poisonous alterations of them, must be considered contamination by man of his own environment and of the environments of all populations that support him. His efforts to so completely destroy microbes are contributing to his gradual destruction by his own hand. Decomposers are not respecters of man when they release their own wastes as contaminants.

The Producers

The second group among the populations, or trophic levels, of the earth are the plants, which produce organic compounds carrying the chemical and other energy transferred from the sun. They are the only means of storing and distributing that supply. Energy is collected by photo-synthesis, the unique process whereby the chlorophyll of the leaves binds it into compounds of carbon, hydrogen, and oxygen in the mole-cular arrangement of carbohydrates. Plants are the source of energy for all biochemical processes, and of their own starter compounds into which they synthesize nitrogen, sulfur, and phosphorus to yield the different amino acids of proteins and living tissues which grow, protect, and reproduce. Plants are the only producers, since they are the sources of food energy and growth potential synthesized directly from the chemical elements and flowing through all the other trophic levels.

Plants root themselves first into the soil and then extend their tops into the atmosphere. They may be vulnerable to contaminants from both di-rections. Their unique position and special processes bring both in-organic and organic decompositions from the soil into biochemical union with water, and carbon dioxide, and nitrogen. Plants, representing that limited zone where earth and atmosphere meet, act as a kind of interface for concentrations of different kinds of matter, becoming the significant stratum for the creation of all that lives. All life is possible because the synthetic power of sunlight operates through the plant enzyme chloro-phyll. It is a mobilizer, or chelator, of the chemical elements, unique be-cause the plant itself creates it. Its chemical structure consists of the inorganic element magnesium as the core, combined with nitrogen, linked with carbon, and all three connected with hydrogen. Even this chelator's composition represents a chemical union between the soil, which furnishes the magnesium, and the atmosphere, which yields the nitrogen, carbons, and hydrogen.

Because plants support themselves by their own capacity for combin-ing elements and using solar energy to create compounds, they surpass all other populations in the struggle for survival. Microbes can use the elements in synthesis but must decompose the organic compounds synthesized by plants to provide the necessary energy. Plants, in turn, profit in their extended survival because the microbes simplify the accumulated organic matter to keep the soil's inorganic elements and the atmosphere's organic elements—carbon and nitrogen—in cycles of reuse. Otherwise the accumulated products of plants would contaminate their own environment.

Plants and microbes may be considered in a symbiosis for survival independent of more complex populations. But even that symbiosis may by disrupted by one or the other symbiont acting as a competitor, a parasite, or a predator. Either may even produce contamination by its waste products: plant compounds may be poisons for microbes and microbes may be poisons for plants. By competing for essential inorganic elements—calcium, magnesium, phosphorus, potassium, nitrogen, sulfur —and the several "trace" elements, one may limit the other via the soil.

All trophic levels above the plants must live by the compounds of the latter's synthesis—carbohydrates for energy; proteins for growth of tissue, protection, and reproduction; and inorgano-organic combinations associated with the proteins. Proteins in plants result, not from photosynthesis, but from the plant's biochemical processes, which require expenditures of stored energy and assembly of inorganic and organic requirements by the roots. The roots penetrate only a limited volume of soil, living there largely through activities of the decomposers. Plants, like microbes, use carbon dioxide waste—from the roots—to produce active hydrogen in the resulting carbonic acid to mobilize the soil fertility elements for plant survival. These two populations, the producers and the decomposers, as contaminants or as transformers, determine the environmental support of all other populations.

The Predators

All the heterotrophic populations crowd each other to get to the food delivered to them by that mundane team of autotrophs, the symbiotic team of microbes and plants. That crowding, under the deficiencies provoking it, makes the wastes of each a contamination for the other whenever the natural processes of the producers and decomposers are disrupted. All populations above plants and microbes are included in the third category: the predators. They prey upon the plant population, and upon each other to an increasing degree, since the plants are not nourished by the living soil completely enough to be ample prey for man and all the other predators and parasites.

Predators—other than man—do not destroy their prey completely before the numbers of predators drop down so far that the numbers of prey mount to domination again. Increase in prey favors an increase in predators, and then, in turn, a decrease in prey, to yield naturally alternating dominations but not the extinction of either. But man is not merely the predator of one trophic level; he also aims his technology at complete extinction of many populations. Thus he breaks the law of predator-prey relations and of survival. When he causes extinction, he reduces the number of basic segments by which the biotic pyramid supports man.

Interpopulation predations increase as the soil becomes less able to grow the vegetation of nutrition in required quality and quantity. When the soil's inorganic elements have been depleted, then the exploited soils must eventually register their damage on all trophic levels. The most serious effects fall first on man, raising the question of whether the baffling degeneration of our bodily health, now increasing our concern about what was once commonly called "disease," may not suggest patterns of hidden causes connected in some way with the climatic-fertility pattern of the soil. Thus, human ecology may develop into the most important science.

Human Life Came Late and Must Go Early

When the numbers in any population are charted as a graph against a base of time, they give a sigmoid curve. Its shape suggests the top of the letter S pulled to the right while the bottom remains attached. The introduction of a single living microbe into a given volume of medium results in a slow increase in numbers with the curve moving along the near-horizontal. But soon the move turns toward the vertical, suggesting a population explosion. Then the increase lessens, ceases, and, finally, there is a population decrease followed by eventual extinction. Contamination by its accumulated non-transformed wastes, coupled with exhaustion of nutritional and other environmental supports, eliminates the population from its limited setting.

Populations of older countries, similarly charted, suggest the final third of the biotic curve. France, Scandinavia, Italy, and Spain, starting as far back as 1900, are illustrations. The United States illustrates the lower two thirds, or the beginning of the chart. Predictions from 1920 onward pointed to the falling percentages of increase, if immigrations were limited.

Since the multiplication of man still conforms to the natural laws of biological phenomena, and since human multiplication is by no means managed to give biological advantages for improved survival, we must characterize man, at this stage, as the main biological liability, not only to himself, but to the other populations supporting him. *He is the contamination in the environment.*

Man's disregard of his ecological limitation to the temperate zone—by the required supply of proteins alone—should be cited as only one powerful factor. As one moves from the temperate to the torrid and humid tropical zone, the desperate struggle for proteins at any trophic level is evident in the carnivorousness and cannibalism that are common. Here, life forms are mainly predators. The same is true as one moves from the temperate to the frigid zone.

The migrations into the frigid zone, into climatic-soil-fertility settings of little or no soil construction, are badly handicapped by the paucity of producers and decomposers. The predators win support by their carnivorousness or through lifelines reaching back into the temperate zone. In the tropics, high rainfall and temperatures have caused excessive decomposition of the rocks to the point of destruction of soils, which then fail to fully nourish plant life. Even proteins are there replaced by

poisonous compounds of many producers. Carnivorousness and cannibalism characterize the survival of decidedly limited populations. The
dry tropics are in the same category. Populations at climatic extremes
are limited because the producers, operating in combination with the
decomposers, are not providing the necessary proteins in complete array,
nor with their natural accompaniments.

Can Man Manage His Own Species?

The epoch of man is but a minute segment in the paleontological
column of the earth's populations as they have come, gone, or remained.
Man has shifted away from the rugged individualism of open country
and its diversity of agriculture according to the laws of nature. He has
collected himself into congested cities which have been said to require
monocultures and chemicalized agricultures; he has controlled the environment of those cities according to the dictates of technology and
economics, disregarding nature's laws and even his own biochemistry.

During the latest part of the brief epoch of man's existence, his
technologies and their political complications have served to harvest the
natural living resources, to exploit soil fertility, and to compel the human
march from east to west. The march has rolled on until the resources of
most recent possession—those of the western hemisphere—are dwindling
rapidly under the political demand for coexistence of the Western world
with those bringing up the rear in the march—a total world population
approaching three billion predators.

Because they must behave according to the natural laws controlling
biological bodies, each population below man has—through evolution—
exhibited itself as a climax crop for a limited time in its limited ecological setting. But man, with mental capacity transcending that of the
others, has used most of the other levels to his advantage and their
disadvantage so that, in general, he does not conform to the pattern of
evolution. His technological powers disrupt the pattern and destroy the
very conformers that support him. Unwittingly, his development and
management of environmental control over materials and energy have
increased the contamination of the soil and the atmosphere. He has
destroyed the decomposer populations to the extent that the natural
basic support of the producers is weakening; the entire biotic pyramid is
tumbling because of man's dominance at the top.

In managing her contaminations, nature either transforms them
through biotic disposers in the surface soil, or buries them safely at
greater depths. Man, managing his contaminations as a helpless novice,
seems to be on his way to his own destruction by and amongst them. In
all probability, nature, not he, will determine the final outcome.

VII. NATURAL FAUNA

The domestication and use of animals and animal products has been a measure of the progress of mankind. Much of the concern of geographers with animal life has been justifiably with domesticated animals —livestock. Nevertheless, natural or wild fauna have been and continue to be of great importance to man. Nearly all of the fish, crustaceans, and other sea life consumed by humans are essentially "wild" animals. Furthermore, through careful observations of animal communities and their apparent social organizations, we may be able to learn some things of value in attempting to solve the many problems confronting that exceedingly social animal—man.

27. Self-Regulating Systems in Populations of Animals

V. C. Wynne-Edwards

Although this brilliant study of population-controlling systems among animals does not address itself directly to the problem of the "population explosion" of humans, we can hardly fail to see the significant correlations possible. It would be no exaggeration to say that we ignore these findings, derived from analysis of the initiatives of many kinds of animals, at our own human peril.

I am going to try to explain a hypothesis which could provide a bridge between two biological realms. On one side is that part of the "Balance of Nature," concerned with regulating the numbers of animals, and on the other is the broad field of social behavior. The hypothesis may, I believe, throw a bright and perhaps important sidelight on human behavior and population problems. I must emphasize, however, that it is still a hypothesis. It appears to be generally consistent with the facts, and it provides entirely new insight into many aspects of animal behavior that have hitherto been unexplainable; but because it involves long-term evolutionary processes it cannot be put to an immediate and comprehensive test by short-term experiments.

SOURCE: *Science*, CXLVII, 3665 (March 26, 1965), 1543–48. Copyright 1965 by the American Association for the Advancement of Science. The author is Regius Professor of Natural History, Marischal College, University of Aberdeen, Scotland.

Human populations are of course increasing at compound interest practically all over the world. At the overall 2 percent annual rate of the last decade, they can be expected to double with each generation. In the perspective of evolutionary time such a situation must be extremely short-lived, and I am sure we are going to grow more and more anxious about the future of man until we are able to satisfy ourselves that the human population explosion is controllable, and can be contained.

Populations of animals, especially when they are living under primeval undisturbed conditions, characteristically show an altogether different state of affairs; and this was equally true of man in the former cultural periods of the stone age. These natural populations tend to preserve a continuing state of balance, usually fluctuating to some extent but essentially stable and regulated. The nature of the regulatory process has been the main focus of study and speculation by animal ecologists during the whole of my working life, and in fact considerably longer.

Charles Darwin was the first to point out that though all animals have the capacity to increase their numbers, in fact they do not continuously do so. The "checks to increase" appeared to him to be of four kinds—namely, the amount of food available, which must give the extreme limit to which any species can increase; the effects of predation by other animals; the effects of physical factors such as climate; and finally, the inroads of disease. "In looking at Nature," he tells us in the *Origin of Species,* "it is most necessary . . . never to forget that every single organic being may be said to be striving to the utmost to increase in numbers." This intuitive assumption of a universal resurgent pressure from within held down by hostile forces from without has dominated the thinking of biologists on matters of population regulation, and on the nature of the struggle for existence, right down to the present day.

Setting all preconceptions aside, however, and returning to a detached assessment of the facts revealed by modern observation and experiment, it becomes almost immediately evident that a very large part of the regulation of numbers depends not on Darwin's hostile forces but on the initiative taken by the animals themselves; that is to say, to an important extent it is an intrinsic phenomenon.

Forty years ago Jespersen showed, for example, that there is a close numerical agreement between the standing crop of planktonic organisms at the surface of the North Atlantic Ocean and the distribution density of the various deep-sea birds that depend on these organisms for food. Over the whole of this vast area the oceanic birds are dispersed in almost constant proportion to the local biomass of plankton, although the biomass itself varies from region to region by a factor of about 100; the actual crude correlation coefficient is 85 percent. This pro rata dispersion of the birds must in fact depend solely on their own intrinsic efforts and behavior. Even though the dispersion directly reflects the availability of food, the movements of the birds over the ocean are essentially voluntary and not imposed against their will by hostile or other outside forces.

Turning to the results of repeatable experiments with laboratory animals, it is a generally established principle that a population started up, perhaps from one parental pair, in some confined universe such as an aquarium or a cage, can be expected to grow to a predictable size, and thereafter to maintain itself at that ceiling for months or years as long as the experimenter keeps the conditions unchanged. This can readily be demonstrated with most common laboratory animals, including the insects *Drosophila* and *Tribolium*, the water-flea *Daphnia*, the guppy *Lebistes*, and also mice and rats. The ceiling population density stays constant in these experiments in the complete absence of predators or disease and equally without recourse to regulation by starvation, simply by the matching of recruitment and loss. For example, a set of particularly illuminating experiments by Silliman and Gutsell, lasting over 3 years, showed that when stable populations of guppies, kept in tanks, were cropped by removal of a proportion of the fish at regular intervals, the remainder responded by producing more young that survived, with the consequence that the losses were compensated. In the controls, on the other hand, where the stocks were left untouched, the guppies went on breeding all the time, but by cannibalism they consistently removed at birth the whole of the surplus produced. The regulating methods are different in different species; under appropriate circumstances in mice, to take another example, ovulation and reproduction can decline and even cease, as long as the ceiling density is maintained.

Here again, therefore, we are confronted by intrinsic mechanisms, in which none of Darwin's checks play any part, competent in themselves to regulate the population size within a given habitat.

The same principle shows up just as clearly in the familiar concept that a habitat has a certain carrying capacity and that it is no good turning out more partridges or planting more trout than the available habitat can hold.

Population growth is essentially a density-dependent process; this means that it tends to proceed fastest when population densities are far below the ceiling level, to fall to zero as this level is approached, and to become negative, leading to an actual drop in numbers, if ever the ceiling is exceeded. The current hypothesis is that the adjustment of numbers in animals is a homeostatic process—that there is, in fact, an automatic self-righting balance between population density and resources.

I must turn briefly aside here to remind you that there are some environments which are so unstable or transitory that there is not time enough for colonizing animals to reach a ceiling density, and invoke their regulatory machinery, before the habitat becomes untenable again or is destroyed. Populations in these conditions are always in the pioneering stage, increasing freely just as long as conditions allow. Instability of this kind tends to appear around the fringes of the geographical range of all free-living organisms, and especially in desert and polar regions. It is also very common in agricultural land, because of the incessant disturbance of ploughing, seeding, spraying, harvesting, and rotating of crops. In these conditions the ecologist will often look in vain for evidences of homeostasis, among the violently fluctuating and completely uncontrollable populations typical of the animal pests of farms and plantations. Homeostasis can hardly be expected to cope unerringly with the ecological turmoil of cultivated land.

I return later to the actual machinery of homeostasis. For the present it can be accepted that more or less effective methods of regulating their own numbers have been evolved by most types of animals. If this is so, it seems logical to ask as the next question: What is it that decides the ceiling level?

Food Supply as a Limiting Factor

Darwin was undoubtedly right in concluding that food is the factor that normally puts an extreme limit on population density, and the dispersion of oceanic birds over the North Atlantic, which so closely reflects the dispersion of their food supply, is certain to prove a typical and representative case. Just the same, the link between food productivity and population density is very far from being self-evident. The relationship between them does not typically involve any signs of undernourishment; and starvation, when we observe it, tends to be a sporadic or accidental cause of mortality rather than a regular one.

Extremely important light is shed on this relationship between population density and food by our human experience of exploiting resources of the same kind. Fish, fur-bearing animals, and game are all notoriously subject to overexploitation at the hands of man, and present-day management of these renewable natural resources is based on the knowledge that there is a limit to the intensity of cropping that each stock can withstand. If we exceed this critical level, the stock will decline and the future annual crops will diminish. Exactly parallel principles apply to the exploitation of natural prairie pastures by domestic livestock: if overgrazing is permitted, fertility and future yields just as fatally decline.

In all these situations there is a tendency to overstep the safety margin while exploitation of the resource is still economically profitable. We have seen since World War II, for example, the decimation of stocks of the blue and the humpback whale in the southern oceans, under the impetus of an intense profit motive, which persisted long after it had become apparent to everyone in the industry that the cropping rate was unsupportably high. The only way to protect these economically valuable recurrent resources from destruction is to impose, by agreement or law, a manmade code of rules, defining closed seasons, catch limits, permitted types of gear, and so on, which restrict the exploitation rate sufficiently to prevent the catch from exceeding the critical level.

In its essentials, this is the same crucial situation that faces populations of animals in exploiting their resources of food. Indeed, without going any further one could predict that if the food supplies of animals were openly exposed to an unruly scramble, there could be no safeguard against their overexploitation either.

Conventional Behavior in Relation to Food

When I first saw the force of this deduction 10 years ago, I felt that the scales had fallen from my eyes. At once the vast edifice of conventional behavior among animals in relation to food began to take on a new meaning. A whole series of unconnected natural phenomena seemed to click smoothly into place.

First among these are the territorial systems of various birds (paralleled in many other organisms), where the claim to an individual piece of ground can evoke competition of an intensity unequaled on any other occasion in the life of the species concerned. It results, in the simplest cases, in a parceling out of the habitat into a mosaic of breeding and feeding lots. A territory has to be of a certain size, and individuals that are unsuccessful in obtaining one are often excluded completely from the habitat, and always prevented from breeding in it. Here is a system that might have been evolved for the exact purpose of imposing a ceiling density on the habitat, and for efficiently disposing of any surplus individuals that fail to establish themselves. Provided the territory size is adequate, it is obvious that the rate of exploitation of the food resources the habitat contains will automatically be prevented from exceeding the critical threshold.

There are other behavioral devices that appear, in the light of the food-resources hypothesis we are examining, equally purposive in leading to the same result—namely, that of limiting the permitted quota of participants in an artificial kind of way, and of off-loading all that are for the time being surplus to the carrying capacity of the ground. Many birds nest in colonies—especially, for example, the oceanic and aerial birds, which cannot, in the nature of things, divide up the element in which they feed into static individual territories. In the colony the pairs compete just as long and keenly for one of the acceptable nest sites, which are in some instances closely packed together. By powerful tradition some of these species return year after year to old-established resorts, where the perimeter of the colony is closely drawn like an imaginary fence around the occupied sites. Once again there is not always room to accommodate all the contestants, and unsuccessful ones have to be relegated to a nonbreeding surplus or reserve, inhibited from sexual maturation because they have failed to obtain a site within the traditional zone and all other sites are taboo.

A third situation, exemplifying another, parallel device, is the pecking order or social hierarchy so typical of the higher animals that live in companies in which the individual members become mutually known. Animal behaviorists have studied the hierarchy in its various manifestations for more than 40 years, most commonly in relation to food. In general, the individuals of higher rank have a prior right to help themselves, and, in situations where there is not enough to go round, the ones at the bottom of the scale must stand aside and do without. In times of food shortage—for example, with big game animals—the result is that the dominant individuals come through in good shape while the subordinates acutally die of starvation. The hierarchy therefore produces the same kind of result as a territorial system in that it admits a limited quota of individuals to share the food resources and excludes the extras. Like the other devices I have described, it can operate in exactly the same way with respect to reproduction. In fact, not only can the hierarchical system exclude individuals from breeding, it can equally inhibit their sexual development.

It must be quite clear already that the kind of competition we are considering, involving as it does the right to take food and the right to breed, is a matter of the highest importance to the individuals that engage in it. At its keenest level it becomes a matter of life and death. Yet, as is well known, the actual contest between individuals for real property or personal status is almost always strictly conventionalized. Fighting and bloodshed are superseded by mere threats of violence, and threats in their turn are sublimated into displays of magnificence and virtuosity. This is the world of bluff and status symbols. What takes place, in other words, is a contest for conventional prizes conducted under conventional rules. But the contest itself is no fantasy, for the losers can forfeit the chance of posterity and the right to survive.

Conventionalized Rivalry and Society

It is at this point that the hypothesis provides its most unexpected and striking insight, by showing that the conventionalization of rivalry and the foundation of society are one and the same thing. Hitherto it has never been possible to give a scientific definition of the terms *social* and *society*, still less a functional explanation. The emphasis has always been on the rather vague element of companionship and brotherhood. Animals have in the main been regarded as social whenever they were gregarious. Now we can view the social phenomenon in a new light. According to the hypothesis, the society is no more and no less than he organization necessary for the staging of conventional competition. At once it assumes a crisp definition: a society is an organization of individuals that is capable of providing conventional competition among its members.

Such a novel interpretation of something that involves us all so intimately is almost certain to be viewed at first sight a bit skeptically; but in fact one needs no prompting in our competitive world to see that human society is impregnated with rivalry. The sentiments of brotherhood are warm and reassurring, and in identifying society primarily with these we appear to have been unconsciously shutting our eyes to the inseparable rough-and-tumble of status seeking and social discrimination that are never very far to seek below the surface, bringing enviable rewards to the successful and pitiful distress to those who lose. If this interpretation is right, conventional competition is an inseparable part of the substance of human society, at the parochial, national, and international level. To direct it into sophisticated and acceptable channels is no doubt one of the great motives of civilized behavior; but it would be idle to imagine that we could eliminate it.

A corollary of the hypothesis that deserves mention is the extension of sociality that it implies, to animals of almost every kind whether they associate in flocks or seek instead a more solitary way of life. There is no particular difficulty of course in seeing, for example, cats and dogs as social mammals individually recognizing the local and personal rights of acquaintances and strangers and inspired by obviously conventional modes of rivalry when they meet. In a different setting, the territory-holding birds that join in the chorus of the spring dawn are acting together in social concert, expressing their mutual rivalry by a conventional display of exalted sophistication and beauty. Even at the other extreme, when animals flock into compact and obviously social herds and schools, each individual can sometimes be seen to maintain a strict individual distance from its companions.

Social Organization and Feedback

We can conveniently return now to the subject of homeostasis, in order to see how it works in population control. Homeostatic systems come within the general purview of cybernetics; in fact, they have long been recognized in the physiology of living organisms. A simple model can be found in any thermostatic system, in which there must of course be units capable of supplying or withdrawing heat whenever the system departs from its standard temperature and readjustment is necessary. But one also needs an indicator device to detect how far the system has deviated and in which direction. It is the feedback of this information that activates the heating or cooling units.

Feedback is an indispensable element of homeostatic systems. There seems no reason to doubt that, in the control of population density, it can be effectively provided simply by the intensity of conventional competition. Social rivalry is inherently density-dependent: the more competitors there are seeking a limited number of rewards, the keener will be the contest. The impact of stress on the individuals concerned, arising from conventional competition and acting through the pituitary-adrenal system, is already fully established, and it can profoundly influence their responses, both physiological and behavioral.

One could predict on theoretical grounds that feedback would be specially important whenever a major change in population density has to take place, upsetting the existing balance between demand and resources. This must occur particularly in the breeding season and at times of seasonal migrations. Keeping this in mind, we can obtain what we need in the way of background information by examining the relatively long-lived vertebrates, including most kinds of birds and mammals, whose individual members live long enough to constitute a standing population all the year round. The hypothesis of course implies that reproduction, as one of the principal parameters of population, will be subject to control—adjusted in magnitude, in fact, to meet whatever addition is currently required to build up the population and make good the losses of the preceding year. *Recruitment* is a term best used only to mean intake of new breeding adults into the population, and in that sense, of course, the raw birth rate may not be the sole and immediate factor that determines it. The newborn young have got to survive adolescence before they can become recruits to the breeding stock; and even after they attain puberty, social pressures may exclude them from reproducing until they attain a sufficiently high rank in the hierarchy. Indeed, there is evidence in a few species that, under sufficient stress, adults which have bred in previous years can be forced to stand aside.

There are, in fact, two largely distinct methods of regulating reproductive output, both of which have been widely adopted in the animal kingdom. One is to limit the number of adults that are permitted to breed, and this is of course a conspicuous result of adopting a territorial system or any other system in which the number of permissible breeding sites is restricted. The other is to influence the number of young that each breeding pair is conditioned to produce. The two methods can easily be combined.

What we are dealing with here is a part of the machinery for adjusting population density. What we are trying to get at, however, is the social feedback mechanism behind it, by which the appropriate responses are elicited from potential breeders.

Birds generally provide us with the best examples, because their size, abundance, and diurnal habits render them the most observable and familiar of the higher animals. It is particularly easy to see in birds that social competition is keenest just before and during the breeding season.

regardless of the type of breeding dispersion any given species happens to adopt. Individuals may compete for and defend territories or nest sites, or in rarer cases they may engage in tournaments in an arena or on a strutting ground; and they may join in a vocal chorus especially concentrated about the conventional hours of dawn and dusk, make mass visits to colony sites, join in massed flights, and share in other forms of communal displays. Some of these activities are more obviously competitive than others, but all appear to be alike in their capacity to reveal to each individual the concentration or density level of the population within its own immediate area.

Communal Male Displays

Some of these activities, like territorial defense, singing, and the arena displays, tend to be the exclusive concern of the males. It has never been possible hitherto to give a satisfactory functional explanation of the kind of communal male displays typified by the arena dances of some of the South American hummingbirds and manakins, and by the dawn strutting of prairie chickens and sharp-tailed grouse. The sites they use are generally traditional, each serving as a communal center and drawing the competitors from a more or less wide surrounding terrain. On many days during the long season of activity the same assembly of males may engage in vigorous interplay and mutual hostility, holding tense dramatic postures for an hour or more at a stretch without a moment's relaxation, although there is no female anywhere in sight at the time. The local females do of course come at least once to be fertilized; but the performance makes such demands on the time and energy of the males that it seems perfectly reasonable to assume that this is the reason why they play no part in nesting and raising a family. The duty they perform is presumably important, but it is simply not credible to attribute it primarily to courting the females. To anyone looking for a population feedback device, on the other hand, interpretation would present no difficulty: he would presume that the males are being conditioned or stressed by their ritual exertions. In some of the arena species some of the males are known to be totally excluded from sexual intercourse; but it would seem that the feedback mechanism could produce its full effect only if it succeeded in limiting the number of females fertilized to an appropriate quota, after which the males refused service to any still remaining unfertilized. I hope research may at a not-too-distant date show us whether or not such refusal really takes place.

The conclusion that much of the social display associated with the breeding season consists of males competing with males makes necessary a reapprasial of Darwinian sexual selection. Whether the special organs developed for display are confined to the males, as in the examples we have just considered, or are found in both sexes, as for instance in most of the colony-nesting birds, there is a strong indication that they are first and foremost status symbols, used in conventional competition, and that the selective process by which they have been evolved is social rather than sexual. This would account for the hitherto puzzling fact that, although in the mature bullfrog and cicada the loud sound is produced by the males, in both cases it is the males that are provided with extra-large eardrums. There does not seem much room for doubt about who is displaying to whom.

Communal displays are familiar also in the context of bird migration, especially in the massing and maneuvering of flocks before the exodus begins. A comparable buildup of social excitement precedes the migratory flight of locusts. Indeed, what I have elsewhere defined as *epideictic* phenomena—displays, or special occasions, which allow all the individuals taking part to sense or become conditioned by population pressure —appear to be very common and widespread in the animal kingdom. They occur especially at the times predicted, when feedback is required in anticipation of a change in population density. The singing of birds, the trilling of katydids, crickets, and frogs, the underwater sounds of fish, and the flashing of fireflies all appear to perform this epideictic function. In cases where, as we have just seen, epideictic behavior is confined in the breeding season to the male sex, the presumption is that the whole process of controlling the breeding density and the reproductive quota is relegated to the males. Outside the breeding season, when the individuals are no longer united in pairs and are all effectively neuter in sex, all participate alike in epideictic displays—in fighting at sundown, like ducks; in demonstrating at huge communal roosts at dusk, like starlings, grackles, and crows; or in forming premigratory swarms, like swallows. The assumption which the hypothesis suggests, that the largest sector of all social behavior must have this fundamentally epideictic or feedback function, gives a key to understanding a vast agglomeration of observed animal behavior that has hitherto been dubiously interpreted or has seemed altogether meaningless.

Maintaining Population Balance

Having outlined the way in which social organization appears to serve in supplying feedback, I propose to look again at the machinery for making adjustments to the population balance. In territorial birds, variations in the average size of territories from place to place and year to year can be shown to alter the breeding density and probably also the proportion of adults actually participating in reproduction. In various mammals the proportion of the females made pregnant, the number and size of litters, the survival of the young, and the age at which they mature may all be influenced by social stress. Wherever parental care of the young has been evolved in the animal kingdom, the possibility exists that maternal behavior and solicitude can be affected in the same way; and the commonly observed variations in survival rates of the newborn could, in that case, have a substantial functional component and play a significant part in regulating the reproductive output. This would, among other things, explain away the enigma of cannibalism of the young, which we noticed earlier in the guppies and which occurs sporadically all through the higher animals. Infanticide played a conspicuous part in reducing the effective birth rate of many of the primitive human peoples that survived into modern times. Not infrequently it took the form of abandoning the child for what appeared to be commendable reasons, without involving an act of violence.

Reproduction is of course only one of the parameters involved in keeping the balance between income and loss in populations. The homeostatic machinery can go to work on the other side of the balance also, by influencing survival. Already, in considering the recruitment of adults, we have taken note of the way this can be affected by juvenile mortality, some of which is intrinsic in origin and capable of being promoted by social pressures. Conventional competition often leads to the exclusion of surplus individuals from any further right to share the resources of the habitat, and this in turn compels them to emigrate. Research conducted at Aberdeen in the last 8 years has shown how important a factor forced expulsion is in regulating the numbers of the Scottish red grouse. Every breeding season so far has produced a population surplus, and it is the aggressive behavior of the dominant males which succeeds in driving the supernumeraries away. In this case the outcasts do not go far; they get picked up by predators or they mope and die because they are cut off from their proper food. Deaths from predation and disease can in fact be substantially "assisted" under social stress.

On the income side, therefore, both reproductive input and the acquisition of recruits by immigration appear to be subject to social regulation; and on the loss side, emigration and what can be described as socially induced mortality can be similarly affected. Once more it appears that it is only the inroads of Darwin's "checks to increase," the agents once held to be totally responsible for population regulation, which are in fact uncontrollable and have to be balanced out by manipulation of the other four components.

Attention must be drawn to the intimate way in which physiology and behavior are entwined in providing the regulatory machinery. It seems certain that the feedback of social stimulation acts on the individual through his endocrine system, and in the case of the vertebrates, as I have said, this particularly involves the pituitary and adrenal cortex or its equivalent. Sometimes the individual's response is primarily a physiological one—for example, the inhibition of spermatogenesis or the acceleration of growth; sometimes it is purely behavioral, as in the urge to return to the breeding site, the development of aggresiveness, or the demand for territory of a given size. But often there is a combination of the two—that is to say, a psychosomatic response, as when, for instance, the assumption of breeding colors is coupled with the urge to display.

Sources of Controversy

There is no need for me to emphasize that the hypothesis is controversial. But almost all of it is based on well-established fact, so that the controversy can relate solely to matters of interpretation. Examples have been given here which show the ability of the hypothesis to offer new and satisfying interpretations of matters of facts where none could be suggested before. Some of these matters are of wide importance, like the basic function of social behavior; some are matters of everyday experience, like why birds sing at dawn. Very seldom indeed does the hypothesis contradict well-founded accepted principles. What, then, are the sources of controversy?

These are really three in number, all of them important. The first is that the concept is very wide-ranging and comprehensive; this means that it cannot be simply proved or disproved by performing a decisive experiment. There are of course dubious points where critical tests can be made, and research is proceeding, at Aberdeen among many other places, toward this end. Relevant results are constantly emerging, and at many points the hypothesis has been solidified and strengthened since it was first formulated. On the other hand, there has been no cause yet to retract anything.

The second source of controversy is that the hypothesis invokes a type of natural selection which is unfamiliar to zoologists generally. Social grouping is essentially a localizing phenomenon, and an animal species is normally made up of countless local populations all perpetuating themselves on their native soil, exactly as happens in underdeveloped and primitive communities of man. Social customs and adaptations vary from one local group to another, and the hypothesis requires that natural selection should take place between these groups, promoting those with more effective social organizations while the less effective ones go under. It is necessary, in other words, to postulate that social organizations are capable of progressive evolution and perfection as entities in their own right. The detailed arguments are too complex to be presented here, but I can point out that intergroup selection is far from being a new concept: It has been widely accepted for more than 20 years by geneticists. It is almost impossible to demonstrate it experimentally because we have to deal with something closely corresponding to the rise and fall of nations in history, rather than with success or failure of single genes over a few generations; it is therefore the time scale that prevents direct experiment. Even the comparatively rapid process of natural selection acting among individuals has been notoriously difficult to demonstrate in nature.

The third objection is, I think, by far the most interesting. It is simply that the hypothesis does not apply to ourselves. No built-in mechanisms appear to curb our own population growth, or adjust our numbers to our resources. If they did so, everything I have said would be evident to every educated child, and I should not be surveying it here. How is this paradox to be explained?

The answer, it seems clear, is that these mechanisms did exist in primitive man and have been lost, almost within historic times. Man in the paleolithic stage, living as a hunter and gatherer, remained in balance with his natural resources just as other animals do under natural conditions. Generation after generation, his numbers underwent little or no change. Population increase was prevented not by physiological control mechanisms of the kind found in many other mammals but only by behavior ones, taking the form of traditional customs and taboos. All the stone age tribes that survived into modern times diminished their effective birth rate by at least one of three ritual practices—infanticide, abortion, and abstention from intercourse. In a few cases, fertility was apparently impaired by surgery during the initiation ceremonies. In many cases, marriage was long deferred. Mortality of those of more advanced age was often raised through cannibalism, tribal fighting, and human sacrifice.

Gradually, with the spread of the agricultural revolution, which tended to concentrate the population at high densities on fertile soils and led by degrees to the rise of the town, the craftsman, and the merchant, the old customs and taboos must have been forsaken. The means of population control would have been inherited originally from man's subhuman ancestors, and among stone age peoples their real function was probably not even dimly discerned except perhaps by a few individuals of exceptional brilliance and insight. The continually expanding horizons and skills of modern man rendered intrinsic limitaton of numbers unnecessary, and for 5,000 or 10,000 years the advanced peoples of the Western world and Asia have increased without appearing to harm the world about them or endanger its productivity. But the underlying principles are the same as they have always been. It becomes obvious at last that we are getting very near the global carrying capacity of our habitat, and that we ought swiftly to impose some new, effective, homeostatic regime before we overwhelm it, and the ax of group selection falls.

28. Problems and Potentials of World Fisheries

Francis T. Christy, Jr. and Anthony Scott

As was suggested earlier, sea animals constitute a natural resource of increasing significance to a hungry world. Much has been made of "harvesting the sea" as a means of increasing substantially the world food supply. In this study, not merely is the potential of the sea assessed, but the serious problems associated with such a harvest are examined in considerable detail.

More than 70 per cent of the earth's surface is covered by ocean. Light and temperature conditions over most of this vast area are favorable to plant and animal growth. Yet though fishing is an ancient calling, the sea produces only a small fraction of the world's food supply. With increasing problems in protein malnutrition in certain areas of the world and the prospect of large increases in world population, it is not surprising that many people should think of the oceans as a major source of tomorrow's food.

In fact, some nations are already making sizable investments in fisheries. Since the Second World War, the total world catch of fish has been increasing at about 6 per cent per year, which means that it doubles about every twelve years. The rate of increase has not been uniform among all fishing nations. The growth in Peruvian output has been by far the most spectacular. In the fifteen years from 1947 to 1962, Peru's catch increased from about 31,000 metric tons live weight to over 6.8 million, a total second only to Japan's. Almost all of this catch is one species—a member of the herring family—caught in Peruvian coastal waters, processed, and shipped abroad as feed for livestock. Both Japan and Russia have also been increasing their catch rapidly and vessels from both nations are now found in almost all of the world's seas. On the other hand, the output of North America and Europe was not much greater in 1962 than it was fifteen years before.

Can the recent rate of increase in world output be sustained in the future or, if need be, stepped up? Although it seems clear that the oceans can yield far larger annual harvests than they now do, the long-range answers are by no means clear. Some of the reasons lie in nature, others in the economics of fisheries. The data now available suggest

SOURCE: *Resources for the Future Annual Report, 1964,* (Washington, D. C.: Resources for the Future, Inc., 1964), pp. 33–41. The authors are engaged in research for Resources for the Future, Inc., Washington, D.C.

that the sea is a large but not limitless source. Also, people have not as yet found uses for many kinds of fish, and the sought-after species are not uniformly distributed throughout the waters of the oceans but are, in fact restricted to relatively small areas. Competition tends to become focused on these areas of high natural fertility. The growth in total catch and the marked shifts in patterns of output create problems that stand in the way of rational and equitable development of marine fisheries. The difficulties are further compounded by the fact that the seas and their resources are the common property of the world community and that no single fisherman or nation has a right to exclude others from the waters beyond the territorial seas. Where the fishery resources are fully utilized the competition tends to become wasteful, leading to a greater amount of effort than is required or is economically justifiable.

Almost every broad discussion of commercial fisheries leads back to the mass of living matter (plants and animals) within the oceans. The characteristics of this biomass depend upon interrelationships between mineral nutrients, sunlight, photosynthesizing organisms, temperature, and other basic factors. Differences in the availability of these essentials lead to differences in fertility and to the concentration of plants and animals in some areas and diffusion in others. Because plants drift and fish swim, the areas of concentration are not rigidly fixed, but are subject to significant displacement, both between seasons and between years. And finally, it is not only the quantity of the living matter that is significant but also the quality in terms of species that are of economic importance to man.

The phytoplankton (microscopic, free-floating plants) are the basic pasture material of the seas, transforming chemical nutrients and light energy into organic matter that is consumed by the marine animals. Such plants can grow anywhere on the oceans, not only on the surface but also down as far as sunlight can penetrate effectively for photosynthesis to take place. This depth depends upon the latitude and the transparency of the water: about 45 feet in high latitudes and as much as 600 feet in the tropics. These favorable areas make up a vast euphotic zone, within which plant production can take place, given the necessary nutrients.

The natural fertilization of floating marine plants, however, is subject to different forces than is natural fertilization of plants on land. Organic matter which decays on the land remains at a level where plant production takes place. In sea water, the remnants of plants and animals sink towards the bottom, thus draining the necessary organic compounds to regions below the euphotic zone. The ultimate release of mineral substances, through decomposition, therefore occurs mostly in depths of the ocean below the zone where photosynthesis can take place. Under these conditions the upper layers of the ocean would become sterile if it were not for the possibility of turnover and upwelling. Plant production could take place only where nutrient salts are washed from the land.

In fact, however, plant production is not restricted to estuaries and shallow coastal waters. The relatively rich deep layers of nutrients are subjected to scouring forces that lead to the replenishment of the euphotic zones and to concentrations of plant life in various regions of the seas. Wind, winter cooling, and turbulence at the interface of different currents serve to "plow" the lower level of nutrients and raise them to the surface.

One major source of upwellings is the transport of surface waters away from coastal areas by winds and the effect of the earth's rotation. Where such transport occurs, the deep bottom waters, rich in settled nutrients, rise to replace the surface waters. Areas where fertile upwellings of this kind take place are found along the coasts of California and Peru, and also along the west coast of South Africa.

Winter cooling also leads to upwellings. Particularly in the North Atlantic, the falling air temperatures of the winter make the surface waters denser and heavier than the deep waters, so that there is an overturn, reaching in some areas down as far as ten or twelve thousand feet. The sinking surface waters are replaced by the nutrient-rich waters of the bottom. The overturn in the North Atlantic also has an important effect on the fertility of Antarctic waters several thousand miles away in the Southern Hemisphere. Within the Atlantic Ocean, the action of the prevailing winds and the character of the coastlines induce a flow of surface waters northward across the equator in amounts that are estimated at about 6 million cubic meters per second or 45,000 cubic miles a year. As these great quantities of surface water flow to the north, they are replaced in the Antarctic regions by the waters from a massive submarine current that originates partly with the sinking waters of the North Atlantic and partly with a deep flow from the bottom of the Straits of Gibraltar. While the deep water flow far south, they pick up additional nitrates, phosphates, and other matter that have settled from the surface, thus enriching the masses of water that upwell around the Antarctic continent.

Another kind of upwelling is caused by the turbulence that occurs where major ocean currents meets.The warm, northerly Kuro-Shio current meets the cold southerly Oya-Shio current off the northern islands of Japan and creates a rich and productive surface water. The high fertility of the Grand Banks is the result of the same kind of action induced by the collision of the Gulf Stream and the Labrador Current.

Besides these areas of upwelling, there are extensive regions of high fertility along most of the world's coasts. In these littoral areas the mineral elements and organic materials that are washed off the land enter the euphotic zones of the continental shelves. The shelves decline gently to a depth of about 600 feet, and then drop off, usually precipitously, into the continental slopes. The plants and animals associated with the ocean bottom (the benthic organisms) thrive in the shallow waters of the continental shelves because the decaying organic matter and the nutrient salts that settle to the bottom are taken up and continuously recycled by the living organisms.

The continental shelves and the areas of upwelling have high natural fertility. The rest of the oceans, however, representing the major part, is quite low in the production of phytoplankton and, consequently, does not support a large animal population.

Within the fertile areas of the ocean there is a tremendous variety of animal life, ranging in size from the microscopic zooplankton to whales. Some of the animals spend their adult life fixed to the bottom of the seas, while others range over entire oceans. And each animal has its own particular requirements for temperature, salinity, and food. The interrelationships among these animals, and between them and their environment, are very complex and, as yet, little understood. The phytoplankton, dependent upon light energy and nutrient salts, is a source of food for the zooplankton. This then may be consumed by herring, which in turn may become a source of food for the larger predatory animals such as tuna. This process is commonly described as the "food chain," each successively upward link of which is made up of smaller numbers of animals of larger size. But the relationships are not really that neat and simple. Some of the largest animals of the sea, the blue whales, live on some of the smallest. Some fish, as young, consume larger animals than they do when fully grown. Some consume both small and large fish of a large number of species. And at different stages in their life cycles, they may be both prey and predator. The term "food web" is therefore more descriptive of the interrelationships in the marine ecosystem than "food chain."

It is generally true, however, that the total mass of the smaller plants and animals is greater than that of the larger animals. As Lionel Walford has pointed out, it takes at least ten pounds of plankton to make a pound of whale or of herring.

And it may take ten pounds of herring, more or less, to make a pound of tuna. This is because most of the food that is consumed is devoted to metabolic processes and only a little contributes to the net growth of the animal. The weight gained relative to the amount of food consumed varies widely among the animals of the sea and, even for specific animals, again may vary widely according to the nature of the food, the conditions of the environment, and the age of the animal.

Simply for the sake of illustration, let us assume that there is a "food chain" from phytoplankton to tuna as described above, and that the feed efficiencies at each link are 10 per cent. On these assumptions, one pound of tuna would require the consumption of ten pounds of herring, which would require consumption of a hundred pounds of zooplankton, which would require consumption of a thousand pounds of phytoplankton. Thus, there would be a ratio of a thousand to one from the base to the top of the "chain." However, only a portion of each link may be consumed by each higher link, the remainder dying of other causes. To quote Mr. Walford again, ". . . in the North Sea about 2 million tons (wet weight) of herring are based on from 50 to 60 million tons (wet weight) of zooplankton annually." This is a ratio of twenty-five or thirty to one between consecutive links, rather than the ten to one assumed above for feed efficiencies. Although there is certainly not enough information to derive such figures for most fishes, if any, at all periods of their life cycle and under all conditions, it is clear that the annual crop of the lower links must be considerable in order to support the higher links, or the predatory fishes.

Wide recognition of the abundance of the lower forms of life is probably one of the reasons for the popular belief in the vastness of the ocean's food resources. This faith, however, fails to take account of the fact that there is little or no demand for plankton itself. Further, it neglects the enormous costs of harvesting plankon in commercial quantities. Thus far, and probably for many decades to come, man finds it more attractive and economical to harvest the large species that, directly or indirectly, have already filtered out the basic organic materials of the ocean. Moreover, not all of the larger species are utilized by man, and not all of the areas of high fertility lead to the kinds of fish that are in demand. Many varieties labeled as "trash" fish, particularly by the Western nations, are avoided by the fishermen or returned to the sea when caught. In short, the oceans are not a limitless storehouse of food materials. There is a wide range in natural fertility, with many areas little more than deserts in terms of animal life. And even where animal life is abundant, the portion of it that is economically useful to man is very small.

Just how small, or large, is a difficult question to answer. Present output is about 45 million metric tons, live weight. Estimates of potential output range from about 60 million tons to twice, or four or more times the present level. The lower figure has been derived by assuming that most of the catch will come from the continental shelves at an average yield of 20 pounds of fish per acre. This average, based upon records from the major fisheries of the North Atlantic, was made prior to the unprecedented development of the Peruvian industry, where output is estimated to be on the order of 300 to 350 pounds per acre.

The wide variations in estimates are due to differences in assumptions about the kinds of species that will be demanded and also to different, but unexpressed, anticipations of the costs of supply. The lower estimates refer to the current patterns of demand and they implicitly assume current techniques and cost structures. The figure of 60 to 70 million metric tons is thus an estimate of supply. The higher figures to a greater or lesser extent ignore the effects of demand and costs and refer primarily to potential physical output. While we cannot come up with a definitive picture of the future situation, we can, at least, draw two conclusions that are of significance for the future.

First, while the oceans may contain a vast and relatively untapped amount of organic life, the resources at present in demand are definitely limited both as to their total availability and as to their distribution throughout the oceans. This suggests that world competition for the resources will become more severe and will tend to be concentrated in certain areas.

Second, the most pressing problems of supply concern not the total availability of all fish that someone, somewhere, may want, but the specific availability of certain kinds of fish. For example, a high demand for salmon has led to strong pressures on that fishery resource. The cost of catching salmon has risen, and so has the price; this, in turn, tends to reduce consumption and lead to the substitution of other species in the market, and perhaps even to the demand for previously unutilized species of fish. This is the natural course of events and provides a safety valve for the release of pressures on scarce resources. However, what is important is not the ability of the total resource base to adjust in this fashion, but the transitional problems that are created for the participants in the industry and also the international controversies that can be avoided only by foresight and by continual co-operation in facilitating the process of adjustment.

For particular species, not only salmon but several others (for example, blue whales, Pacific halibut, and fur seals), it is clear that the resource has been depleted. Whale and salmon stocks are very low at present, and the yields are much smaller than they used to be or than they could be again under management controls. The Pacific halibut and the fur seals were formerly severely depleted, but international agreements on management measures have permitted the stocks to recover and the annual yields to increase.

As demand for fish increases throughout the world and as fishing fleets extend and intensify their operations, the problems of depletion are becoming more severe and widespread. The usual economic restraints that impede depletion of renewable resources that are under single ownership do not apply to marine resources that are the common property of all fishermen. Because no one fisherman or nation can exclude other fishermen from the high seas fishery, there is no incentive to restrain one's effort. Where a fishery is depleted, it is necessary to cut back on present catch in order to improve future yields. But no individual fisherman will voluntarily and unilaterally take this step because any fish that he leaves today will be taken by others tomorrow;

nor will any group of fishermen from any single nation. Open and un-restrained competition on most of the major fishing grounds is therefore damaging to the resource.

In order to prevent this, management is required; and, where fisheries are in international waters, management requires international agree-ment and control. A number of such controls have been tried, and more often than not they have succeeded in improving the physical yields from the fishery. The record of international amity and co-opera-tion on marine fisheries is encouraging. However, there are serious ques-tions of whether the management goals selected have been in the long-range interest of the world community. In almost every case, the objec-tive has been to obtain the largest physical yield that can be sustained.

Sustainable yields vary, of course, with the amount of effort applied. At low levels of effort, yields are low and the fish population and addi-tions to it are both high. There is also a high natural mortality that keeps the population relatively level over time. At higher levels of ef-fort, there will be higher yields, and at some point there will be a maxi-mum yield that can be sustained over time. At levels of effort beyond that point, the population will be lower, additions will be low, and the catch that can be taken and sustained will also be reduced.

Where effort is applied beyond the point of largest sustainable catch, there is obvious waste, since a greater yield could be obtained with less effort. The maximum sustainable physical yield, though it has been the objective of most management treaties, is not an economic goal because it takes no account of the costs of the effort or the values of the yields. Only under the most peculiar conditions would the sole owner of a fishery find that his profit would be greatest at the point where the physical yield is highest. Economic efficiency will almost always be obtained at a point where less effort is applied.

This can be shown by examining the economic consequences of ex-ploiting a common property resource such as a fishery. The chief conse-quence is that there will tend to be an excessive application of capital and labor. The fishermen are operating as individuals, each seeking to achieve the greatest difference between his own revenues and costs. But with no restrictions on the number of fishermen that can enter the indus-try, any true profit will attract additional fishermen. This will mean that the total revenues will be shared by more and more producers until no true profit at all remains to be distributed. If fishing grounds were not open to all comers, fishermen might arrange to apply effort only to the point where maximum *net* economic revenue was obtained. Then the industry might utilize capital and labor efficiently and produce a profit. Economic efficiency, therefore, implies some restrictions on the number of producers.

That is the theory. In practice, large difficulties stand in the way of reaching a goal of maximum net economic revenue. If entry into an international fishery is to be restricted, who is to be permitted to participate and how much effort should be applied? Two countries contemplating the same fishery may rightly make different choices about the intensity and combination of fishing activities. Given the same knowledge of the oceans and their biology, one country may decide, for example, that to catch a large volume of small fish will maximize the net economic revenue of the region; another may favor a smaller volume of larger fish, perhaps of another species that might be ecologically competitive. Such a situation can arise whenever the two countries differ in the relative valuations they place on labor, capital, and each of the possible types of fish. In Japan, for example, the cost of labor relative to the cost of vessels and equipment is less than it is in North America. Again, the Japanese valuation of cod relative to that of halibut exceeds the North American. It is not surprising that Japanese ideas about the best use of the Bering Sea and the Gulf of Alaska are at odds with those of Canada and the United States.

These are real difficulties, but it does not necessarily follow that improvements in economic efficiency are beyond reach. It seems quite possible to find ways of distributing the profit to be gained by restricting effort among the participants that will leave each better off than he would be under the conditions of unrestrained competition. But this has not yet been clearly demonstrated. There is need for considerable economic research in this area, as well as on many other aspects of international fishery exploitation.

Such research must be undertaken soon, for the problems of congestion and the possibilities of open conflict are growing very rapidly. There are already serious controversies over the extent of territorial waters. Foreign vessels are being impounded by coastal states in many areas of the world. Congestion, which is a clear manifestation of economic inefficiency, is becoming severe on some of the major fishing grounds. And as demand rises and technological innovation takes place, there will be more significant and widespread depletion of fish stocks.

VIII. WATER RESOURCES

For better or worse, the distribution of fresh, potable, or otherwise usable water over the land surface of the earth is extremely uneven, and even in those areas most abundantly endowed, persistent problems of pollution and future shortages exist. Vast areas of the earth remain virtually unsettled and unproductive as a result of the lack of an available water supply. Egypt's survival as a nation and the present disproportionate distribution of its people are almost entirely direct consequences of the Nile and the arid land around it. The economy of other areas is endangered by man's use of surface or ground water more rapidly than it can be renewed by nature. Water is a renewable resource normally taken for granted, and its critical importance is realized only when it is not available.

Knowledge of the regional distribution of water on the earth and of the problems involved in man's use of water in various regions provides an important link in the understanding of our environment. In this section a variety of approaches to the problems of water is presented, indicating not only the great importance of water to man's whole development but also the serious problem of supplying sufficient water for our enormous and increasing urban populations and thirsty industries, and considering some ideas about future sources and consumer patterns of water.

29. The Story of Water as the Story of Man

Bernard Frank

Here is an epic view of the role of water in man's progress through the ages, with some provocative comment and questions about the future. This selection provides an overview of the importance of water similar to that of Zon in the selection "Forests and Human Progress" in the section on vegetation.

SOURCE: *Water, The Yearbook of Agriculture* (Washington, D.C.: U.S. Department of Agriculture, 1955). The author is assistant chief of the Division of Watershed Management Research of the U.S. Forest Service.

You could write the story of man's growth in terms of his epic concerns with water.

Through the ages people have elected or have been compelled to settle in regions where water was deficient in amount, inferior in quality, or erratic in behavior. Only when supplies failed or were made useless by unbearable silt or pollution or when floods swept everything before them were centers of habitation abandoned. But often the causes lay as much in the acts or failures of men themselves as in the caprices of Nature. So, too, man's endeavors to achieve a more desirable relationship with the waters of the earth have helped mold his character and his outlook toward the world around him.

People always have preferred to meet their water troubles head-on rather than quit their places of abode and industry. So people have applied their creative imagination, and utilized their skills, and released heroic energy. The ancient wells, aqueducts, and reservoirs of the Old World, some still serviceable after thousands of years, attest to the capacity for constructive thinking and cooperative ventures which had a part in human advancement.

Fifty centuries ago the Mohan-Jo-Daro civilization of the Indus Valley in India enjoyed the benefits of well-designed water supply and drainage systems and even public swimming pools and baths. Excavated ruins of that period have revealed a surprising variety of waterworks, including tanks and irrigation canals.

The people of Assyria, Babylonia, Egypt, Israel, Greece, Rome, and China built similar facilities long before the Christian era. Egypt has the world's oldest known dam, a rock-fill structure built 5,000 years ago to store drinking and irrigation water and perhaps also to hold back floodwaters. Its length was 355 feet, and its crest was 40 feet above the riverbed. Apparently it was poorly designed, for it failed soon after, and no other was erected for 3,000 years afterward. Jacob's well was excavated through rock to a depth of 105 feet. The well is reported to be still in use. About 950 B.C., Solomon directed the construction of sizable aqueducts to provide for the needs of man, beast, and field. Ancient Arabia's enterprising farmers utilized extinct volcanic craters to store surface flows for irrigation and drove deep wells to get drinking water. Babylonia's King Hammurabi supervised the digging of an extensive network of irrigation canals and promulgated laws for their repair.

Among the early Greeks, Hippocrates recognized the dangers to health of polluted drinking water and recommended that water be filtered and boiled. The Romans used their poorer waters for irrigation and fountains.

The Tukiangyien system, built in China some 2,200 years ago, is another tribute to the genius and toil of ancient peoples. This skillfully designed multi-purpose engineering project was intended to divert the flows of the Min River, a tumultuous stream that rises on the high plateau of Tibet. By building a series of dams and dikes on the main river where it first enters the broad plain from the mountain canyon, the farmers divided its flow into many parts so they could irrigate one-half million fertile acres. The structures—composed of bamboo frames weighted down by rocks—also reduced greatly the heavy toll of life and property from spring and summer floods.

The habits of men and the forms of their social organizations have been influenced more by their close association with water than with the land by which they earned their bread. This association is reflected in the Psalms of the Hebrew poets and in the laws, regulations, and beliefs among the civilizations of the Near East, the Far East, and South America.

Read, in the Old Testament: ". . . A good land, a land of brooks of water, of fountains and depths that spring out of valleys and hills . . ." (Deuteronomy 8: 7). "I did know thee in the wilderness, in the land of great drought" (Hosea 13:5). "Drought and heat consume the snow waters . . ." (Job 24: 19). "He sendeth the springs into the valleys, which run among the hills. They give drink to every beast of the field: the wild asses quench their thirst. By them shall the fowls of the heaven have their habitation, which sing among the branches. He watereth the hills from his chambers . . . He causeth the grass to grow for the cattle, and herb for the service of man . . ." (Psalm 104:10–14).

Property in water long antedated property in land in the arid lands of antiquity. Property rights were associated primarily with the uses of water—first for drinking, next for irrigation. Mohammed saw water as an object of religious charity. He declared that free access to water was the right of every Moslem community and that no Moslem should want for it. The precept of the Holy Koran, "No one can refuse surplus water without sinning against Allah and against Man," was the cornerstone of a whole body of social traditions and of regulations governing the ownership, use, and protection of water supplies.

All persons who shared rights to a watercourse were held responsible for its maintainance and cleaning. The whole community was responsible for the care of large watercourses. Cleaning was to start at the head of the stream or canal, descending in order to each waterside family. All users shared the cost in proportion to their irrigation rights.

Even marriage might be influenced by the difficulties of obtaining water. The inhabitants of one rural community in southeastern Asia must walk 9 miles to the nearest sources of drinking water—a group of wells. Local custom decrees that wives must fetch the water. One wife can make only one trip a day with her bucket—not enough for the family's needs—and so a man finds it desirable to have several wives.

All life depends on water. For us today water is as necessary for life and health as it was for our prehistoric ancestors. Like air, water is bound up with man's evolution—and doubtless his destiny—in countless ways. One of the basic conditions for life on earth is that water be available in liquid form.

The origin of all life on our planet is believed to be the sea, and today, after millions of years of evolution, modern man's tissues are still bathed in a saline solution closely akin to that of the sea when the earlier forms of life first left it to dwell on the land.

Every organic process can occur only in the watery medium. The embryo floats in a liquid from conception to birth. Breathing, digestion, glandular acivities, heat dissipation, and secretion can be performed only in the presence of watery solutions. Water acts as a lubricant, helps protect certain tissues from external injury, and gives flexibility to the muscles, tendons, cartilage, and bones.

The role of water in metabolism, in regulating body temperature, and in nourishing the tissues explains why we could not long survive without adequate amounts of water. Yet our direct bodily needs for water are relatively small in terms of our total body weight (itself more than 71 percent water) and infinitesimal in relation to the total demands upon water by human societies, even among primitive cultures.

The average person in the Temperate Zone can get along with about 5.5 pints of water a day if he is moderately active. Slightly more than 2 pints are taken in with a normal mixed diet or created in the body by the oxidation of food, especially sugars, starches, and fats. Another 3 pints are taken in as fluids. Altogether it takes 5 or 6 pints to replace the daily losses in perspiration, exhalation, and excretion.

The amount for a given individual varies with his weight, age, activity, health, and other factors, but basic needs must be satisfied if life is to go on. The consumption of lesser amounts than those needed to replace losses will lead to a diminished appetite and eventually to undernutrition. A man in good health might be able to survive without water for a few days in a desert if he is only slightly active. If he tried to be more active he might not last a single day, because the consequent losses of water—as much as 10 pints an hour—from the body would greatly exceed the losses incurred under slight activity. Unless water were promptly made available, the losses would cause dehydration, incapacity, and painful death. By contrast, in the parts of the Tropics where high temperature and high humidity prevail, high rates of activity cannot be maintained even if abundant water were available, since the body is unable to dissipate heat and rid itself of waste products fast enough to prevent a breakdown in body functions.

Water serves in many other ways to maintain life, health, vigor, and social stability. The nutritive value of food crops may be affected by the amount of moisture available to them when they are in active growth. Because the minerals in the soil can be taken up by plants only when they are in solution, the amounts thus made available are greatest when the soil is moist.

The oceans, lakes, and flowing waters and their shores furnish food and clothing. Men always have looked to such places for a goodly part of their diet of proteins and carbohydrates.

The gathering of fish, lobsters, crabs, and other crustacea, the waterfowl, fur bearers, and other wildlife that frequent riparian environments, and the stems, roots, bulbs, or fruits of bulrush, watercress, marshmarigold, water chinquapin, wildrice, and other water-loving vegetation have furnished sustenance to people the world over.

The occurrence of water in a locality confers advantages on the people who own or use the lands. The lakes, beaver ponds, the waterfalls, cascades, bogs, swamps, springs, or snowfields that feature wilderness, park, and the other recreational places and the colorful plants and wildlife that thrive there provide an appeal that attracts many people to the outdoors.

Natural waterways—oceans, lakes, and rivers—have greatly facilitated the worldwide spread of population and of commerce. Most of the permanent setttlements in the arid regions—today as in antiquity—have concentrated along river valleys. Even along the seacoasts, habitation clustered around or near the convenient sources of fresh water.

The early Egyptians along the Nile and the Incas at Lake Titicaca in Peru employed rafts cleverly constructed of native plants. Solid logs filled with double outriggers and platforms made seaworthy craft in Africa and Polynesia; later craft were constructed from logs hollowed out by fire and crude tools.

Inland transportation since early times has been facilitated by canals, first for irrigation and later for transport, as among the early Assyrians, Egyptians, and Chinese. The Grand Canal, built in China in the 13th century, served irrigation needs and also provided an important artery of commerce for the products of its millions of people. European countries, notably Holland, France, and England, later developed extensive systems of canals between natural waterways. So, too, in the Andes region of South America, rivers are the arteries on which rubber, lumber and other products of the interior are carried to the coast.

Early settlement in the United States, at first restricted to the coastal strips, soon moved westward through the mountains by utilizing such streams as the Mohawk River in New York, the upper Potomac in Maryland and West Virginia, and the Ohio. By 1790, shortly after our country achieved independence, all but 5 percent of the 4 million inhabitants still lived along the Atlantic seaboard, but the way westward was rapidly being charted. River craft had navigated up the coastal rivers to the fall line. Canals to bypass the unnavigable parts of rivers were already built in Pennsylvania—connecting the town of Reading on the

Schuylkill River with Middletown on the Susquehanna—and around the rapids at Harpers Ferry, W. Va., on the Potomac. Following the successful tests of steam-propelled craft, large fleets began to haul wheat, coal, and iron on the Ohio River, the Great Lakes, and the Mississippi.

As the country expanded and prospered, eyes turned increasingly to the opportunities on the major rivers. Today, notwithstanding the intensive networks of railoads, highways, and airways, our improved navigation waterways—developed largely by the Corps of Engineers—total more than 25,000 miles and in 1953 carried a volume of raw and manufactured products amounting to nearly 225 million tons. It is possible to travel by boat from the Gulf of Mexico to Sioux City, Iowa, a distance of 2,030 miles.

Modern civilization imposes heavy demands on water. Merely to sustain life takes relatively little water. But even in pastoral or other simple societies, additional amounts are needed in preparing food and washing our bodies and clothes. The total daily requirement for all purposes, including drinking, in ancient villages may have average 3 to 5 gallons a person. Now a person uses 60 gallons or more each day for household and lawn-watering purposes in the average electrified farm or urban home in the United States! The figures are for homes with running water; the corresponding average for homes without that convenience is only 10 gallons a person a day.

At the minimum comfort level of 5 gallons a day—corresponding to the needs of primitive living conditions—our country's 165 million people would have few serious water difficulties. That daily total consumption of 825 millions of gallons would represent 0.07 percent of the Nation's average daily runoff of 1,160 billion gallons a day and 1.2 percent of the amount used up (not available for reuse) in the United States.

But our technological civilization could not have been attained at a level of water consumption geared to the requirements of primitive societies, even in our humid sections, where the need for irrigating crops is relatively slight. The steady rise in the consumption of water in industrially advanced countries explains why we now regard our water supplies with great concern.

The impact of new inventions and new developments and growth in population and industry has not commonly been given the attention it has merited.

Many critical local water shortages therefore have occurred that could have been forestalled. For example, rural electrification has brought about such heavy increases in the use of water for household and production purposes that the limited well-water supplies of many farms have been severely strained.

Similarly, factories have been built without prior studies to determine whether water would be available to operate the factories and to provide for the communities around them.

Towns, cities, industries, and farms have kept expanding beyond the safe limits of available water. Often makeshift efforts have been necessary to meet emergencies, especially in years of low rainfall. Such efforts have often hastened the depletion of the limited reserves in underground reservoirs, generated disputes with other cities or industries drawing on the same sources of water, introduced conflicts with the use of water for recreation, and threatened the permanent flooding of lands valuable for farming, forestry, wilderness, or wildlife.

To meet the difficulties, more thought is being given to the advance planning of storage reservoirs, aqueducts, canals, methods of recharging ground water, reclamation of waste waters, and other devices. Still the search for more and better water goes on. Use continues to rise; advancing standards of health and comfort, the application of more intensive farming practices, and the development of new products all impose additional demands. In fact, the proportion of our total economic and recreational activity—both in rural and urban areas—that depends on handy and abundant supplies of clean, safe water is greater than ever before in our history.

Our water needs are indeed great. Yet they do not begin to compare with the needs of the millions of people in Asia Minor, India, Africa, and South America who must still scoop up water from shallow pools or foul streams or haul it up by hand from wells. Travelers relate how in Madagascar the women carry water home in jars on their heads across miles of hot sands. In parts of the Egyptian Sudan, water is stored in the trunks of large, hollow trees. The openings are sealed with wet clay to keep it uncontaminated. Thousands of these small reservoirs —which hold 300 to 1,000 gallons each—appear along routes of travel. In one province all the trees are registered and the contents noted for information on the extent of the water resource.

Among the early pioneers, especially in the southern Appalachian Mountains, the ownership and control of a clean, abundantly flowing spring was considered an indispensable prerequisite to staking out a homestead. Once chosen, the spring was cherished. It meant cleanliness, health, and comfort. It was sheltered against contamination and protected against trespassers.

How far have most of us strayed from the old family spring! Generations of men and women have grown up without experiencing the joy of satisfying their thirst from cool, sparkling, spring water. Modern living standards have made it necessary to rely upon water supplies of far greater volumes than the one-family—or even the community—spring could furnish. Many of us have lost contact with the land and the pure waters that came from its depths. We must get water from distant rivers or reservoirs, and then only after it has been made safe by filtration and chemicals.

The task of finding, developing, and maintaining suitable water supplies has not been limited to modern times. It has had to be faced wherever large numbers of people have crowded together in small spaces.

Paul B. Sears, discussing climate and civilization (in the book *Climatic Change,* edited by Harlow Shapley), wrote that the highly developed civilization of Babylon finally disintegrated because "for centuries the operation of agriculture had been increasingly burdened by heavy loads of silt in the life-giving [irrigation] canals." He added: "So much labor was required for their annual cleaning that little leisure remained for anything else, and the long piles of silt . . . grew steadily in height and volume. Presumably this was due to increasing pressure, through cutting and grazing, upon the vegetation of the highlands whose runoff supplied the water. Under those conditions, the landscape became increasingly vulnerable to the effects of climate with its infrequent but violent rains and dryseason winds."

During the several centuries of stability under the Roman Empire, vast and intricate systems of waterworks had been constructed to provide the millions of people with safe supplies. Disposal of sewage was well developed for the times, and, in general, the value of clean household water and of sanitation was well understood. But when the empire disintegrated, chaos reigned, and the hard-won gains were rapidly dissipated. The constant warfare and political disturbances broke down the social concerns over water supplies, among other important public services. As ignorance and poverty increased, sanitary precautions came to mean less and less, and in time cleanliness was frowned upon as evidence of wicked thoughts and self-indulgence. Bathing, formerly widely practiced for its therapeutic values, was abandoned. The citizens no longer took pride in clean homes and streets, which became filthier and filthier. Worst of all, the water, obtained mostly from wells, eventually became so fouled as to be unfit for use.

Illness and death from waterborne diseases have plagued one country after another down to the present time. And not only were the poor people struck down. Records indicate that many famous characters of history also fell victim to waterborne diseases. Among them was King Louis VIII of France, Charles X of Sweden, Prince Albert of England, his son Edward VII, and his grandson George V. George Washington was known to have suffered from dysentery. And Abigail Adams, wife of the second President of the United States; Zachary Taylor; and—ironically enough—Louis Pasteur's two daughters are said to have died of typhoid fever.

Apparently the popular indifference toward safe, clean water prevailed well into the 19th century, even in England and the United States, where the dangers from the polluted supplies were generally known.

The effects of polluted waters now are considered to be the foremost obstacle to raising the living standards of underdeveloped countries.

Great strides have been made since 1900 toward meeting our needs for water—and we have been going farther and farther away to get it. Today, for example, Los Angeles obtains its water not only locally— from the Sierra Madre in southern California—but also from the Owens River on the east side of the Sierra Nevada, 240 miles away; Mono Lake, 350 miles away; and from the Colorado River, 450 miles away.

But the end is not yet. New sources of water are sought for the swelling population of southern California. Sewage, formerly discharged into the ocean, is reconditioned for irrigation and industrial use; eyes are turning to the better watered, less densely peopled northern part of the State; and the possibilities of converting sea water are being studied by scientists.

Each one of us is affected by the water problems now before us. L. K. Sillcox, a sanitary engineer, estimated that about one-quarter of our total population is up against actual water shortages or poor quality of water or both. Population has doubled since 1900, but the per capita use of water has quadrupled, mostly because of industrial and agricultural demands. The 17 Western States, with about 37 million people, use a daily average of 85 billion gallons (77 billion for irrigating arid farmlands alone) as against 80 billion gallons in the 31 Eastern States with their 128 million people. Industrial water in the East amounts to 65 billion gallons, as against 3 billion in the West. Farm irrigation in the East has taken only 3 billion gallons, but this use is growing so fast, and its impact on other uses has become so heavy, that many States—South Carolina, Georgia, Minnesota, and Wisconsin, for example —are closely reexamining their water policies with a view to developing new and more adequate legislation on this problem.

Mr. Sillcox estimated the Nation's annual water supply bill at 3 billion dollars, of which the urbanites' share is 500 million dollars. Farmers spend 200 million dollars (mostly for irrigation water). Investments in reservoirs, aqueducts, and other works to use or control water already total about 50 billion dollars—as against an outlay of 32 billion dollars to build our railways. (During the next 50 years we can expect to see further such investments by private, State, and Federal interests of 75 to 100 billion dollars.)

What to do about industrial wastes is another urgent and perplexing question. The Public Health Service estimates that it would take 9 billion to 12 billion dollars to rid our rivers of pollution and another 12 billion to 15 billion dollars to keep them unpolluted.

A special case of pollution as it relates to human health concerns the protection of the municipal and rural water supplies from radioactive wastes.

The coming years will bring an increase in the use of radioactive materials in manufacturing, for the production of electric power, and for experimentation in medicine, agriculture, and industry. The operation of nuclear power reactors alone will produce a manifold increase over the amount of radiation released to the air.

Radioactive materials released into the air are deposited sooner or later on the surface of the earth, including streams and lakes. Much of the radiation is noninjurious, and most of that which enters municipal reservoirs or other surface waters is rendered harmless by the application of modern detection and treatment methods. Not yet known, however, are the longtime, cumulative effects on human beings of the very small amounts of harmful radiation that still remain in the water we drink after it has been treated.

Studies indicate that the water that comes from underground sources, such as deep wells, is much less susceptible to contamination by airborne materials than are the surface waters. Other researchers indicate that the distillation methods of purifying water are effective in eliminating sources of harmful radiation, even in large amounts; perhaps the future may bring radically different ways of handling our water supplies. Perhaps the same watershed conditions that favor the slow movement of water through the soil into underground storage may prove to be highly desirable also in facilitating the natural purification of contaminated waters. If so, watershed management, especially in localities that represent sources of underground water recharge, will take on added significance by providing an important safeguard to the protection of human health.

A serious challenge to our ingenuity is how to convert to useful service the savage energies of runaway floodwaters. The rapid growth in population in new and settled localities, on the flood plains and hill lands, and the corresponding expansion in highways, airports, factories, and homes have aggravated the tendencies of rivers, streams, and brooks to break loose when rain comes or snow melts. Despite heavy expenditures for levees, dikes, reservoirs, and other devices for curbing overflows, the damages from floods average about 1.2 billion dollars a year, including the value of the soil lost from productive farms and the deposition of silt and debris in irrigation canals and reservoirs and on the farms and city streets.

We have to pool our efforts if we expect to apply appropriate and durable prescriptions for our water ills. Few activities have so clearly brought out the interdependence of all individuals, communities, States, regions, and nations as have our harried concerns with this product of the heavens. How it moves over the land and whether it aids or harms us depend on its behavior during its return to sea and atmosphere. The behavior of water directly reflects the conditions and uses of the lands from which it drains. Since drainage basins are composed of many kinds of land in many kinds of ownerships, our efforts to ameliorate those traits of water that we consider harmful bring into play the deep-seated, although often submerged, instincts of cooperation inherent in all forms of life. In that sense, water, perhaps to a greater extent than any other resource, takes on social significance.

Planning for the maximum development of our water resources for the longtime benefit of all of our people, when properly conceived, can bind together individual and community, farmer and urbanite, as few other conservation activities can do. Conservation has received perhaps its greatest impetus since our dealings with soil, forest, wildlife, recreation, community betterment, and industrial development have come to be viewed in terms of their interrelationships with water. More and more people have become informed and interested in all these fields because our water troubles and our attempts to resolve them on the watershed lands and in the river channels have had a direct impact upon their personal, economic, social, or recreational affairs. Thus, farmers on the Rifle River watershed in Michigan, who once seemed indifferent to rebuilding their eroding land, now enthusiastically participate in a watershed improvement program because they became convinced that fishing on their local streams would thereby be greatly improved.

Similarly, indifference toward stream channels, as exemplified by their use as dumps for garbage and trash, is changing with the development of individual and group awareness of what clean waters mean for their well-being. Men, women, and boys and girls in hundreds of communities are studying, thinking, planning, and carrying out programs to restore the attractiveness and utility of their local watercourses. In so doing they are developing a positive appreciation of the meaning of harmonious living with their fellowmen and their natural environment. As these wholesome cooperative endeavors spread through the land, we Americans cannot help but become richer in mutual understanding, more secure in spirit, more united in purpose.

30. Will There Be Enough Water?
John C. Maxwell

At present, every projection of future water needs indicates some concern for the future, and most answers to the above question are a categorical no. Yet faced with such prospects,

*it appears that solutions to these shortages are available, or
will be in the near future; but at the same time, little is
being done to use and conserve presently available supplies
and to reduce if not avoid pollution. By putting waters now
available on a quality/cost ratio basis, the nature and scope
of future problems of water supply are clarified. Maxwell
also indicates several problems involved with some of the
proposed solutions to water shortages.*

For centuries we in the well-watered East have taken for granted that
clean water in almost any desired quantity will flow from the tap whenever we require it. Now, quite suddenly, we are deluged with newspaper and magazine articles suggesting an imminent and general water
crisis throughout the country. Why all the fuss? Without trying to give
the definitive answer, I would like to share a few concepts with you,
and perhaps raise some points not generally considered in discussions
of our national water situation.

For our purposes, "water" will mean water of a quality usable for
domestic, industrial or agricultural purposes. Immediately, the concept
of *quality* becomes important. Let us arbitrarily set up the following
categories:

1. Low cost water (a few cents per thousand gallons).
   (*a*) High quality water, usable without treatment. (Many wells and
   springs and a few lakes and streams.)
   (*b*) Medium quality water requiring treatment (usually filtering
   and/or chlorination.) Most urban water supplies are included here.
2. High cost water (several tens of cents per thousand gallons).
   (*a*) Brackish water.
   (*b*) Sea water, etc.

These latter require large expenditures of energy to separate the
water and dissolved salts. At present only low cost water, category (1),
is considered in the annual water budget, although the distinction between fresh and brackish water varies somewhat with the usage to
which the water is put.

A map of the average annual rainfall in the United States tells us
immediately a great deal about water problems and water potential.
Approximately half of the country is semiarid or desert, whereas only
the extreme northwest and southeast are abundantly watered. The map
does not tell us the whole story, because a large proportion of annual
rainfall, approximately 70%, is subsequently lost to the atmosphere by
evaporation and transpiration. The remaining, or "run-off," water is
available for development. The total average annual rainfall is approxi-

Source: *American Scientist*, LIII, 1, (1965), 97–103. The author is chairman of the
Department of Geological Engineering, Princeton University.

mately thirty inches per year, five billion acre feet on two billion acres of land surface, or approximately 4300 billion gallons per day. About 3000 billion gallons per day are lost to the atmosphere. The run-off is then approximately 1300 billion gallons per day. This is the water available for man to use as he sees fit.

Now we plunge into the numbers game of water budgets, where it seems to be possible to prove almost any point and with well-founded calculations! The confusion arises partly from absence of data, but largely from the extreme complexity of the subject itself and from the difficulty of defining terms precisely.

Semantically it seems simple enough. The *water budget* is usually expressed thus: *total precipitation* minus *evaporation and transpiration* equals *available water* (run-off to streams plus ground water recharge). As mentioned above, the run-off, or available water is about 1300 billion gallons per day.

Some 240 billion gallons per day of metered water are sold in the United States. Much of this metered water is reused, that is, water that has been sold one or more times previously. Farms, cities, industries and septic tanks discharge both treated and untreated waste water and aqueous sewage into streams or into the ground water supply. The next water user down gradient then reuses a part of this water, and so on, to the sea. In computing the water budget then, it may be asserted that only water actually lost to the atmosphere is no longer available for use. Various experts estimate that only about one quarter of our available 1300 billion gallons per day is actually consumed. It should, therefore, be relatively easy and painless to enlarge our population and/or standard of living to about four times its present size. But wait.

Let us take a quick look at the life process as related to water. The lowly colonial coral is an instructive example. This primitive animal consists of individual polyps, each occupying its own "house," each ingesting food and water and ejecting watery waste within the boundaries of its own domain. Quite obviously, the coral recycles some of its own body wastes. A continuing movement of the surrounding water brings the coral clean water and food, and also removes the waste which otherwise would quickly smother it. Each coral colony grows to an equilibrium size and shape controlled by rate of food supply and waste removal.

Let us now modify the scale, to duplicate any one of thousands of suburban developments which depend on individual wells and cesspools. It is immediately obvious that here also a balance between waste removal (dilution) and water supply will develop, depending on rainfall and geological conditions, and that below some critical lot size (it usually works out to be between three quarters of an acre and two acres here in the Northeast) the poor suburbanite will slowly smother in his own waste. The suburbanite also has the added blessing of detergents to give him a head of foam on his water supply, a benefit unknown to the coral.

In the national water supply picture the coral-suburbia comparison can be scaled up through villages and towns to great cities and gigantic irrigation water districts, but the same principle holds. The *supply* of *usable water* is *always* a *function* of *total pure water versus waste*. It becomes obvious, therefore, that we cannot begin to use *all* of the remaining three quarters of our available water to expand our economy. Many of our streams are already so laden with waste that a much increased concentration would be intolerable.

For the moment however, let us assume that three quarters of our run-off water is indeed available for expansion (some 800 million gallons per day). We find that this water is available only in certain parts of the country, especially the southeastern states and the Pacific northwest. Already the water supplies of the western interior half of the country are largely pre-empted. Indeed, in parts of this area, water is being mined from underground storage at an alarming rate. This will not surprise you. You may, however, not be aware of the fact that the eastern Great Lakes–St. Lawrence area, the Delaware-Hudson drainage, and the Ohio River drainage have only limited reserves to meet pressures upon them. In our own state of New Jersey, the entire northwestern half is close to its maximum safe sustained yield of surface and ground water. Only in the coastal plains of southeastern New Jersey are large fresh water reserves still available.

The foregoing summary, not particularly optimistic, is nevertheless probably much *too* optimistic. A more realistic and penetrating analysis has been suggested by Professor Charles Bradley of Montana State College in a recent article in *Science*, subtitled, incidentally, "A permanent water shortage affecting our standard of living will occur before the year 2000." Professor Bradley points out that the 70% of water lost by evaporation and transpiration, and therefore disregarded in most water budget studies, is actually that part of the total water budget which is most important to man, for it is this part which sustains plant and animal life. Assuming that man *can* live by bread alone, and that his daily ration is two and one-half pounds, then some 300 gallons of water are transpired by the wheat which produces the grain for this much bread. About 300 gallons per day per person is therefore the minimum to sustain human life. For the meat diet so dear to our hearts, the water consumption is much higher. Alfalfa has a transpiration ratio of 800 to one; that is, 800 pounds of water are consumed in producing one pound of dry alfalfa. A steer drinks about twelve gallons of water a day, but consumes some thirty pounds of alfalfa which, in turn, consumed 24,000 pounds of water. Assuming 700 pounds of meat per two-year old steer, *one pound of meat per day* represents a *consumption of 2900 gallons of water per person per day*. Something between 300 and 3000 gallons per day would appear to be the bare subsistence water cost for one human being, and I do mean *bare:* cotton consumes 800,000 gallons of water per acre, and wool an even larger amount.

Approximately three quarters of the nation's average daily rainfall of 4300 billion gallons falls on one half of the nation's area, and it is this three quarters that does the job of raising crops for America. Perhaps a tenth of the rain falls on unproductive areas. Hence about 3000 billion gallons per day are productive of crops or surplus water.

For our 1960 population of 180 million people, about 13,800 gallons per day per person were consumed and some 240 billion gallons of metered water sold. The per capita daily use in the U.S. is therefore in excess of 15,000 gallons per day per person, 95% of which is consumed, that is, lost to the atmosphere. For 180 million people and a daily average rainfall of 4300 billion gallons, each person theoretically has 24,000 gallons per day for his own use; also, theoretically, the population could nearly double without appreciably lowering the standard of living. A moment's reflection will show this is not possible, because all surface water would be consumed and none would be left to generate power, float ships, and carry away the national sewage and waste. Bradley suggests that something of the order of one third of our remaining river waters, or 400 billion gallons per day, *might* be available for future consumptive use, plus water that now falls on unproductive areas which could be utilized. We then have available some 750 billion gallons per day. At 15,000 gallons per day per person, we might accommodate fifty million more, or a population of 230 million, without much of a change in our way of life. Presumably, this population figure will be reached during the 1980's or 1990's.

This type of analysis is particularly compelling because it shows that the major part of our water budget is already working hard for us, feeding us, clothing us, providing us with cheap power and cheap manufactured goods of all types, and diluting and carrying away to the sea the resulting wastes. If we plan for future population growth, we must provide not only the relatively modest amounts of water needed for domestic and industrial use, but the vastly larger quantities required by the animal and vegetable crops upon which life depends. Where can we find large quantities of water?

Man looks longingly at the sea as an inexhaustible source of water; and so it is, but at a high cost. Large quantities of energy are required to reduce the salt content to tolerable levels. Many methods have been tried, and work satisfactorily, but cost hovers at a level about ten times that of present water systems. Considerable publicity has been given recently to a report of a Task Committee headed by Dr. Roger Revelle for the Office of Science and Technology. This report proposed the development of nuclear-fired plants to produce large volumes of water by distillation of sea water, plus vast quantities of by-product electric power. The proposed reactors and distilling units are larger than existing facilities by a factor of several hundred. Allowing for necessary research, scaling up of plants in several steps, and financing, the estimated water and power costs for one of the largest facilities contemplated (an 8300 thermal megawatt nuclear plant capable of producing 620 million gallons per day of water and 1460 megawatts of electric energy) is something of the order of twenty-five cents per thousand gallons, depending on the price paid for the electric power generated. Delivery costs are not included.

One nasty and expensive problem was not discussed in the Task Committee report. A reactor of the size contemplated would produce as by-products immense quantities of heat, hundreds of millions of gallons of concentrated brine and quantities of radioactive isotopes. The brine and heat must be dissipated in some way in the surrounding sea. Unless carefully engineered, resulting heating of the water and enrichment in salts would drastically alter the ecologic balance. One can imagine a thick algal soup lapping the golden beaches of California. Far more serious is the problem of disposing of some tons of highly lethal radioactive by-products each year. At first glance this doesn't seem to be much of a problem, until we realize that the waste will remain deadly for periods approximating 1000 years. The search for ways of permanently containing such waste, in a manner to be absolutely certain that it will not enter the biosphere, is one of the urgent problems facing scientists today. The present solution, recognized as temporary, is to hold the "hot" waste in tanks. Other more desirable disposal methods are being investigated. Let us fervently hope that the building of giant reactors will be delayed until the problems of waste disposal are solved.

Accepting the cost estimates of the Task Committee as realistic, what is the competitive position of water from a large nuclear-fired plant? The householder may pay thirty-five to forty cents per thousand gallons for water delivered to his home. Except for high value crops, the agricultural user apparently can not afford to pay more than about five cents per thousand gallons. Nuclear plants may therefore be acceptable in some areas for household and industrial water, but not for the much larger quantities required by agriculture.

Experiments with the application of atomic energy and of other types of energy to desalination will be, and certainly should be, continued. Some islands and desert areas simply have little hope of developing other supplies. However, we should not ignore potential sources of natural water which may still be developed for most areas by diligent pollution control and by imaginative engineering. For example, the north and northwestern half of this continent is blessed with mighty river systems of unpolluted water in an environment where food-raising potential is small. The Ralph M. Parsons Comapny, a Los Angeles engineering firm, has computed costs of diverting part of this supply to the western half of the United States. They estimate that a $100 billion project, to be completed in thirty years, could supply the following each year: 147 million acre feet irrigation water at $3 per acre foot (a little less than one cent per thousand gallons); 37 million acre feet of industrial water at $10 per acre foot (about three cents per thousand gallons); plus 100 million kilowatts generating capacity at $32 per kilowatt year. It is estimated that this project would yield an income of over $4 billion per year.

A less ambitious though equally imaginative plan has recently been proposed by a Canadian engineering firm (T. W. Kierans of Sudbury, Ontario) to stabilize water levels in the Great Lakes–St. Lawrence system. The vast quantities of fresh water now lost to James Bay will be intercepted and returned southward across the divide to the Ottawa River and thence to the Great Lakes. Through this water-way, designated the "Grand Canal," 100,000 cfs or more of new water may eventually be obtained, equal to about half the present flow of the Niagara River. A pump-power system is envisaged along the "Grand Canal" to supply peak load electric power, and the new water in the Niagara River would also allow greatly increased power output as well as other nonconsumptive and consumptive uses. Again it is estimated that revenues will balance costs.

Even allowing for optimism on the part of the engineers making these analyses, here is a way of getting vast amounts of water for a small fraction of the indicated unit cost of water produced by desalination plants. Equally importantly, this water may be obtained without further polluting our environment with undesirable wastes.

In the first century A.D., the city of Rome was supplied with some 300 million gallons of water daily by fourteen aqueducts totaling 1300 miles in length. Certainly our engineers are quite able to meet a similar challenge today. Let us hope the Congress will be as enterprising as the Senate of ancient Rome in meeting the water needs of an expanding population.

31. The Nodal Water Region of North America

Allen K. Philbrick

Desalination of sea water may well hold the key to solving water problems of the future. Philbrick raises substantive questions about what the pattern of future water use in

*North America may be and suggests an approach to the
problem. In this analysis he uses the approach of cultural
geographers as well as a fundamental unit of area and areal
interaction—the nodal region. This concept of an area as a
region, and consideration of the connections between areas,
is basic to the whole study of regions and regional
delimitation. It is one of the serious concerns of geographers,
a problem that is considered at length elsewhere in this
series (Volume III). It should be noted that Philbrick does
not consider the serious problems for the nodal region raised
by Maxwell in an earlier selection on water: dissipation of
the heat, brine, and radioactive materials attendant on the
use of nuclear power for desalinization of sea water.*

By way of introduction this is a paper in applied cultural geography
emphasizing the importance of innovative perception. Human culture
is a complex cyclical phenomenon operating at three distinct levels
simultaneously. These are the levels of human values or tradition, ways
of doing things, and works expressed in patterns of the human organization of area, like a palimpsest in successive stages upon the face of the
earth.

The cyclical nature of the culture process may be formalized by
writing the three words, *values, ways, works* under one another in a list
with directional arrows pointing downward on the right and upward
on the left.

$$\uparrow \quad \begin{matrix} \text{VALUES} \\ \text{WAYS} \\ \text{WORKS} \end{matrix} \quad \downarrow$$

The downward arrow on the right signifies that already-formulated,
widely held cultural values are implemented by established routines of
conduct which produce familiar and dependably predictable results.
The upward arrow on the left signifies that innovative perception in the
fulfillment of felt need requires new procedures which continuously
pose increments of change in the creating of new human values.

Old traditions are well established and conservative. They are difficult
to change or dislodge because they have the strength of long-established
commitment. Fragments of emergent tradition are weak and may easily
be pushed aside because they normally have few adherents.

Where water is concerned there are two very strong traditional views
First, all water that is to be of any use to satisfy the needs of land animals and vegetation must be derived either directly or indirectly from
precipitation through the hydrologic cycle. Secondly, because the hold
which living matter has over its water content is purely temporary

SOURCE: *Canadian Geographer*, VIII, 4 (1964), 182–87. The author is a membe
of the Department of Geography, University of Western Ontario.

practically no water is ever withdrawn permanently from the cycle; so there cannot be said to be any real shortage of water, only problems of distribution and of human stupidity in water use, which proper attention to correct conservation practices can set right.

But these traditional views are not necessarily the last word on the subject. In innumerable situations over the face of the earth, practical problems of a pressing nature over a long period of time have led men to yearn for other ways of doing something about a water supply than to accept complete dependence upon the natural hydrologic cycle.

Let us suppose, for the sake of the record, that the American Atomic Energy Commission is correct in reporting on its experimental *work* (the final word of the three describing the culture cycle) and that fresh water may, in the future, be produced by desalinization of sea water for eight cents per thousand gallons in a plant delivering a billion gallons per day using breeder reactors, and for possibly as low as five cents per thousand gallons with electricity for one-half cent per kilowatt hour into the bargain. Ask yourself, what is the impact of such conjecture upon the possible *ways* (the second of the three words in the cultural cycle) of supplying water at the right time in the right places to accommodate human need? And ask yourself, also, what is the impact of such implications with respect to ways of getting fresh water upon our *traditional ideas* concerning water supply (the first concept of the culture cycle)?

Is there a difference in the kinds of policy and programme appropriate for developing run-off water of the natural hydrologic cycle from those appropriate in quest of fresh water from the sea? The answer is so emphatically yes that we should re-examine how we really do expect to obtain the fresh water for our ever increasing multi-purpose uses.

In the case of capture, storage, and use of controlled run-offs from precipitation in the natural hydrologic cycle, *river basins* are inherently logical planning units. In projecting use of desalinized sea water, on the other hand, an entirely different kind of functional and planning unit becomes necessary. We are no longer required to think only in terms of given natural drainage units. What I shall call the *nodal water region* now becomes an effective operational unit. A nodal water region is one of human organization, unifying water resources of any type in some optimum way for the delivery of maximum amounts of water of the most appropriate quality to the greatest number of users with maximum effectiveness at minimum cost.

When one considers the possible location of sea-water desalinization plants in terms of resource versus market orientations, one is struck by the apparent but deceptive simplicity of the problem. There are, after all, so many millions of square miles of ocean and so very many tens of thousands of linear miles of sea coast, to say nothing of the numerous large underground sources of saline waters from which to choose! When we imagine desalinization plants all along our coats to supply water deficit areas, then we begin to ask where are we going to store water processed in this manner? How are we going to deliver it to users? How are we going to minimize costs of production by concentrating a relatively few large producers for maximum efficiency in the most wisely selected places? In response to such thoughts we begin to feel the need for coordinated nodal systems of strategically located desalinization and pumping plants. We begin to cast our eyes about the world for the most suitably distributed circumstances for natural storage and delivery which are also adjacent to large populations in need of additional supplies of water.

If past experience is any criterion, we shall both scatter and concentrate desalinization projects, just as we have experienced similar results in the controversy between advocates of the big dams on the major rivers and the advocates of far upstream control. Man-made hydrologic cycles serving large locally market-oriented needs may, indeed, justify localized individual desalinization works; yet, it remains true that the public interest will be best served generally by the policy of the broadest possible effort to secure optimum co-ordination among diverse water resource and market-oriented interests within the context of a new water resource tradition—the nodal water region based upon development of a man-made hydrologic cycle.

Such a policy statement is background for discussion of the specific illustration of a nodal water region which is the geographical focus of this paper—a co-ordinated international programme of engineering facilities and political statesmanship which will assure the status of the Great Lakes of North America is perpetuity as the mid-continent fresh water reservoir for both Canada and the United States. Indeed, there are four separate statements of policy needed to complete that background, including the above.

(1) *The nodal water region rather than the river basin* is the most appropriate unit for planning and operation under co-ordinated policy and engineering developments.

(2) From prior tradition, *let there be continued and ever strengthened conservation, purification, and multiple re-use of existing water supplies.* Such measures can delay and reduce the need for supplemental man-made hydrologic cycles, extend the time period over which development of desalinization works can take place, and thus facilitate their construction by allowing them to be in response to a more gradually increasing need than otherwise would be the case.

(3) *Water used in excess of annual precipitation will be replaced* within a reasonable time. Surface and ground water are to be regarded as a "water bank" against which our people have been borrowing since the beginning of European settlement. Prospects of man-made hydrologic cycles at strategic locations raise possibilities for the de

liberate reinvestment in this water bank through recharging of aquifers.

(4) *Users must pay* for water so that the capital as well as current operating costs may be met. Such policy will encourage thrift. Private works for purification and re-use of water taken into closed systems from public sources will be cheaper over the long range for many to construct and maintain than the continuing purchase of large amount of new water.

Research and development on an international scale can implement such policies. Plans and programmes must take into account continuing advances in engineering technology which can reduce costs of desalinization and power production, the selection of optimum locations for facilities and distribution channels, and the direct as well as indirect effects of such policies and developments upon local, regional, and national economies in the equitable distribution of benefits among the political entities involved.

The Great Lakes Nodal Water Region of North America will be used to illustrate these ideas. The states of the United States bordering the Great Lakes and the province of Ontario, Canada, combined, withdraw from ground and surface sources approximately 80 billion gallons per day (66 billion English gallons, 303 million kiloliters)—one fourth of the total water withdrawn by the two countries. It is estimated that at any given time no more than one fourth of this amount is unavailable for re-use and that existing quantities of water are withdrawn for use and re-use at least four times. Given adequate control, we could thus double the available water supply by desalinization and introduction into the Great Lakes of 20 billion U.S. gallons (16.5 billion English gallons, 75 million kiloliters) of fresh water per day processed from the world ocean. On an annual basis this is 7,300 billion U.S. gallons.

In round numbers there are 20,000 billion U.S. gallons in the top one foot of the Great Lakes' surface water (91 billion kiloliters). One year's additional supply of water for the Great Lakes region could therefore be stored in less than five inches (12.7 cm.) of rise in the level of lakes. This vast 95,200-square-mile (246,558-square-kilometer) alignment of the Great Lakes, shown in Figure 1, containing 9,511 cubic miles of fresh water (39,641 cu. km.), already in unregulated use, is not only the world's largest fresh water supply, but it is also the world's largest natural storage reservoir, available free for use without the building of a single dam, large or small.

The responsibility for the quality control and re-supply of these waters so that they may be used in excess of their natural supply is a grave trust. The long-range prosperity of North America is at stake in the wise development and multiple-purpose use of these waters.

Diversion of rivers draining into Hudson Bay is one source for additional water for the lakes. Precedent for use of this source already exists in diversion of water from the Albany River. The amount of water

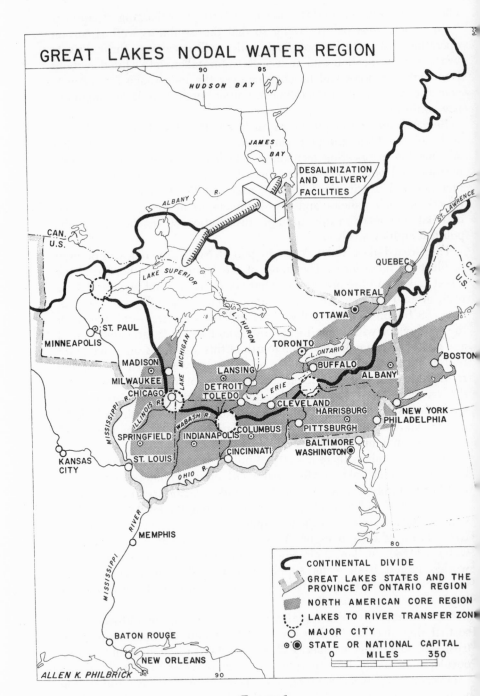

GREAT LAKES NODAL WATER REGION

DESALINIZATION
AND DELIVERY
FACILITIES

HUDSON BAY

JAMES BAY

ALBANY R.

ST. LAWRENCE

CAN.
U.S.

LAKE SUPERIOR

QUEBEC

MONTREAL

OTTAWA

ST. PAUL

MINNEAPOLIS

L. HURON

TORONTO

CA.
U.S.

LAKE MICHIGAN

L. ONTARIO

BOSTON

MADISON

LANSING

BUFFALO

ALBANY

MILWAUKEE

DETROIT

MISSISSIPPI R.

CHICAGO

TOLEDO

L. ERIE

CLEVELAND

NEW YORK

ILLINOIS R.

WABASH R.

HARRISBURG

PHILADELPHIA

SPRINGFIELD

INDIANAPOLIS

COLUMBUS

PITTSBURGH

KANSAS
CITY

ST. LOUIS

CINCINNATI

BALTIMORE

WASHINGTON

OHIO R.

RIVER

MEMPHIS

80

MISSISSIPPI

BATON ROUGE

NEW ORLEANS

ALLEN K. PHILBRICK

CONTINENTAL DIVIDE

GREAT LAKES STATES AND THE
PROVINCE OF ONTARIO REGION

NORTH AMERICAN CORE REGION

LAKES TO RIVER TRANSFER ZONE

MAJOR CITY

STATE OR NATIONAL CAPITAL

0   MILES   350

Figure 1.

which can be diverted, however, is less than the potential requirement; and there are limits beyond which supply from this source will adversely affect the ecological balance of the region. In principle it is a poor policy, which requires us perpetually to rob Peter to pay Paul.

An unlimited supply of sea water for desalinization is accessible from Hudson Bay, 350 miles (563 km.) northeast of the highest of the Great Lakes, Lake Superior, 602 feet (183.5 m.) above mean sea level. When engineering pilot plants now in operation and others being developed demonstrate that desalinization, power, and pumping phases for a coordinated continental desalinization and water delivery system are economically competitive, a programme for such a large-scale man-operated hydrologic cycle should be ready for construction and operation.

The choice of James Bay and Lake Superior as the salt water source and reservoir of initial storage, respectively, for such a system is geographically logical from many viewpoints. Each point in the following summary should be considered in relation to the man in Figure 1; and it should be understood that their combined significance is multiple rather than additive.

(1) *Storage.* From Lake Superior water can flow eastward by gravity, throughout the system.

(2) *Salt.* Salt from demineralized seawater may be returned to the sea, stored as sludge for final evaporation in the processing of by-product minerals and chemicals, or used as a basis for storing fissionable wastes.

(3) *Access.* Including the St. Lawrence River to the Lambert Locks at Montreal, water users have access to supply from 10,000 miles (16,093 km.) of fresh water coast, divided approximately evenly between the United States and Canada. The region thus served is the industrial heart and the greatest nodal regional market for water on the continent.

(4) *Access.* Because of the circumstances of glacial origins in the formation of the Great Lakes–St. Lawrence drainage system, there are many widely distributed points of near contact between the lakes and the outstretched headwaters of the Mississippi's dendritic drainage pattern. By short siphon-pumping transfers at many points, fresh water could be made available to downstream communities in controlled amounts all along the major Mississippi tributaries.

(5) *Power.* Power derived from the head of water stored at various points down-river could, within a co-ordinated international system, at least reduce costs of original pumping of desalinized water into Lake Superior.

(6) *Evaporation control.* Winter storage of desalinized water produced during late summer and fall would minimize evaporation loss because much of the lake area is roofed by ice during the winter.

(7) *Seasonality*. Conversely, heavy withdrawal during early spring would correspond with the season of greatest natural re-supply from run-off. Varying degrees of seasonal and regional co-ordination of production, delivery, storage, and consumption are possible within an international nodal system serving half a continent.

(8) *Silting*. Silting, which plagues builders of reservoirs within river basis because of upstream erosion, would not represent a major inherent difficulty in using the Great Lakes as a continental reservoir supplied in this manner. The savings through avoidance of eventual reconstruction costs would be very large.

(9) *Balance*. Uncontrolled use of surface and ground waters under present and probable future demands promises increasingly to upset the balance of nature. Implementation of a more positive policy of water production by man-made and operated hydrologic cycles will create the opportunities for people to restore and to stabilize such balance as investment in the natural "water bank" for any dry day in the future.

(10) *Cost*. A policy of scarcity ensures disagreement over rights and privileges of water use. Controlled-production water policy provides the basis for enlightened international agreement and a wise division of responsibility within a co-ordinated system. Under such a system the only limitation on water withdrawal would be the willingness to pay a reasonable cost of guaranteed water replacement. As already indicated, responsible estimates of future costs of as little as five cents per thousand gallons and cheap electricity into the bargain have been made by the Atomic Energy Commission. Even if one doubles this figure to ten cents and redoubles it to pay power and financing costs of mass water production, it is reasonable to predict on a long-range pay-as-you-go basis the doubling of the region's annual water supply for twenty cents per thousand gallons.

To treat water as a mineral to be mined, beneficiated, and delivered through use of existing lakes and rivers, by the construction of a minimum of concentrated engineering facilities, to provide and absolute increase in fresh water available for industrial, agricultural, domestic, municipal, and all other purposes *is* a revolutionary idea. Its full impact can be appreciated only when the manner in which its multiple advantages reinforce one another is understood. This can best be appreciated by viewing the spatial association of the variables as outlined above in this article in applied cultural geography, emphasizing the role of innovative perception.

From the sea around us water seems as universal as the world ocean But the mathematics of optimum location and the significance of geographical position of supply and demand gives to *human perception* the opportunity to plan and execute a programme of water development which will give an entirely new and more positive direction to future water policy in North America and the world.

32. The Geography of New York City's Water Supply: A Study of Interactions

Anastasia Van Burkalow

Because Los Angeles tends to get wider publicity for what are undoubtedly more spectacular "water works," one may forget that the New York area, although in the humid northeast, has the greatest water supply problem in the United States, and considering the "plumbing orientation" of the affluent American society, quite possibly in the world. In recent years, serious shortages have developed, and some rationing has been necessary to make sure of adequate supplies for the needs of more than ten million people in one of the largest industrial complexes anywhere. Van Burkelow examines all aspects of the New York problem and relates these to the larger problem of future demands and developments.

A city must often look outside its own boundaries for its water. Smaller communities can usually obtain an adequate water supply from local ground or surface waters, and even a large city can meet its water needs from local sources if it is near a large river (London, Philadelphia, Washington, Pittsburgh, and St. Louis) or lake (Chicago and Buffalo). New York City, however, has no nearby lake and no usable river; for the Hudson River, being an estuary, is brackish.[1] And early in the nineteenth century the city began to outgrow its local ground and surface water supplies. It has therefore had to go gradually farther and farther

[1] Farther up the Hudson a layer of fresh water, brought in by tributary streams, floats on top of the brackish water, and from that fresh surface layer some Hudson Valley communities (Poughkeepsie, Rensselaer, and Waterford, for example) take their public water supplies. Treatment is necessary, of course, to counteract the fairly heavy pollution. In the early 1950's, when the most recent expansion of New York City's water supply was being planned, some citizens' groups favored a Hudson source instead of the Cannonsville Reservoir. However, the nearest the city has come to using Hudson River water was to build a temporary pumping plant near Chelsea, 10 miles south of Poughkeepsie. This plant, capable of pumping 100 million gallons per day (mgd) of river water into the city system, was authorized by the state Water Power and Control Commission for emergency use only, in case of shortage before completion of the first two stages of the Delaware system, and was not to be used after 1957. It was never needed and has now been demolished.

SOURCE: *Geographical Review*, XLIX, 3 (1959), 369–86. The author is a member of the Department of Geology and Geography, Hunter College, New York City.

afield, eventually as much as 125 miles, to tap the surface waters of other watersheds.

New York first did this as early as 1842, when the Croton water system went into operation. This ended the use of local wells and ponds for public supply in Manhattan (New York City did not then include the other boroughs), though some Manhattan industries still use water from their own private wells. Other parts of the present city continued to depend on local sources for a longer time: the Bronx until it was annexed to the city in 1874 (west Bronx) and 1895 (east Bronx); Richmond until it received Catskill water in 1917; parts of Brooklyn until 1947, when pumping for public supply was stopped because of depletion of the ground water; and parts of Queens even today.[2] However, the inadequacy of the local sources was felt in Brooklyn and Queens as early as the 1890's, and it is said that need for additional sources of water helped influence Brooklyn, at least, to become part of Greater New York in 1898. One of the first concerns of the Greater City was to add to its water supply, which by then consisted of an enlarged Croton system and the Bronx-Byram watershed.[3] Construction of the Catskill system, authorized in 1905, was begun in 1907, and in late 1915 Catskill water first reached the city. By the time this system was completed in 1927, plans were already being discussed for the Delaware system. Construction was finally begun in 1937 (court action and the depression had delayed it) but was interrupted by World War II. Finally, in 1951, the Rondout Reservoir was completed. It was followed by the Neversink in 1952 and the Pepacton (East Delaware watershed) in 1955. The final stage, the Cannonsville Reservoir (West Delaware watershed), now under construction, is slated for completion in 1962.

[2] Wells of the Jamaica Water Supply Company and the New York Water Service Corporation provide the public supply for parts of Queens, furnishing an average of nearly 50 mgd in recent years, which is about 3½ per cent of the average daily consumption of the entire city. Little additional ground water is now used in the city for public supply. City-owned wells in Brooklyn have long been out of use, and those in Queens and Nassau Counties, with a dependable yield of 70 mgd, and in Richmond County, with a dependable yield of 5 mgd, have been kept as stand-bys in recent years. They were used extensively only in the dry period of 1949–1950 and in 1957–1958 while the Delaware Aqueduct was closed for cleaning. Now that Delaware water is available, the Long Island well water is not considered necessary, and the city plans to sell its Long Island wells.

[3] This consisted of the Bronx River watershed above Kensico Dam, from which water still enters the city's water-supply system, and the adjacent Byram River watershed. From its Byram Lake and Wampus Pond a dependable yield of 5 mgd could be led into the Bronx River by a tunnel and open channel. However, since April 12, 1955, none of this water has been allowed to enter the New York City system. In 1958, Byram Lake was bought by a resident of Mt. Kisco and presented to that village, which had for many years met about half its public water-supply needs by buying that very water from New York City.

The Bronx-Byram watershed, too small to be shown clearly on Figure 1, lies close to the southeastern edge of the Croton watershed, near the New York-Connecticut boundary.

Thus New York City now depends on seven distant watersheds—Croton, Bronx River, Esopus, Schoharie, Rondout, Neversink, and East Delaware—and is developing an eighth, the West Delaware. Their dependable yields are given in Table I, and their locations are shown on the map, Figure 1. Within their combined area of 1969 square miles, half again as large as Rhode Island, water is taken from more than a thousand streams, big and little. It is stored in 27 reservoirs and controlled natural lakes and is brought to the city through more than 350 miles of aqueducts and tunnels (Fig. 1).

Several aspects of the physical and cultural geography of the source areas have affected the amount and quality of the water available to

TABLE I. New York City's Watersheds

Watershed	Area (sq. mi.)	Dependable Yield (mill. gal. daily)	Watershed	Area (sq. mi.)	Dependable Yield (mill. gal. daily)
Croton	375	325	Neversink	93	115[b]
Bronx River	13	5	East Delaware	372	375[b]
Esopus	257	345	West Delaware[a]	450	310[b]
Schoharie	314	220			
Rondout	95	120[b]	TOTAL	1,969	1,815[c]

[a] Under construction.
[b] Additional water must be held to replenish the stream in dry weather (see text, pp. 322–23).
[c] To this must be added the 5 mgd dependable yield that can be drawn from wells in the Borough of Richmond if necessary, which will make a total dependable yield of 1820 mgd available in 1962.
SOURCE: "Brief Descriptive Outline of New York City's Water Supply Works" (Board of Water Supply, City of New York, June, 1958).

TABLE II. Watershed Precipitation *(in inches)*

Watershed	Average	Minimum	Year	Maximum	Year
Long Island	43.22[a]	29.90	1931	56.50	1889
Croton	47.68[b]	32.29	1935	63.76	1901
Esopus	49.32[c]	33.70	1957	73.08	1928
Schoharie	42.68[d]	30.68	1911	60.35	1928
Rondout	49.03[c]	33.65	1941	73.54	1928
Neversink	51.55[e]	37.36	1941	71.24	1938
East Delaware	43.79[e]	33.38	1957	54.43	1938
West Delaware	41.74[e]	33.22	1957	51.53	1938

Averages are for (a) 78 years; (b) 89 years; (c) 51 years; (d) 50 years; (e) 20 years. All periods end with 1957.
SOURCES: *52nd Ann. Rept. New York City Board of Water Supply, 1957; Ann. Rept. New York City Dept. of Water Supply, Gas and Electricity, 1951* (for Croton's maximum and minimum).

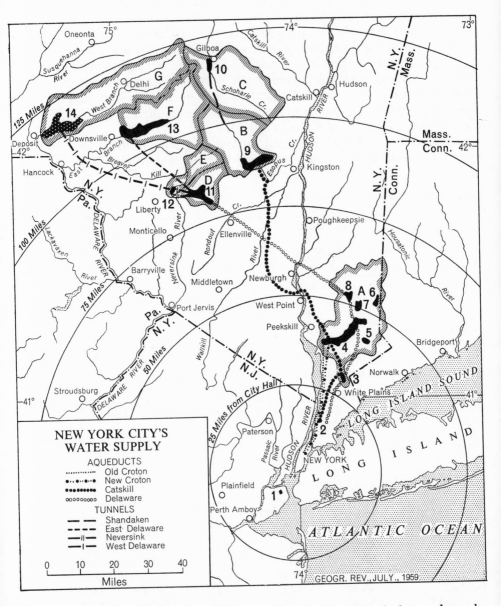

FIGURE 1: The sources of New York City's water supply. Watersheds are shown by heavy boundary; key: A, Croton; B, Esopus; C, Schoharie; D, Rondout; E, Neversink; F, East Delaware; G, West Delaware. Reservoirs are shown in black; key: 1, Silver lake; 2, Hill View; 3, Kensico; 4, Croton; 5, Cross River; 6, East Branch; 7, Middle Branch; 8, West Branch; 9, Ashokan; 10, Schoharie; 11, Rondout; 12, Neversink; 13, Pepacton; 14, Cannonsville (under construction). Adapted from map in "The Water Supply of the City of New York," pp. 40-41.

New York City and the construction problems encountered in building the dams and aqueducts. And the development of this extensive water-supply system has left its imprint on the physical and cultural geography of the source areas and also of still more distant areas in the lower Delaware Valley. It is with these interrelationships that the present paper is concerned.

How the Geography of the Watershed Areas Affects The City's Water Supply

Factors That Influence the Amount of Water Available

PRECIPITATION / In the watersheds the average precipitation is well over 40 inches a year, but the amount received in individual years may vary a good deal from the average (Table II).

It is the amount of water available in the driest year on record that is the dependable yield of a watershed, the minimum with which a city might have to get along and below which consumption should be kept. Unfortunately, in many cities of the United States consumption equals or exceeds dependable yield, and no reserve is left for emergencies or for future growth of the city. As a result there are water shortages from time to time, when the use of water must be curtailed. This is what happened in New York in 1949. Consumption was about 25 per cent greater than dependable yield of the then existing facilities, and a severe drought in the summer and fall caused a serious water shortage. Disaster was prevented only by an intensive water-saving campaign, which in about three months reduced the consumption by nearly 25 per cent. Completion of the Rondout, Neversink, and Pepacton Reservoirs has increased the dependable yield (now 1510 million gallons per day, counting ground-water resources on Staten Island but not on Long Island) comfortably beyond current consumption (1153 mgd in 1958), and completion of the Cannonsville Reservoir will give a total dependable yield of 1820 mgd, which it is thought will be adequate until about the end of the century.

In the rainiest periods the reservoirs cannot hold all the available water, and large amounts spill over the dams and are lost. Carrying capacity of the aqueducts also limits the amount of water that can reach the city. Thus nature determines the minimum amount of water available to the city, but man has determined the maximum, because the reservoirs and aqueducts he has built will not accommodate nature's maximum.

INTERSTATE CHARACTER OF THE DELAWARE RIVER DRAINAGE BASIN / In the Delaware system man has placed still another limit on the maximum supply available to the city, this time by court decree. The Delaware

River serves as boundary first between Pennsylvania and New York and then, for many miles, between Pennsylvania and New Jersey, and its broad estuary lies between Delaware and New Jersey. Its headwaters, however, from which New York City takes water, are in New York State, and when the Delaware plan was first announced in 1928, the approval of the Water Power and Control Commission of New York State was granted. Residents of New Jersey, Pennsylvania, and Delaware were at once concerned lest they be deprived of water for their needs. Accordingly, in 1929 New Jersey went to the United States Supreme Court to enjoin New York City from taking any water from the Delaware River or its tributaries. Pennsylvania acted as intervener. The Court decision in May, 1931, permitted the city to take 440 mgd, enough only for the first two stages of the Delaware plan (Neversink and Pepacton Reservoirs), instead of the 600 mgd originally proposed. Efforts were made to provide for the third stage, the Cannonsville Reservoir, as part of an interstate development of the river, proposed by the Interstate Commission on the Delaware River Basin (Incodel) for power development and control of floods and pollution as well as for water supply. New York, New Jersey, and Delaware accepted the plan, but in 1952 Pennsylvania rejected it. Thereupon New York City reopened the original case before the Supreme Court and asked for an additional 50 mgd from the Neversink and Pepacton Reservoirs and 310 mgd from the proposed Cannonsville Reservoir. This request was granted by a decision in 1954. In both Court decisions the city was directed to release water from its reservoirs in dry periods, to maintain a certain minimum flow in the main valley.

Factors That Influence the Quality of the Water

GEOLOGY / In the Westchester watersheds there are long, narrow outcrops of metamorphosed limestone, a soluble rock, but most of the area is underlaid by relatively insoluble schist and gneiss. In the Catskill and Delaware watersheds most of the rocks are dark sandstones and shales, also insoluble. As a result the water is soft, with only 17 parts per million of dissolved matter in the Catskill and Delaware water and 40–50 ppm in the Croton water. Both home and industrial users are thus relieved of the expense and difficulties caused by hard water.

Because of the composition of the rocks in the watersheds, New York City's water contains little or no dissolved fluorides. It has been widely recognized by dental and medical authorities that about 1 ppm of fluorides in drinking water makes teeth more resistant to decay (but only if such water is drunk in early childhood while the permanent teeth are forming.) Lack of natural fluorides can easily be offset by addition of the desired amount, as has been done in many community water supplies. Whether or not New York City's water will be so treated has yet to be decided. Some groups strongly oppose this so-called "mass medication."

In the Catskill and Delaware watersheds especially, the banks of the streams and reservoirs consist in some places of easily eroded glacial clays. During heavy rains these are washed into the water and temporarily increase its turbidity.

VEGETATION / In the Catskill and Delaware watersheds large areas have been set aside as state parks and forest preserves, within which most of the surface is covered with trees. Because the forests retard soil erosion, and therefore siltation in the reservoirs, the useful lifetime of the reservoirs is prolonged, and there is little need to treat the water for turbidity. In Westchester a smaller part of the watershed is forested, but here, as in the Catskills, the land close to the reservoirs has usually been planted with evergreens. These are used instead of deciduous trees because the thin, broad leaves of the latter would tend to blow into the water, where they would clog outlets, discolor the water as they decayed, and so on. For these tree belts a program of planting, pruning, thinning, and insect control is carried on by the Department of Water Supply, Gas and Electricity as part of the maintenance of the water-supply system.

POPULATION DENSITY / In 1950 the population densities per square mile in the various watersheds were as follows: Bronx-Byram, 184; Croton, 128; Esopus, 17; Schoharie, 26; Rondout, 17; Neversink, 19; East Delaware, 18; West Delaware, 30. Except in the Westchester area (Bronx-Byram and Croton) these densities are very low, and there is relatively little danger of pollution of the water. Where this danger exists, the city builds and operates sewage-disposal plants.

SIZE OF THE SYSTEM / The large size of New York City's reservoirs, due both to nature's potentialities and to man's decisions, makes it possible for water to remain in them for a long time—in the Catskill reservoirs for as much as six months, in Kensico (the Westchester storage reservoir for the Catskill and Delaware systems) for about three weeks. This permits natural purification of the water before it finally enters the aqueducts on its way to the consumers. In 1954, for example, it was found that the period of storage in Ashokan Reservoir reduced turbidity 62 per cent and bacterial count 71 per cent.

Factors That Influenced the Construction of the Dams and Aqueducts

GEOLOGY / The nature and general conditions of the surface materials and bedrock in which dams and aqueducts are to be built determine the kind of structure required and the cost. Geological information, gained by surface exploration and test drilling, is therefore necessary during both planning and construction. With foreknowledge of the difficulties that will be met it is often possible to plan the route of an aqueduct or the location of a dam so as to avoid some of them. Where they cannot be avoided, construction can be planned to deal with them.

Because geological advice proved helpful in the construction of the New Croton Dam, completed in 1905, the city has employed geologists on the Catskill and Delaware systems from the earliest planning stages. Their careful exploratory studies have discovered, for example, places where ground water, seeping into the tunnels in large amounts, would complicate construction; caverns in limestone that might weaken tunnel walls; masses of deeply weathered rock, along faults or in places that had been protected from glacial erosion, that would require extra strengthening of tunnels; resistant rock formations that a tunnel should avoid; thick covers of glacial moraine filling deep preglacial or glacially eroded valleys that would require tunnels to be unusually deep to pass beneath them.

ELEVATION OF THE WATERSHED AREAS / The Catskill water drops from 590 feet above sea level in the Ashokan Reservoir to 295 feet at the Hill View Reservoir (the distributing reservoir for both Catskill and Delaware water), 92 miles away, near the city line in Yonkers. Thus in the Catskill Aqueduct the water can move downhill under the influence of gravity. But since the drop is fairly slight, it was necessary to build about 80 per cent of the aqueduct with just enough slope to make the water flow. Where the surface is about at the level necessary for gravity flow, the aqueduct is a cut-and-cover structure—a channel cut into the surface and covered over with a mound of earth. In higher areas the gravity-flow level is maintained through tunnels. Where valleys cut below this level, the aqueduct goes under them in pressure tunnels.

Flow in the Delaware Aqueduct is by gravity also, and the drop from the outlet of the Roundout Reservoir, flow line 840 feet above sea level, to Hill View is even greater than that from Ashokan. However, this aqueduct is a deep pressure tunnel throughout its length, for reasons discussed below.

Incidentally, the elevation of the distributing reservoirs determines how and where the water will be delivered within the city. Catskill and Delaware water, distributed from the Hill View Reservoir, can flow by gravity to all parts of the city except the highest, where pumping is needed. In contrast, Croton water, distributed from the Jerome Park Reservoir, elevation about 133 feet, can reach by gravity flow only the parts of the city less than 40 feet in elevation. But since these consume only about one-third of the total Croton supply, the rest must be pumped to higher areas. Long Island well water must always be pumped, of course.

CULTURAL AND PHYSICAL GEOGRAPHY ALONG THE DELAWARE AQUEDUCT ROUTE / The Delaware Aqueduct could have been constructed like the Catskill—a combination of cut-and-cover sections and tunnels (gravity and pressure). However, because of various conditions along the route it was built as a deep pressure tunnel throughout. By the time it was built, in the late 1930's, villages, houses, roads, and other structures were much more numerous than they had been in the early years of the century, and property values had greatly increased. Building deep below the surface avoided conflict with these surface developments and eliminated the necessity of paying high taxes for surface rights of way. Only underground easements were needed. West of the Hudson the aqueduct crosses a number of deep valleys, under which pressure tunnels would have been required anyway, and a number of high ridges, under which deep tunnels were necessary (the deepest of these is 2500 feet below the ridge crest). A deep pressure tunnel for the entire length was therefore simpler to build, and it will have lower maintenance costs and greater safety from damage. Choice of the exact route was often guided by surface conditions. For building the access shafts (there are 31 of these) room was needed on the surface, and both for this reason and to keep down the cost of the sites the more heavily built-up areas were avoided whenever possible.

Effect of the City's Water-Supply System on The Source Areas

Changes in Physical Conditions

THE UPLAND WATERSHEDS / Most obvious among the physical changes in the upland watersheds are the reservoirs—twelve in the Croton watershed, two in the Catskill system, and four in the Delaware. These, with their borders of pine trees (another change introduced by the water system), add greatly to the scenic beauty of the areas and to their recreational facilities. By state law the city must allow boating, fishing, and ice cutting on the reservoirs, subject to reasonable regulations. Ice cutting is no longer carried on, of course. But permits for boating and for fishing, from shore or boat, are available free of charge from the Department of Water Supply, Gas and Electricity.

More localized is the change in Esopus Creek, which now carries, in addition to its own water, the water from the Schoharie Reservoir diverted southward under the mountain divide by means of the Shandaken Tunnel. Because of the resulting great increase in the volume and depth of Esopus Creek, some adjacent areas have been flooded.

In the spring and summer of 1950 New York City tried to change conditions in the Catskill and Croton watersheds in still another way–artificial rain making. As one of its efforts to ease the critical water shortage of 1949–1950 the city employed Dr. Wallace E. Howell, a meterorologist, to seed the clouds over the watersheds with silver iodide. In 31 weeks Dr. Howell carried out 36 seeding operations. During that period the rainfall in some months was greater than average, and in the watersheds it was 14 per cent greater than in surrounding areas that had not been seeded. Whether the increased rainfall was caused· by the seeding can never be proved, of course, since natural variations in rainfall from year to year are marked.

THE LONG ISLAND WATER TABLE / When ground water is withdrawn more rapidly than it accumulates, the water table is lowered. Many parts of the country have been damaged in this way, some of them seriously; a notable example is western Long Island. During the early decades of this century the water table here dropped rapidly because of the combined effects of (1) decreased replenishment as buildings and pavements covered more and more of the surface and (2) increased use. Water was withdrawn both for public use, from wells owned by the city and by several private water companies, and for industrial use from wells owned by the industries themselves. How great the over withdrawal was becoming was not realized until 1933, when a detailed survey of the island's ground-water resources revealed that the water table was below sea level, more than 15 feet below in some places, in an area of more than 40 square miles, including nearly all of Brooklyn and adjacent parts of Queens. Sea water was infiltrating into the wells and moving farther and farther inland each year.

It was because of this situation that in 1933 the New York State Legislature passed a law requiring that new Long Island wells yielding more than 100,000 gallons a day and not to be used for agriculture must be approved by the state Water Power and Control Commission. When such new wells are to supply water for industrial cooling and air conditioning, the water must be returned after use to the aquifer from which it was taken. This can be done by pumping the water back through a recharge well (the method commonly used in crowded Brooklyn and Queens because it requires little surface area) or by allowing it to accumulate in a recharge basin and soak back into the ground (the method often used in the more open areas of Nassau and Suffolk Counties). The returned water has been found to be 2°–20°F. warmer than when it was first pumped from the ground and is therefore less effective for subsequent cooling; however, only where there are numerous recharge wells close together is the effect marked. Nassau County has also provided eleven recharge basins for the accumulation and seepage of storm runoff discharged into the sewers.

In spite of these conservation measures, the water table continued to drop for several years and in the late 1930's reached levels as much as 35 feet below sea level. Recovery did not begin until about 1941 and was slow at first. An element of gradual change was the decrease in the number of plants manufacturing ice. As their business was curtailed by the increasing use of electric refrigerators in homes, their pumping of ground water decreased from 18 mgd in 1936 to 4 mgd in 1947. A more abrupt change came in 1947. In that year net withdrawal of ground water in Brooklyn was reduced by more than half because the city required the New York Water Service Corporation to stop pumping from its Flatbush wells, source of the infamous "Flatbush" water. Against this unsatisfactory public supply—brackish, corrosive, and hard—there had been public outcry for years, and the change in 1947 to Catskill water brought rejoicing. It also initiated a more rapid recovery of the water table, which by the early 1950's had been raised above sea level in the entire south half of Brooklyn. In the northwest, where there are large industrial wells that predate the conservation measures of 1933, heavy industrial use keeps the water table well below sea level. And in western Queens it stays slightly below sea level because of pumping for public supply by the Jamaica Water Supply Company and the New York Water Service Corporation.

Effects on People and Communities

DISPLACEMENT OF PEOPLE AND THEIR WORKS / To strangers driving past, the city's reservoirs may look like natural lakes. Old-timers, however, cannot forget that they are man's work, in a sense a new cultural landscape blotting out the old one they remember so well. Inundated under many feet of water are hundreds of farms, among them prosperous dairy farms in the valleys tributary to the Delaware; resort hotels and camps that drew numerous summer visitors to the mountain valleys of the Catskill and Delaware watersheds; more than 20 villages, with their homes, churches, schools, and businesses; and more than 60 cemeteries. From these last some 10,000 bodies were removed for burial elsewhere. And from the farms and villages some 6,000 permanent residents have been displaced.

By state law the city is allowed to acquire the property it needs through condemnation proceedings, but it is also required to pay generously. As a matter of course it must pay the value of the property, buildings, and equipment taken—and this requires a separate negotiation for each piece of property, 557 of them in the Pepacton Valley alone, for example. But in addition the city must pay claims for business losses, loss of wages, and so on, both to those whose property has been taken and to people in nearby areas. In the Pepacton Valley there were 475 such claims.

BENEFITS TO LOCAL COMMUNITIES / To residents in the watershed areas the city water system brings several benefits: an easily available water supply if they wish to tap it; a real-estate tax income that may be sizable; and in many localities sewage-disposal plants at no cost.

By state law the city must allow communities and water districts in Delaware, Greene, Orange, Putnam, Schoharie, Sullivan, Ulster, and Westchester Counties to take water from city acqueducts or reservoirs, subject to reasonable regulation. The users must pay a reasonable rate for the water and all costs of their connections with the city system. Use has been made of this privilege chiefly in Westchester, where 58 per cent of the water supplied by comunities in 1957 came from the city system. To these communities, and to a handful west of the Hudson, the city furnishes an average of nearly 50 mgd. for which it is paid more than $1.5 million yearly.

Land owned by the city for water-supply use totals 73,000 acres, with an assessed value of about $75 million. The 1957 state, county, town, village, and school-district taxes on this land amounted to about $5.5 million. In some localities the city's payments make up a large part of the total realestate tax income—90 per cent, for example, in the little village of Olive in Ulster County and 25 per cent even in the prosperous township of North Castle in Westchester County.

By state law New York City can, with the approval of the state Health Department, set up sanitary regulations in its watershed areas. This permits the city (at its own expense, of course) to improve sewage-disposal facilities on private property and, in villages with public water supplies, to build sewage-disposal plants, which it must maintain and operate forever. Such plants have been built in a number of places in all the city's watersheds, and one was built outside the watersheds at Port Jervis, N. Y., on the Delaware River as directed by the United States Supreme Court in its decree of 1931.

Effect of the City's Water-Supply System on More Distant Areas

Control of Volume in the Delaware and Its Tributaries

Water diverted from the Delaware headwaters for use in New York City is permanently removed from the Delaware drainage system. And yet because of the diversion the headwaters below the dams and the main valley downstream from them have more water available for use not less, as many residents of the valley feared would be the case. Without the dams the volume of these streams varied greatly, from flood stage, when there was more water than could be used, to a mere trickle in the dry summer months. The dams help to reduce the volume of floods, with their destruction and waste of water, as was demonstrated in 1955 when Hurricane Diane brought heavy rains to the region. And the dry-season volume is increased by releases of stored water from the reservoirs. For the main valley these were ordered by the United States Supreme Court in its decisions of 1931 and 1954, in amounts great enough to maintain a specified minimum flow (according to the 1954 decision, 1525 cubic feet per second at the United States Geological Survey gauging station at Montague, N.J.). This is chiefly to provide adequate water for community water supplies navigation, sewage disposal, and pollution control; however, camps and resorts in the upper valley and the shad-fishing industry downstream should also benefit. In the very dry summer of 1957 these releases made up about two thirds of the average flow of the river. Within New York State the minimum volume of the streams below the dams is controlled in the same way (Rondout Creek, a tributary of the Hudson, is included), in accordance with regulations of the Conservation Department of New York State and the state Water Power and Control Commission. These releases, made whether or not any are needed for the main valley, are solely for conservation of fish. As a result, the streams are kept full even in droughts. In the dry summer of 1957, for example, 1201 million gallons of water were released daily from the Pepacton Reservoir, and 345 million from the Neversink Reservoir, at a time when the natural flow in the streams would have been only 133 and 83 million gallons daily.

Control of Salinity in Delaware Bay

Salinity of the water in Delaware Bay, of great importance to the oyster industry, is affected by the volume of fresh water flowing in. The boundary line between fresh and brackish water surges upvalley at times of low stream flow and downvalley in floods. It is close to this boundary that the oysters flourish best; for there the salinity is too low for their chief enemies—oyster drills, starfish, and mussels. Some oystermen feared that New York City's withdrawal of Delaware River water would cause a permanent upvalley shift of the critical border zone, bringing saltier water to the oyster beds they were working. Instead, the decreased variation in stream volume will mean a decrease in the naturally great variation in salinity. This should benefit the oyster industry, which yields five million bushels a year here and is important to residents of both New Jersey and Delaware.

The story of New York City's water supply is thus one of interactions: between various elements of the earth environment within the watershed areas; between man and the earth environment both locally and in more distant areas; between the city and individuals in the watershed areas; between the city and other political units or agencies (the United States Supreme Court, New York State and adjoining states, state agencies and departments, counties, townships, villages, school districts);

and between man's resource needs and government regulations. On the one hand the amount and quality of the water available to the city have been affected by the physical and cultural geography of the watersheds and by the political organization of the main Delaware Valley. On the other hand the development of the city's water supply has affected the physical and cultural geography of the watersheds and of the Delaware Valley. In these more distant areas it has not influenced political organization, but the city's own political organization, resulting from the creation of the Greater City, may have been partly influenced by water needs and developments. And both locally (on Long Island) and in the Delaware Valley the utilization of water resources has resulted in government regulation, which in its turn has influenced the availability of water.

To understand the geography of New York City's water supply, we must know the locational facts of where the water comes from, where it is stored, and by what routes it reaches the city. And we must know descriptive facts about the source areas. But these facts, locational and descriptive, are only the raw materials of geography. From them must come an understanding of the interactions discussed above, a compound of physical, cultural, and political geography.

IX. MINERAL RESOURCES

It has been said that the consumption of mineral products during the twentieth century, including all the more important minerals and metals that provide the sinews of modern industry, far exceeds that for the whole preceeding period of man's existence. The present importance of minerals varies with the stages of industrial development of a nation or region. Other factors, such as accessibility and world market conditions, enter into the importance of any particular mineral deposit. The three key minerals of modern society are coal, iron, and petroleum. These minerals, of low value per unit weight, are used in huge quantities and usually cannot stand the cost of transportation as well as minerals less utilized and of higher value per unit weight. Large industrial areas are generally found near deposits of one or more of these key minerals, or they have easy access (by efficient transportation) to abundant supplies.

The uneven distribution of minerals is a geographic fact of great economic and political importance, and the world pattern of mineral production is irregular and unpredictable. No nation possesses all the minerals necessary to supply the needs of its industry. The number, abundance, and quality of minerals and the need for them varies from nation to nation.

Although the primary concern of this volume is with the physical earth—the occurrence and distribution of mineral resources—the importance of minerals as useable materials must not be overlooked. The actual or potenial use often distinguishes mineral ore from an almost valueless rock formation. The existence of exploitable minerals is closely related to the geologic structures of the earth; many minerals such as iron are extremely abundant in the earth's crust, but generally in such small amounts that they are not considered as commercial ore deposits. Concentration by nature or man must take place for the deposit to become profitable.

33. Geographical Factors in the Utilization of Mineral Deposits

Alan M. Bateman

Minerals are often exploited in many remote corners of the earth under exceedingly adverse geographical conditions; nitrates in the driest desert in existence (northern Chile), and gold in barren, cold, northern Siberia are only two examples. "If a mineral deposit is indicated to be valuable, adverse geographical factors are a hindrance, rather than a preventative, to utilization" according to Bateman, one of the leading economic geologists of the United States. Although man has the ingenuity and ability to overcome many of the handicaps of nature, various environmental factors play an important part in the successful exploitation of the world's mineral resources. Some of these factors are discussed in this selection.

This subject may perhaps best be approached by a brief glance at the mineral background. If we study the development of the industrial nations we will note that their rise coincided with their utilization of mineral resources, notably that of coal and iron. Coal supplied the energy that made the wheels go around, and the wheels were made of steel. We have come to realize that the energy of fuels and the solidity of metals spelled industrial growth and those countries abundantly endowed with both attained predominance over their competitors and became the great manufacturing and trading nations. It is no accident that great industrial cities sprang up in central England, in the Ruhr, in France, and around the Great Lakes regions of the United States; for there coal and iron met and the products of the junction spread to the far corners of the world. Those nations lacking these substances became agricultural or handicraft nations, and mineral resources came to be regarded as one of the chief goals of economic sufficiency.

The world realization that industrial development of modern life depended upon a liberal endowment of mineral resources, or access to them, created such an insatiable appetite, for minerals that within the period embracing the two world wars we have dug and consumed more minerals than in all previous history. This has made deep inroads into

SOURCE: *Proceedings of the United Nations Scientific Conference on the Conservation Utilization of Resources,* (New York: United Nations, Department of Economic Affairs, 1951), pp. 13–16. The author is Silliman Professor of Economic Geology, Yale University.

unreplaceable mineral resources. They do not grow again like a crop of corn. Former adequate supplies now look meagre, and sources of large supplies are becoming fewer and fewer. The more manufacturing proceeds, the greater the inroads upon the very basis of manufacturing, and the greater the depletion in mineral resources. It is fitting therefore that conservation and wise utilization of mineral resources should command the attention of this congress. It is further fitting that attention should be directed to all factors that bear upon the development of new resources to replace those that are undergoing such rapid depletion, and this includes geographical factors.

Background

Geographical factors in the development of the Western Hemisphere offer a clue to the part that such factors may play in the development and utilization of other mineral resources in the future.

The lure of a gold strike in California one hundred years ago initiated a gold rush that spread rapidly over California. Crude mining was initiated, followed almost immediately by farming to supply the miners with food, and small hand-craft industries to supply them with tools and equipment. Then, further farming and industries arose to supply those who were supplying the miners. A little known, sparsely settled region, was rapidly transformed by the initiation of development of mineral resources into a productive, flourishing, and wealthy state.

The gold rush of California in 1849 spread to the search for gold and silver in the unsettled states of Nevada, Arziona, New Mexico, Utah, and the Rocky Mountain states of Colorado, Montana, Idaho. Wild regions, roamed by bands of Indians and herds of buffalo became dotted by scattered mining centers. Local resources were tapped to supply these centres, transportation was initiated, supplies began to flow, and communities independent of mining came into being and existed for their own account and for export. The discovery of bulky non-ferrous metals created more lasting communities and demands for heavy transportation facilities. Likewise the gold rush to the forbidding Yukon and Alaska in 1898, midst hardship and tragedy was the forerunner of geographic changes that led to the development of this harsh country.

Today, in the unsettled wilderness of northeastern Quebec and Labrador, two new large mineral deposits, one of iron ore and the other of titanium ore, are undergoing development and exploitation. Geographic factors had to be carefully studied before decision was reached to go ahead with expenditures that would amount to scores of millions of dollars. The geographic factors chiefly involved are present lack of land transportation; availability of water transport at the rail terminal for ocean-going vessels, whereby transportation costs could be cut; bulk of product versus cost of transportation and market price of product; questions of freezing of ore in railroad cars, and consequent unloading difficulties, during the long sub-arctic winters; problems of mine operation during the many low temperature and high-snowfall months; problems of protecting water supplies during the winter months; availability of timber for mining operations; availability of fuel or water power in sub-arctic lands for mining and domestic purposes; effect of a bleak, lonely country, and harsh climate on retention of labour. These, and many other geographical factors, had to be carefully studied and balanced against cost of mining, processing, transportation, and the value of the product at the place of delivery. In these two cases the effect of geographical factors is largely that of determining feasibility, and of costs. If the deposits had been located in New Jersey for instance, practically all of the geographical factors mentioned above would not need to be considered and one could consider at once that, provided the quality of the ores was satisfactory, economic exploitation could be assured.

Similarly, geographical factors, although of different character, will have to be considered in the contemplated development of iron ore deposits in Venezuela, low-grade chrome deposits in Turkey, iron-ore deposits in Brazil, zinc deposits in Bolivia, manganese deposits in the hinterland of Brazil, and in many other cases.

The Geographical Factors

Geographical factors may determine whether a mineral deposit can be utilized, or whether it is economic to attempt to utilize it. In general, if a mineral deposit is indicated to be valuable, adverse geographical factors are a hindrance, rather than a preventative, to utilization. Mostly, they can be overcome provided scientific and engineering skills, ingenuity, and venture capital, are available. Geographical obstacles become then chiefly a matter of cost and economics. The intrepid British, American, Canadian, Australian, French, Dutch, and Belgian mineral pioneers, with their knowledge and skills, have not hesitated to initiate mining developments in far off remote parts of the United States, Canada, Alaska, Mexico, South America, Australia, Africa, Russia, and other parts of Asia. They are the ones who have developed most of the world's mineral resources.

The various geographical factors that bear on the utilization of mineral deposits may now each be considered separately, with some examples of deposits in which such factors have had to, or will have to be taken into consideration. Although each factor is dealt with separately, it should be realized that in actuality several geographical factors may enter into the problem of development and utilization of a single deposit.

Location

The geographical situation of a mineral deposit is perhaps the most important single item that determines whether it may be utilized. Location immediately raises a number of questions as to utilization that must be resolved before consideration of development can proceed. As an extreme case, the location of a non-ferrous mineral deposit on Northwest Greenland would entrain many geographical problems that would be absent with a similar type of deposit located alongside the Canadian Pacific railroad or on the banks of the River Plate. Location may involve not only transportation but elevation, climatic and health conditions, labour supply, availability of water, timber and fuels, accessibility to market and other conditions. Most obstacles of location, however, can be overcome provided the increased cost of doing so is not prohibitive or provided the material is desired regardless of cost.

Transportation

Transportation ranks first among geographical factors in the utilization of mineral resources. For the most part recent discoveries of minerals have taken place in sparsely settled regions where transportation is absent. Two questions immediately arise, namely the feasibility of establishing transportation and the transportation cost of shipping the product to market. These in turn depend upon the character of the mineral product to be utilized and whether water, rail, truck, or air transportation is utilized.

Low-value, bulk mineral products such as coal, iron ore, or phosphate rock must move in large volume at low transportation cost to compete in world markets and require therefore, water or rail transport. If such means of transport are not available, the mineral deposits must contain tonnages large enough to repay the capital expenditures of transportation installation. If the rail or water transport cannot be installed because of the physical geography, or because the tonnage would not justify the expenditure, the deposits are then uneconomic under present conditions. If the tonnage of the deposit does not justify the capital expenditures for transportation construction, other geographical factors may weigh in favour of construction, namely, the development of the products of forest or agriculture that may spread the cost of transport and lower it on the mineral products. Or transport construction may be politically advisable for the development of a frontier region.

In the case of ores amenable to beneficiation, concentration processes may be installed at the place of extraction and the volume of the shipping product may thereby be so greatly reduced that the cost of transportation becomes a minor part of the cost of the product. For example, a copper ore containing 2 per cent metal, may be concentrated so that the copper minerals in twenty tons of ore are reduced to one ton of concentrates, thereby reducing the cost of transportation to approximately one-twentieth of the cost on the original ore. If the concentrates can be smelted at the point of extraction, the volume is further reduced, with additional saving in transportation costs. Although rail or water transport is most desirable for the shipment of such non-ferrous metals, movement by trucks may be feasible if the terrain and accessibility to market permits.

High-value, low-volume products such as gold and silver may not even require the building of railroads or roads, but may be serviced by air. The output of a successful gold mine may be packed in hand-bags. Successful gold mines at Bululo, New Guinea, in British Guiana, in the Andes, and in Northern Canada, are serviced entirely by airplanes.

Topography

Topography generally determines the means of transportation to be used and the effect of cost of transportation on the utilization of mineral deposits. Flattish topography such as that of the African plateaus favours construction at low coast of railroads or highways and this feature alone may determine the utilization of a given mineral deposit. Rugged mountainous areas may defy the building of railroads or highways but oftentimes the inaccessible parts may be spanned by aerial tramways, or tunnels may be bored beneath them. Few valuable deposits, however, have been left undeveloped in rugged mountainous regions because of inability to bring them within reach of some kind of transportation.

Water Supply

The availability of fresh water supply may be a determining geographical factor in the utilization of mineral resources. This problem is, of course, particularly acute in arid or desert regions and may be the largest single cost in development, or even render a deposit uneconomic. Most mining operations are accompanied by ore beneficiation which requires huge quantities of water, and in Chile and Australia water supplies have to be brought scores of miles and involve large capital expenditures. In one large Chilean mine the quantity of water available determines the capacity of operations. Water scarcity is not restricted solely to arid regions; it is a problem of many flattish regions and of regions of perennial frost. Water purification commonly has to be resorted to in many areas, particularly in tropical ones.

Power Sources

Sources of available power supply rank next to transportation and water supply in the geographical factors affecting utilization of mineral resources. Much power is required for mineral extraction and its generation usually constitutes one of the chief items of capital outlay and cost. Most new mineral developments of the future will come from frontier regions where existing power supply is lacking. Consequently, power must be developed, and one must look to the availability of water power, coal, coal, oil, gas, wood, subterranean heat or atomic power.

Water power is the most preferred energy since it saves transportation and storage of fuels, but unfortunately it is not often available. Because of its high installation cost, the ore reserves of the deposit must be sufficiently large to repay over their life the capital cost involved. Lacking water power, other energy sources, presumably fuels, must be utilized, and the choice is determined by the geographic location of the deposit and of the fuel. The preferred fuel, of course, is natural gas or petroleum if available. In the case of deposits of small-to-medium size, one must resort to the less expensive power installations, using fuels, and the proximity of the fuel may be the determining economic factor. Even a diesel plant using fuel oil might not be economic under adverse transportation. In many place for small deposits, where transport cost prohibits the use of imported fuels, local wood has been used, as in parts of Africa, Northern Canada, Alaska, and South America.

In most cases, large deposits that indicate a satisfactory margin of profit will justify the building of transportation to them and this solves the problems of power supply.

Climate

The factor of climate is seldom a deterrent to the development of mineral resources. Man has an amazing ability to adapt himself and his operations to climatic conditions, however severe. Hence, an unfavourable climate imposes only additional costs of operation made necessary to provide physical comfort or satisfactory operating conditions. A sub-arctic climate requires for many months additional heating for plants and houses, at a cost; it requires special means of handling and transporting ores to prevent freezing, or methods of defrosting; it involves problems of winter water supply and of snow disposal; it involves high expense to keep lines of communication open; it may even restrict operations to a short summer season, as in the placer-mining operations in Alaska. Water transportation may also be restricted to summer months, necessitating much winter storage capacity for the mineral products. All of these features add to the cost of operations, and in the case of "near-marginal" properties may even render them uneconomic.

At the other extreme, a humid tropical climate, likewise adds to the cost of operations although to a lesser amount. This comes about by lower labour and managerial efficiency in a debilitating climate and the necessity for long vacations. Also, air conditioning may be necessary, as in the oil regions of Saudi Arabia. The problems of health and sanitation in tropical climates also generally add to the cost of operations.

Timber

The availability of timber is another geographical factor pertinent to the development of minerals. Mines are great consumers of timber and lumber, both for surface and underground operations, and a large mine needs its own forest. If local timber is not available or suitable, other timber must be brought in and that demands a means of transportation.

Labour Supply

In the development of minerals, indigenous labour is desired, but, the geography may decree that none is available and an added cost to the minerals is imposed in recruiting, transporting, housing, and returning labour. For the New Caledonia nickel operations labour had to be imported from far off Java; for Northern Canada and Alaska labour has to be brought in; this is true also of the hinterland regions of South America; and for most African operations labor has to be recruited elsewhere.

Food Supplies

If local food supplies can be raised in the region surrounding mineral deposits it adds to health, comfort, lower living cost, and lower operating cost. The lack of nearby fertile areas has been no great handicap in the utilization of mineral deposits in such unfertile regions as Saudi Arabia, Alaska, Northern Canada, and parts of South America.

Health and Sanitation

The geographical location of mineral deposits often necessitates elaborate precautions for health and sanitation—problems particularly pertinent to unsettled tropical and subtropical regions where fevers, plague, dysentery, or other diseases are apt to be present. Such problems are generally absent in cold northern and high mountain climates. Thus, in the development of the Northern Rhodesia copper belt an intense and successful health and sanitation programme was initiated to inhibit malaria, typhoid, dysentery and other diseases. Similar steps were taken in Katanga, Belgian Congo, Tanganyika gold districts, Bulolo, New Guinea, Persian Gulf, Venezuela, and Colombia oil fields, Netherland Indies and Malayan tin fields, Gold Coast manganese fields, and in many other localities. Such precautions are essential for the safety and maintenance of labour and have to be considered as an integral cost of mining operations.

Juxtaposition of Resources

The most ideal conditions for the utilization of mineral resources are the juxtaposition of several favourable geographical factors. Indeed, for some mineral industries, such as a steel project, it is almost essential for economic operation that supplies of iron ore, coal, and limestone flux, be closely grouped. That has been a fundamental factor in the development of such great steel centres as Pennsylvania, Great Lakes region, Birmingham, Alabama, and the Ruhr. The lack of such grouping near the large iron ore deposits of Itabira, Brazil, Orinoco region of Venezuela, Chile, or even Kiruna, Sweden, is a deterrent to large steel industries in those localities. The iron ore, perforce, must move to coal and limestone.

Similarly, a precious and base-metal smelting industry, must have available to it ores that can serve as collectors for precious metals, ores to supply the proper proportions of bases and silica, and necessary fluxes.

Markets for By-Products

Oftentimes the economic possibilities of a mineral deposit may depend upon the utilization of by-products which can find a market near by. This in turn may depend upon the physical, geographical and industrial development, and the density of population. To illustrate the forthcoming exploitation of the large titanium deposit in northern Quebec, referred to earlier, will be economically feasible only because by-product iron can be marketed in the industrialized St. Lawrence waterway. The sale of by-product pyrite for sulphur burning for the paper pulp industry has made marginal copper deposits profitable. Similarly other by-products whose utilization nearby has helped make marginal deposits economic are: fluorspar for steel making or chemicals; manganese carbonate for manganese ore; magnetic iron from titanium ore; barite for industrial use and oil drilling; feldspar for ceramics; quartz for silica glass and abrasives; crushed rocks for highways, building construction, and concrete aggregrates; and minerals for abrasives, lithium, strontium, and other compounds.

Some Recent Mineral Developments

Some new, large mineral developments going on today, where geographical factors have had to be carefully weighed and overcome, illustrate the relationship between geography and utilization.

In addition to the huge iron-ore and titanium properties undergoing development in sub-arctic Quebec, a sub-arctic gold district at Great

Slave Lake, Northwest Canada, is being developed where the heavy transportation is by water for only a few months, and the airplane is necessary. In the unsettled tropical hinterlands of Venezuela, near the Orinoco River, large iron ore deposits are undergoing development for ocean transport delivery to northeastern Atlantic ports. There, geographical factors revolve around transportation and the problems of developing a low-cost product in a low-lying tropical region. Similarly, large manganese deposits are being investigated in the sparsely-settled, tropical regions of Brazil where transportation is crude or lacking. New, large sulphide copper ore installations are taking place in Chile, Northern Rhodesia, and Katanga. Large-scale new gold developments are being pushed under the favourable geographical conditions of the Orange Free State in South Africa, and lead-zinc-copper developments in the remote regions of South West Africa.

These are but a few of the many new mineral deposits undergoing exploration or development in remote lands where geographical factors are ever to the fore.

Again, some of the noteworthy developments completed in the last decade or so have demonstrated the successful overcoming of severe geographical factors in utilizing mineral resources. A few examples will serve as illustrations.

In the rigorous sub-arctic of Canada, the uranium-silver deposits of Great Bear Lake were brought into production where transportation over a distance of 500 miles from railhead was by inland waterways open only from June to September. In Finland, the development of nickel deposits at Petsamo, on the Arctic Ocean, was under way when World War II broke out. In Africa, the great Northern Rhodesian Copper Belt was opened up in forested wilderness, infested with fever and roamed by lions, and numerous other mineral deposits of lesser importance have been brought into production throughout other parts of geographically difficult Africa. Latin America has witnessed the recent development of the $33,000,000 Nicaro Nickel project in northeastern Cuba, the large copper deposit of Yauricocha in the high Andes of Peru, the development of oil in Eastern Bolivia and southern Chile, and the further development of the Itabira iron deposit in Brazil.

Each of the above examples of recent successful utilization of mineral resources has demonstrated the necessity of the co-operation and interweaving of technical skills. The mining geologist has been called upon to appraise the size, value, and potentialities of the deposit and whether the tonnage involved and its value merit further consideration. He has also been called upon to guide the exploration to obtain data to furnish answers to the above questions. The mining engineer has been called upon to appraise the mining possibilities, to determine the location of mine openings, to choose the mining and beneficiation methods and to determine the means and cost of transportation and power development.

The metallurgical engineer is called upon to determine the character and design of beneficiation, refining and smelting plants. The mining or civil engineer may be called upon to design and construct aerial or gravity tramways, haulage ways, highways, or railways adapted to the topography and climate of the region. The engineer's skills are also utilized to design and construct housing, public utilities, and health and recreational facilities adapted to the peculiarities of the people, or the topography, and the climate. All of these are interwoven with financing.

Thus, the utilization of mineral resources necessitates the co-operative effort of the skills of geologists and of engineers to investigate and attempt to overcome the many and varied geographical factors in order to strive to make the property an economic success. But skills alone will not avail unless the costs of production and transportation can be made less than the selling price of the product.

34. Fossil Fuels in the Future

Milton F. Searle

Although we head a great deal about the soon-to-be-reached era of plentiful power through widespread use of nuclear energy, sober analysis indicates that the batic fossil fuels— coal, petroleum and natural gas—will be in increasing demand throughout the rest of the twentieth century. From time to time, prophets of gloom forecasting rapid depletion of these resources have arisen, only to be silenced almost immediately through new discoveries. How real are these concerns? What will the fossil fuel demand be in the year 2000? Can we meet this demand? This study, prepared for the Atomic Energy Commission, provides some of the answers.

Summary

World fossil-fuel consumption in the year 2000 will be over five times consumption in 1958. Cumulative fossil-fuel consumption from 1958 through the year 2000 is estimated at 11.65 Q.* This compares to 3.70 Q used through 1958. Thus, during the remainder of the century, mankind is expected to use over three times as much fossil fuel as used in all previous time unless the burden on fossil fuels is eased by some other source of power.

SOURCE: Office of Operations Analysis and Forecasting, United States Atomic Energy Commission, TID 8209, Washington, D.C. (October, 1960), 1–15. The author is an economist with the U.S. Atomic Energy Commission.
One Q equals one quintillion or 10^{18} British thermal units of heat.

Residents of the United States are expected to use over four times as much fossil-fuel energy in the year 2000 as they used in 1958. Cumulative use of fossil fuels from 1958 through the year 2000 will aggregate 3.81 Q. This is over 2½ times as much fossil fuel as the total amount used in the previous history of the nation.

The prospect of such tremendous consumption in the United States and in the world has raised the specter of energy shortages and high energy costs. Fortunately fossil-fuel resources are also large. The world has an estimated 111.02 Q remaining to be produced if undiscovered reserves as well as presently proved reserves are considered. Resources are thus almost ten times requirements during the remainder of the century, although these resources are predominantly solid fuels rather than presently preferred fluid fuels. Out of the 111.02 Q remaining, 19.22 Q should be available at real prices not over 25 per cent above 1958 prices.

Domestic fossil-fuel resources are also large in comparison to energy requirements. An estimated 28.57 Q remain to be produced, of which 5.57 Q are in the low-cost category (not over 25 per cent increase in real prices). Requirements during the remainder of the century are 3.81 Q; however, the distribution of fuel resources with respect to fuel consumption patterns is poor.

This study does not place great emphasis on energy requirements by fuel type since technological developments may well have radically altered consumption patterns before the end of the century. If, however, the possibility of such technological changes is ignored, the present world trend toward an increased use of fluid fuels can still be met. More specifically, it is estimated that over 63 per cent of the world's fossil-fuel requirements can be produced from petroleum and shale oil in the year 2000. This compares with less than 44 per cent of the world sources in 1958.

The real cost per unit of producing fluid fuels in the year 2000 should be less than 50 per cent above 1958 costs. Such an increase should not prove particularly burdensome. The cost of fossil fuels, at mine and wellhead, is only a small part of national income, and thus even a large increase in these costs over a long period of time will not seriously impair economic growth. In the United States, fossil-fuel costs, at the mine and wellhead, are less than 2 per cent of national income. Prices to consumers should increase by considerably less than costs at the point of production since a large part of the cost to the consumer is in processing, transporting, and marketing costs, which should not rise significantly in terms of real dollars.

The United States currently uses about 75 per cent of its fossil fuels in fluid form. About 10 per cent of the fluid-fuel total is now imported. If the United States should cease to import fuels in the near future domestic fluid-fuel resources could supply domestic requirements for fluid fuels into the 1970's. Before 1980 it would become necessary to produce large amounts of shale oil to help meet fluid-fuel requirements. Together, shale oil and fluid hydrocarbons could meet domestic requirements for fluid fuels for the remainder of the century, although the cost would be somewhat higher than if some petroleum fuels were imported.

Thus the conclusion of this study is that fossil fuels can meet energy requirements in both the United States and the remainder of the world for the rest of the century without difficulty and with only moderate increases in real costs. In fact, requirements twice as large as those predicted could be easily met, providing that both the world and the United States adjusted consumption patterns to large increases in the use of coal. Similarly, estimated requirements could be met if resources are only one-half as large as predicted, providing again that consumption patterns are adjusted toward increased use of solid fuels.

Beyond the year 2000 the adequacy of fossil-fuel resources is less certain. Although over 90 per cent of the world's fossil-fuel resources considered in this report will still be available after the year 2000, continued compounding of fossil-fuel requirements at the same rate as predicted for the remainder of this century (slightly over 4 per cent per year) would exhaust fossil-fuel resources by the middle of the next century. That time, the year 2050, is within the life span of children now being born. It is therefore expedient that new sources of power be capable of supplying the increase in energy requirements after the turn of the century.

. . . . .

Energy Requirements

Only the so-called commercial fuels are considered in this paper. While noncommercial fuels such as wood and other vegetable fuels, dung, and windpower presently supply about 11 per cent of the world's energy, the tendency is for them to be replaced by coal, petroleum, and hydroelectric power. Such replacement is inherent in the historic rate of growth of commercial fuels.

Key-year Requirements

Forecast energy requirements for the world and the two areas of primary interest, the United States and the Organisation for European Economic Co-operation (OEEC) countries, are shown in Table 1. . . .

The world figures shown in Table 1 are the summation of the individual area figures plus an allowance for the fuel used by ships on the high seas (bunkering). . . .

The different rates of growth shown in Table 1 imply substantial changes in the relative amounts of world energy used in the various

TABLE 1. Energy Consumption*

	United States	OEEC countries	World
Key-year consumption quadrillions (10^{15}) of Btu			
1958	41	22	109
1980	86	41	266
2000	170	71	615
Key-year consumption, compared to 1958 consumption, %			
1958	100	100	100
1980	210	186	244
2000	415	323	564
Compounded rate of annual increase, %			
1958–1980	3.4	2.9	4.2
1980–2000	3.5	2.8	4.2

* Commercial energy only.

areas. In 1958, the United States consumed 38 percent of the world's energy, whereas in the year 2000 the United States will consume only 28 per cent of the world energy supplies. Western Europe will also take a decreasing percentage of the world's energy. In 1958, the OEEC countries took 20 per cent of world requirements, but by the end of the century they will use only 12 per cent of total world energy production.

Changes in the relative amounts of energy consumed in various areas are, of course, a reflection of changes in more fundamental and inter-related variables such as population, economic structure, and per-capita consumption of goods and services, to mention only a few. In fact, energy consumption is often projected by forecasting population and per-capita energy consumption separately and then combining them to obtain a figure for energy use. Actually, population and per-capita energy consumption are not independent variables, and this technique is not entirely satisfactory, but for many areas of the world available data do not justify the use of more sophisticated techniques. In this report a heterogeneous set of forecasting techniques has been used, includ- ing per-capita and population type projections for some areas. These various techniques have been employed in an attempt to make the best use of the available data in each area. Regardless of the methods used it is still informative to examine the resulting forecasts in terms of popu- lation and per-capita use. Forecasts of population and per-capita con- sumption are shown in Tables 2 and 3.

U.S. population figures used in this report through 1980 are Series 1 of the latest projection by the Bureau of the Census. The figures beyond

TABLE 2. Population

	United States	OEEC countries	World
Key-year population, millions of persons			
1958	174	294	2852
1980	260	356	4250
2000	388	425	6387
Key-year population compared to 1958 population, %			
1958	100	100	100
1980	149	121	149
2000	218	145	224
Compounded rate of annual increase, %			
1958–1980	1.8	0.9	1.8
1980–2000	1.9	0.9	2.1

TABLE 3. Per-Capita Energy Consumption *

	United States	OEEC countries	World
Key-year consumption, millions of Btu per person			
1958	236	73	38
1980	332	114	63
2000	439	166	96
Key-year consumption compared to 1958 consumption, %			
1958	100	100	100
1980	141	156	166
2000	186	227	253
Compounded rate of annual increase, %			
1958–1980	1.6	2.0	2.3
1980–2000	1.4	1.9	2.2

* Commercial energy only.

1980 represent an extension of the Series II figures. Population figures for the rest of the world are from the medium series of the latest United Nations forecast (1958). . . .

The per-capita energy consumption figures shown in Table 3 are obtained by dividing the energy requirements on which Table 1 is based by the population figures from which Table 2 is derived.

This study does not place great emphasis on energy requirements by fuel type. There are several reasons for this. Technology may have drastically changed the pattern of energy use by 1980 and almost certainly will have done so by the year 2000. The internal combustion engine may even become obsolete and mobile equipment may cease to be highly dependent on hydrocarbons. Even if the natural evolution of technology does not change the pattern of fuel consumption, it is very likely that technology could adapt our consuming devices to a changed pattern of supply if necessary, or could convert available fuels to desired forms.

Finally it is likely that the first areas of fossil-fuel shortage will occur among the hydrocarbon fuels, and it does not appear that such a shortage can be met any better by nuclear power than by coal and oil shales, if as well.

Although estimates of energy requirements of fuel source are considered to be of secondary importance in this study, it is of some value to compare possible requirements for specific fuels with the estimates of reserves developed later. Table 4 shows the historical division and a possible future division of energy requirements by fuel types. The world figures for the years 1980 and 2000 are based on a continuation of present trends, although at a gradually decreasing rate, toward the increased use of petroleum fuels. The figures for the United States assume that the percentage supplied by hydroelectricity will continue to decrease, as it has in recent years, and that the percentages supplied by oil and natural gas will have passed their peak and be decreasing by 1980. The anticipated rate of decrease is slow, however, and petroleum will still be supplying a larger portion of U.S. energy in the year 2000 than it did in 1950. Coal will supply increasing percentages as petroleum and hydroelectricity decline. These percentages take into account any limitations imposed by the supply figures developed in later sections. The distribution between fuel types is that which might prevail in the absence of any nuclear power. Such nuclear power as is produced will mainly displace coal, although some oil may be displaced in maritime uses.

The ultimate form into which the world's fossil fuels are transformed before they reach the final consumer, like the production requirements for various fossil fuels, is judged to be of secondary importance in this paper. Historically, increasing percentages of total fossil-fuel production have been converted to electricity. It seems likely that consumers throughout the world will continue to use electricity to fill an increasing percentage of their total energy requirements.

Philip Sporn, president of the American Electric Power Co., has predicted that electricity production in the United States (measured in terms of the amount of fuel required for the production of the electricity) will increase from 18 per cent of total energy requirements in 1957 to 25 per cent by 1975 and to 40 per cent by the year 2000.

TABLE 4. Percentage Distribution of Commercial Fuel Requirements by Fuel Source °

	Coal, lignite and nuclear	Crude oil, natural gas liquids, and shale oil	Natural gas	Hydro-electric †	Total
1929					
World	75.7	14.8	4.1	5.4	100.0
United States	64.9	23.3	8.2	3.6	100.0
1950					
World	58.0	25.4	9.4	7.2	100.0
United States	37.8	39.5	18.0	4.7	100.0
1958					
World	49.0	30.9	12.6	7.5	100.0
United States	24.3	45.0	26.5	4.2	100.0
1980					
World	32.8	40.6	18.9	7.7	100.0
United States	29.7	44.3	23.0	3.0	100.0
2000					
World	30.5	41.0	22.5	6.0	100.0
United States	36.5	42.0	20.0	1.5	100.0

° Based on heat content.
† Heat content of the amount of coal required to produce the same amount of electricity in thermal stations assuming the evarage thermal-station efficiency prevailing in the given year.

TABLE 5. Cumulative Fossil-Fuel Consumption in Q °

	United States †			World		
		CUMULATIVE			CUMULATIVE	
	During period	From 1958	All time	During period	From 1958	All time
Through 1958			1.39			3.70
1959–1980	1.34	1.34	2.73	3.75	3.75	7.45
1981–2000	2.47	3.81	5.20	7.90	11.65	15.35
	Free World			Soviet Bloc †		
	During period	Cumulative from 1958		During period	Cumulative from 1958	
1959–1980	2.79	2.79		0.96	0.96	
1981–2000	5.63	8.42		2.27	3.23	

° Assuming no nuclear power.
† U. S. and Soviet Bloc figures do not contain any amounts for fueling ships engaged in overseas trade (bunkers).

Although total energy requirements for the United States, as envisioned by this report, are much higher than those forecast by Sporn, there would not be any difficulty in producing 40 per cent of this higher level as electricity. In fact, since all of the fossil fuels can be readily used in thermal generating plants, there is, from the production standpoint, no practical upper limit to the percentage of total energy requirements which can be produced as electricity. In particular, large electricity requirements do not automatically mean a larger need for nuclear power as long as fossil-fuel reserves are adequate and the cost of electricity from nuclear plants is above that for electricity from fossil-fuel plants.

Cumulative Requirements

Although the key-year energy consumption figures shown in previous tables are important indications of consumption levels, it is the cumulated consumption over the years that measures the depletion of resources. Table 5 shows cumulative fossil-fuel requirements by periods. Estimated hydroelectric production has been subtracted from total consumption estimates, and, as previously mentioned, the fossil-fuel figures have been based on the assumption of no nuclear power.

The 11.65 Q of energy which the world will consume from 1958 through the year 2000 is over three times the 3.70 Q consumed from the beginning of time to the end of 1958. The 3.18 Q which the United States will use in this period is almost 2¼ times the 1.39 Q consumed in this country through 1958.

If the assumptions of Table 4 with regard to the distribution of energy requirements among fuel types are realized, then the cumulative consumption figures for the world and for the United States shown in Table 5 may be broken down as shown in Tables 6 and 7.

It is prospective rates of consumption such as those shown in Tables 5, 6, and 7 above that led to statements that the nation and the world are running out of fossil fuels and must develop alternative sources of power. While these statements are true in a general sense, a more precise evaluation of the time when alternative power sources will be needed is required as an aid in guiding the rate, and perhaps the direction, of development of alternative power sources. In order to make this evaluation, an analysis of energy supplies is required.

Energy Supplies Compared with Energy Requirements

The energy requirements previously discussed have been based on the tacit assumption that energy materials will continue to move in international trade with no greater restrictions than before and perhaps with gradually diminishing restriction. Under this assumption the three main areas of interest from the standpoint of energy supply are the United States, the Free World, and the Soviet Bloc.

Figures for the United States are of interest both because this country is one of the major energy-producing and -consuming areas of the world and because there is some question as to the length of time during which the United States could continue to consume energy at anticipated rates if cut off from Free World sources.

TABLE 6. World Cumulative Consumption of Fossil Fuels by Fuel Form in Q

	Coal and lignite	Crude oil, natural gas liquids, and shale oil	Natural gas	Total
1959–1980	1.51	1.60	0.64	3.75
1981–2000	2.65	3.50	1.75	7.90
TOTAL	4.16	5.10	2.39	11.65

TABLE 7. U.S. Cumulative Consumption of Fossil Fuels by Fuel Form in Q

	Coal and lignite	Crude oil, natural gas liquids, and shale oil	Natural gas	Total
1959–1980	0.38	0.62	0.34	1.34
1981–2000	0.85	1.08	0.54	2.47
TOTAL	1.23	1.70	0.88	3.81

Consideration of the energy resources of the Free World, particularly the United States and western Europe, assumes continued access to Middle East and South American oil. If the resources of these areas should be denied to the United States and western Europe, energy consumption would be much less, particularly in western Europe (at least until other forms of energy could assume the burden).

Energy supplies of the Soviet Bloc are of interest for two reasons. Any great excess or deficiency in this area may well affect the supplies

TABLE 8. World Fossil-Fuel Reserves *

	COST INCREMENT REQUIRED FOR AVAILABILITY			
Fuel type	Low	Medium	High	Total
Coal and lignite, billions of short tons	681	825	1241	2747
Liquid hydrocarbons, billions of barrels	553	271	270	1094
Natural gas, trillions of cu ft	715	1030	2905	4650
Oil shale and tar sands, billions of barrels	0 †	2400	4200	6600

* Discovered and yet to be discovered as of Dec. 31, 1958.
† Small amounts exist in this category, but probably less than 500,000,000 barrels.

TABLE 9. World Fossil-Fuel Reserves in Q *

| | COST INCREMENT REQUIRED FOR AVAILABILITY | | | |
Fuel type	Low	Medium	High	Total
Coal and lignite	15.27	18.49	27.81	61.57
Liquid hydrocarbons	3.21	1.57	1.57	6.35
Natural gas	0.74	1.07	3.01	4.82
Oil shale and tar sands	0	13.92	24.36	38.28
TOTAL	19.22	35.05	56.75	111.02

* Discovered and yet to be discovered as of Dec. 31, 1958.

TABLE 10. World Fossil-Fuel Production Schedule in Q *

Period	Date of end of period	Production during period	Reserves at end of period
	Dec. 31, 1958		111.02
1959–1980	Dec. 31, 1980	3.75 †	107.27
1981–2000	Dec. 31, 2000	7.90 †	99.37
2001–2020	Dec. 31, 2020	18.35 ‡	81.02
2021–2040	Dec. 31, 2040	41.02 ‡	40.00
2041–2052	Dec. 31, 2052	40.00 ‡	0

* Assuming no nuclear power.
† Based on Table 5.
‡ Based on assumption of 4 per cent annual growth.

available to the Free World, and the availability of fossil fuels in the Soviet Bloc countries will have a bearing on the rate at which those countries develop nuclear power.

The figures for petroleum reserves to a large extent, and the figures for coal and oil shale to a lesser extent, represent reserves yet to be discovered. However, the estimates are based on the work of geological and mining experts in their respective fields, and the estimates used are, in general, among the lower estimates available. The reserve estimates include only those amounts of resources in place which it is estimated will actually be recovered. Allowance has already been made for lack of complete recovery.

Reserves are classified according to the estimated increment in real costs over 1958 costs which would be necessary for their recovery. The cost-increment categories used are low, medium, and high. These refer to increments in real cost over 1958 costs of up to 25 per cent, from 25 to 50 per cent, and from 50 to 300 per cent respectively. Reserves recoverable at still higher costs are not considered.

World

Table 8 shows the amounts of fossil fuel, discovered and yet to be discovered, upon which the conclusions of this paper are based. Although the data are not in comparable units, the table serves to bring the fossil-fuel figures together in one place. Interpretations of the data are made in subsequent tables and text.

In Table 9 the figures of Table 8 are converted to a common unit, British thermal units. Although this increases the comparability of the data, it is not a perfect solution since a Btu from one type of fuel may not be equivalent to a Btu from another type, at least not with the same efficiencies in a given use, and may even require different consuming equipment.

Over 55 per cent of the remaining energy reserve is in coal. The position of coal is even more dominant in the low-cost area. Coal reserves contain over 79 per cent of the energy which can be produced at real dollar costs of less than 25 per cent above 1958 costs.

While coal clearly provides the bulk of the world's energy reserve, oil shales and tar sands are easily in second place with over 27 per cent of total energy. Since there is currently little commercial oil shale production, 1958 crude oil costs are used as a base in determining the amounts of oil shale in the various cost categories. In Table 9 no reserves are shown for oil shale in a low-cost category. The amounts of low-cost shale oil reserves are judged to be too small to show in this class.

Table 10 shows fossil-fuel production by periods and remaining fossil-fuel reserves at the end of the period. The consumption figures through the year 2000 are . . . summarized in Table 5. This report does not attempt to forecast consumption rates beyond the year 2000. Obviously limiting factors on the rate of growth of energy consumption will be reached eventually. For illustrative purposes only, Table 10 is carried beyond 2000 on the assumptions that total energy use grows at 4 per cent per annum and that all of the increase is supplied by fossil fuels. These assumptions result in fossil fuel being exhausted in 2052. Of course, the assumption of a fixed growth rate until all fossil fuels are exhausted is unrealistic. Long before that time the growth rate will become negative, and it is most likely that some fossil fuels will be produced for centuries, although probably for chemical raw materials rather than fuel.

Even if fossil-fuel requirements during the remainder of the century were twice as large as predicted or if low-cost fossil-fuel supplies turn out to be only half as large as now appears likely, total energy requirements could be met by making only moderate demands on the medium cost category of reserves. The first possibility, doubling of fossil-fuel requirements, would imply long-term growth rates without precedent in world history. The second possibility, that low-cost fossil-fuel reserves are only half as large as estimated, is also extremely unlikely since over 7 per cent of the low-cost reserves is coal, and coal reserves are among the better substantiated reserve figures.

The 4 per cent growth rate used in this report as an assumed value for the post-2000 period seems to be a reasonable contingency for which to prepare, although a somewhat lower figure might be more logical as an expected value. The dates by which world fossil-fuel resources would be exhausted if energy demand grew at slower rates and if fossil fuels were called upon to provide all of the increase are as follows:

Rate of growth beyond year 2000, %	Year by which all fossil fuels would be consumed
4	2052
3	2060
2	2072
1	2100
0	2171

Since the projections of Table 10 for the post-2000 period are a reasonable possibility, it would appear that after the year 2000 nuclear and solar power should be prepared to supply amounts of energy equal to the increase in consumption that occurs after that date. This would extend fossil-fuel reserves to the year 2171. The fossil-fuel equivalents of the required amounts of nuclear power are shown in Table 11. Actual nuclear power requirements may be ever larger than this since nuclear power costs are expected to decline to competitive levels with fossil fuels before the end of the century.

The large percentages of total energy requirements which Table 11 shows being supplied by nuclear power will require considerable change in consuming equipment. Most heating will probably be by electricity. Mobile equipment will be either directly powered by electricity or indirectly powered by means of improved batteries or chemical fuels produced through the use of nuclear fuels. Process heat will also be electrical, nuclear, or by means of chemical fuels produced through the use of nuclear power. At present these prospective changes may seem somewhat radical, but in the perspective of historical rates of change and the present state of technology they are probably conservative.

Comparison of world fossil-fuel reserves with expected requirements for various forms of energy as shown in Table 6 is made in Table 12. This table shows the amount of fossil-fuel reserves remaining at the ends of the years 1980 and 2000 after the energy requirements of the periods are met. The figures for oil shale and tar sands are shown separately because there is a considerable amount of interest in the establishment of an oil shale industry; however, as far as the consumer is concerned, the ultimate product will be essentially the same. In connection with these tables attention is again called to the fact that the conclusions of this paper are not particularly sensitive to the predicted form of energy requirements.

Table 12 indicates a rather satisfactory fuel situation for the remainder of the century. A substantial amount of coal will still be available in the year 2000 at low increments in cost.

Some liquid hydrocarbons will still be available at medium increments in cost, and large amounts of shale oil and tar sands will be available at medium increments in cost to replace diminishing liquid

TABLE 11. World Nuclear Power Requirements (in Q) If Nuclear Power Supplies All the Increase in Energy Requirements After the Year 2000 *

Period	Fossil-fuel production	Nuclear power production †	Total production ‡ (excluding hydroelectric)
1959–1980	3.75		3.75
1981–2000	7.90		7.90
2001–2020	11.60	6.75	18.35
2021–2040	11.60	29.42	41.02
2041–2060	11.60	79.09	90.69

* Assumes no nuclear power before the year 2000.
† The figures in this column represent the additional amounts of fossil fuels which would be required without nuclear power. They are not convertible to megawatt hours produced by nuclear plants without further assumptions.
‡ Based on a 4 per cent growth rate in the amount of energy required after the year 2000 as in Table 7. Nuclear power is derived as the difference between total production and fossil-fuel production.

TABLE 12. Remaining World Fossil-Fuel Reserves in Q *

| Fuel type | COST INCREMENT REQUIRED FOR AVAILABILITY | | | |
	Low	Medium	High	Total
Coal and lignite				
Dec. 31, 1958	15.27	18.49	27.81	61.57
Dec. 31, 1980	13.76	18.49	27.81	60.06
Dec. 31, 2000	11.11	18.49	27.81	57.41
Natural gas				
Dec. 31, 1958	0.74	1.07	3.01	4.82
Dec. 31, 1980	0.10	1.07	3.01	4.18
Dec. 31, 2000	0	0	2.43	2.43
Liquid hydrocarbons				
Dec. 31, 1958	3.21	1.57	1.57	6.35
Dec. 31, 1980	1.63	1.57	1.57	4.77
Dec. 31, 2000	0	0.40	1.57	1.97
Shale oil and tar sands				
Dec. 31, 1958	0	13.92	24.36	38.28
Dec. 31, 1980	0	13.90	24.36	38.26
Dec. 31, 2000	0	13.20	24.36	37.56

* Discovered and yet to be discovered; assuming no nuclear power.

hydrocarbon reserves. Only high-incremental-cost natural gas remains, but this is not too serious. To begin with, most gas at the wellhead is currently underpriced with respect to other fuels. Furthermore, much of the delivered price of natural gas represents transportation costs, and a doubling of the wellhead pice may only mean a 25 per cent increase to consumers.

In addition, coal or shale oil can readily be substituted for most uses of natural gas. There is also a strong possibility that reasonably efficient processes for converting coal or oil shale to natural gas will be perfected.

Even if the division of energy requirements should turn out to be considerably different from that shown in Table 6, no serious problem would exist. A doubling of liquid-hydrocarbon requirements would be met from increased production of shale oil. The required technology for the production of shale oil is already fairly well developed. On the other hand, a doubling of coal requirements could be met from existing coal reserves without trouble and at moderate cost.

Free World and the Soviet Bloc

Energy supplies are divided between the Soviet Bloc and the Free World as shown in Tables 13 and 14.

The various fossil-fuel reserves are unevenly distributed between the Free World and the Soviet Bloc as can be seen from Tables 13, 14, and 15. The Free World contains a large proportion of the oil and gas but only a little over one-half of the coal reserves.

In relation to expected consumption levels during the remainder of the century, Free World reserves are adequate but relatively less than those of the Soviet Bloc. From 1958 to 2000 the Free World will account for 72.3 per cent of world consumption although the Free World has only 59.6 per cent of world energy reserves.

The prospective depletion rate of Free World reserves is shown in Table 16. It assumes a zero net trade balance in fossil fuels between the Soviet Bloc and the Free World.

United States

Recoverable domestic fossil-fuel reserves are shown in Table 17. Table 18 shows the same reserves in British thermal units.

The United States has 25.7 per cent of the world's fossil-fuel reserves and will consume 32.7 per cent of the energy used by the world during the remainder of the century. If only the Free World is considered, U.S. energy consumption and reserves, considered in total, are about in balance. This country will consume 45.2 per cent of the energy consumed by the Free World and has 43.2 per cent of the Free World's energy reserves.

If energy requirements by fuel type are disregarded, and if it is assumed that this country is neither a net importer or exporter of energy, then the depletion of reserves would proceed according to the pattern shown in Table 19.

The energy reserve of the United States is clearly adequate to supply the nation's needs for the rest of the century. Predicted consumption is 3.81 Q, leaving reserves of 24.76 Q at the end of the year 2000 if all the energy required is produced domestically. Of the 24.76 Q, at least 1.76 Q would still be reserves in the low-cost increment category. Actual production from domestic reserves will probably be somewhat less than the 3.81 Q needed, due to the importation of some petroleum fuels.

TABLE 13. Free World Fossil-Fuel Reserves in Q *

| Fuel type | COST INCREMENT REQUIRED FOR AVAILABILITY | | | |
	Low	Medium	High	Total
Coal and lignite	7.87	9.49	14.31	31.67
Liquid hydrocarbons	2.54	1.23	1.24	5.01
Natural gas	0.62	0.88	2.46	3.96
Oil shale and tar sands	0 †	9.28	16.24	25.52
TOTAL	11.03	20.88	34.25	66.16

* Discovered and yet to be discovered, as of Dec. 31, 1958.
† Less than 0.005 Q.

TABLE 14. Soviet Bloc Fossil-Fuel Reserves in Q *

| Fuel type | COST INCREMENT REQUIRED FOR AVAILABILITY | | | |
	Low	Medium	High	Total
Coal and lignite	7.40	9.00	13.50	29.90
Liquid hydrocarbons	0.67	0.34	0.33	1.34
Natural gas	0.12	0.19	0.55	0.86
Oil shale and tar sands	0	4.64	8.12	12.76
TOTAL	8.19	14.17	22.50	44.86

* Discovered and yet to be discovered, as of Dec. 31, 1958.

TABLE 15. Free World Fossil-Fuel Reserves as a Per Cent of World Fossil-Fuel Reserves

Fuel type	Per cent
Coal and lignite reserves	51.4
Liquid hydrocarbons	78.9
Natural gas	82.2
Oil shale and tar sands	66.7
TOTAL FOSSIL FUELS	59.6
CONSUMPTION 1959–2000	72.3

TABLE 16. Free World Fossil-Fuel Production Schedule in Q *

Period	Date of end of period	Production during period	Reserves at end of period
	Dec. 31, 1958		66.16
1959–1980	Dec. 31, 1980	2.79 †	63.37
1981–2000	Dec. 31, 2000	5.63 †	57.74
2001–2020	Dec. 31, 2020	13.08 ‡	44.66
2021–2040	Dec. 31, 2040	29.26 ‡	15.40
2041–2047	Dec. 31, 2047	15.40 ‡	0

* Assuming no nuclear power.
† Based on Table 4.
‡ Based on assumption of 4 per cent annual growth.

TABLE 17. U. S. Fossil-Fuel Reserves *

Fuel type	COST INCREMENT REQUIRED FOR AVAILABILITY			
	Low	Medium	High	Total
Coal and lignite, billions of short tons	235	285	426	946
Liquid hydrocarbons, billions of barrels	64	57	46	167
Natural gas, trillions of cu ft	160	220	472	852
Oil shale and tar sands, billions of barrels	0	400	700	1100

* Discovered and yet to be discovered, as of Dec. 31, 1958.

TABLE 18. U. S. Fossil-Fuel Reserves in Q *

Fuel type	COST INCREMENT REQUIRED FOR AVAILABILITY			
	Low	Medium	High	Total
Coal and lignite	5.06	6.14	9.18	20.38
Liquid hydrocarbons	0.34	0.32	0.26	0.92
Natural gas	0.17	0.23	0.49	0.89
Oil shale and tar sands	0	2.32	4.06	6.38
TOTAL	5.57	9.01	13.99	28.57

* Discovered and yet to be discovered as of Dec. 31, 1958.

The problem of requirements by fuel types will be considered later, but the conclusions regarding fuel supplies by type are consistent with the analysis of total supply given here.

Although U.S. reserves will still be large at the end of the century, an annual rate of increase of 3 per cent in requirements would exhaust reserves soon after the middle of the next century. The situation here is

TABLE 19. U. S. Fossil-Fuel Production Schedule in Q [*]

Period	Date of end of period	Production during period	Reserves at end of period
	Dec. 31, 1958		28.57
1959–1980	Dec. 31, 1980	1.34 [†]	27.23
1981–2000	Dec. 31, 2000	2.47 [†]	24.76
2001–2020	Dec. 31, 2020	4.66 [‡]	20.10
2021–2040	Dec. 31, 2040	8.45 [‡]	11.65
2041–2057	Dec. 31, 2057	11.65 [‡]	0

[*] Assuming no nuclear power and no net import or export balance in fossil fuels.
[†] Based on Table 4.
[‡] Based on assumption of 3 per cent annual growth.

analogous to the world situation. World reserves also will be adequate at the end of the century, but continued growth in requirements at the rate of 4 per cent per year would exhaust the reserves shortly after the middle of the next century.

Since the rate of growth of total energy consumption in the United States will be well below 4 per cent in the pre-2000 period, a growth rate of 3 per cent is assumed for the post-2000 period. This compares with 4 per cent assumed for the world in Table 16. Again, the conclusions drawn are not particularly sensitive to the growth rate selected.

The dates by which U.S. fossil-fuel resources would be exhausted if energy demand grew at different rates and if domestic fossil fuels were called upon to provide all of the increase are as follows:

Rate of growth beyond year 2000, %	Year by which all fossil fuels would be consumed
4	2049
3	2057
2	2069
1	2091
0	2148

It may be that energy requirements in the United States will not be as large as predicted, but it is well within the realm of possibility that they will be. Until future requirements are better delineated, it seems desirable to prepare for the contingency of large energy needs. It therefore appears that nuclear and solar power should be prepared to supply amounts of power equal to the increments in total requirements after the year 2000.

Since present plans call for the development of competitive nuclear power in large central-station generating plants in high-cost areas before 1970, the required technology and operating experience should be easily available before the turn of the century. If the costs of nuclear power become substantially less than those of conventional power before the turn of the century, energy consumption may be stimulated and may rise even higher than forecast.

Some idea of the possible magnitude of the demands upon nuclear power in the United States after the turn of the century, if nuclear power is called upon to supply all of the increase, is shown in Table 20.

The composition of this country's fuel reserve is vastly different from present consumption patterns. This disparity between reserves and requirements is shown in Table 21.

TABLE 20. U. S. Nuclear Requirements (in Q) If Nuclear Power Supplies All the Increase in Energy Requirements After the Year 2000 *

Period	Fossil fuel	Nuclear power †	Total production ‡ (excluding hydroelectric)
1959–1980	1.34		1.34
1981–2000	2.47		2.47
2001–2020	3.40	11.26	4.66
2021–2040	3.40	5.05	8.45
2041–2060	3.40	11.90	15.30

* Assumes no nuclear power before year 2000.
† The figures in this column represent the additional amounts of fossil fuels which would be required without nuclear power. They are not convertible to megawatt hours produced by nuclear plants without additional assumptions.
‡ Based on a 3 per cent annual growth rate in the amount of energy required after the year 2000. Nuclear power is derived as the difference between total production and fossil-fuel production.

TABLE 21. Comparison of the Composition of U. S. Fossil-Fuel Reserves with the Composition of 1958 U. S. Fossil-Fuel Consumption

Fuel type	Amount in fossil-fuel reserve, %	Amount in 1958 fossil-fuel consumption, %
Coal and lignite	71.33	25.38
Liquid hydrocarbons	3.22	46.96
Natural gas	3.12	27.66
Oil shale and tar sands	22.33	0
TOTAL	100.00	100.00

Although the United States can supply currently, and certainly for a number of years into the future, sufficient fossil fuels to meet present and anticipated consumption patterns, it is not presently doing so. In 1958 net imports of liquid hydrocarbons were equal to almost 16 per cent of the liquid hydrocarbons consumed in this country. Small amounts of natural gas were also imported. These imports are for economic reasons and not because of domestic shortages.

In the peaceful world postulated in this study, the United States will almost certainly continue to increase its petroleum imports for at least several decades as the result of economic factors which favor foreign oil. However, if a national emergency should require self-sufficiency, the domestic situation, assuming no change in requirements, would be as follows. Low-cost-increment coal and lignite reserves could meet all requirements for that type of fuel during the remainder of the century with ease, since low-cost-increment reserves are 5.06 Q as compared with coal requirements during the balance of the century of 1.23 Q. Even if underground gasification of coal or processes to synthesize hydrocarbons from coal should become economically attractive, coal reserves would still be adequate since total energy requirements are only 3.81 Q. Neither of the above processes appears to have even approached feasibility for commercial purposes at present. In fact, most of the research effort on them has been dropped.

The liquid hydrocarbon situation is less favorable. Without imports, amounts of reserves almost equal to the total of the low- and medium-cost increments would be consumed by 1980. Amounts in the high-cost category would supply less than an additional ten years' requirements. Actually, it is doubtful if the remaining reserves could be found and produced as fast as this, since oil discovery is a function of both effort and time, and since there are maximum rates at which oil reserves can be produced without reducing ultimate recovery.

In all likelihood, large-scale production of medium-cost oil shale would be started long before medium-cost oil reserves were exhausted. In fact, even if oil imports are not cut off, it is quite likely that shale oil will be produced commercially before 1980. Oil shale reserves in the medium-cost-increment category are 2.32 Q. Combined with the low- and medium-cost increment oil reserves this gives a total of 2.98 Q available to meet the demand of 1.70 Q to the end of the century. Demands could be met without imports, but large-scale investment in oil shale facilities would be necessary.

Low- and medium-incremental-cost reserves of natural gas would suffice until the early 1980's, and high-cost natural-gas reserves would be exhausted shortly before the turn of the century, subject, as with oil, to some qualification regarding discovery rates.

Natural gas reserves can probably be supplemented by gas made from oil shale. The gasification technology is less advanced than the technology for converting the oil shale to shale oil, but gasification is a definite possibility. Of course the shale that is used to produce gas will not be available to produce liquid hydrocarbons.

It appears that the nation could meet the expected demands for the various fuel types during the remainder of the century without importing energy from outside sources. The cost would be somewhat higher than if imported fuels are also utilized. This assumes, of course, that the price of imported fuels bears a reasonable relation to costs and is not unduly burdened by additional taxes or regulations.

In the United States, as in the world, the first area of shortage and higher costs will apparently be in the petroleum fuels, and not in coal or oil shales. Unless nuclear energy can be produced at lower costs than energy from coal, can be adapted to supplement petroleum fuels, or can facilitate the conversion of coal or oil shale to petroleum-type fuels, it may play a minor role until near the close of the century.

35. America Still Needs Foreign Mineral Supplies

Hans H. Landsberg

Today, the United States is the greatest producer and consumer of a wide variety of minerals, and a growing market is indicated by estimates of consumption and available resources up to the end of the twentieth century. In spite of substantially increased mining activity in the United States, it is unlikely that internal demand can be satisfied without larger imports of minerals from foreign producers. Landsberg examines the present and future import needs of the United States.

Gold and silver apart, it is now 25 years since the United States last enjoyed an export balance in the trade of minerals, and I am using the term in this instance as denoting non-fabricated commodities of mineral origin, exclusive of scrap. World War II caused sharp increases in the import of a number of metallic commodities, not merely those in which the United States is a "have-not"—manganese, chromium, nickel, etc.— but also others like copper, lead and zinc, and with a few years' delay iron ore, in which there is substantial domestic production. This shift was reinforced by a drop or levelling off in the exports of some non-metallic minerals, like phosphate rock and sulphur, and, more importantly, by the emergence in the late 'forties of an import balance in the third of the major mineral groups: fuels.

The transformation of the United States into a minerals importer was

SOURCE: *Optima*, June, 1964, pp. 111–24. The author is an economist for Resources for the Future, Inc., Washington, D.C.

accompanied by a steady decline in the share that domestic production (and consumption) constitute of corresponding world totals. However, the United States market is not about to shrink to insignificance. Indeed, the United States remains the world's largest single consumer of mineral commodities, absorbing (with exceptions, of which coal and iron are the most significant) between three tenths and four tenths of the world's mineral output. The magnitude of future United States demand and the manner in which it is met will, therefore, remain major factors in the markets of the world.

Research recently concluded at Resources for the Future allows such a glimpse into the future. In an effort to appraise future adequacy of major domestic resources and to analyze the alternatives where adequacy appears doubtful, projections of demand were developed up to the end of the century and compared with estimates of the availability of resources. In the following, the focus is on metals and especially the major-tonnage metals. The outlook in fuels has recently been well described, and in non-metallic, non-fuel minerals the rôle of supply sources outside the United States is, with the principal exception of diamonds, a highly special case, too small to warrant discussion in a non-American publication.

Estimating Future Demand

There is no great art involved in letting the calculator or computer grind out the numerical consequences of a variety of assumptions. But when one undertakes to project future growth for the entire economy, the requirement that the parts be consistent with each other and with the whole raises many conceptual and mechanical problems. Yet coping with these is indispensable, for serious projections need at least a modicum of protection against the isolated wild guess that tends to be either oblivious or neglectful of the consequences it implies for other segments of the economy.

It is only too common, for example, to find the electric utility industry projecting its future without carefully analyzing or even inquiring into the consequences of its calculations for other branches of the energy industry, ignoring the likelihood that the executives of oil, gas, and other energy-producing facilities are equally striving to pre-empt the largest possible share of future energy demand. Similarly, promoters of metal "X" must consider the future of metals "Y" and "Z" in looking ahead, and also that of lumber, plastics, concrete, glass, paper, and perhaps other substances, if they wish to protect themselves—and their stockholders—from surprises. In practice, this turns out to be more complex than projections of the past rate at which substitution has occurred.

All of which is a more concrete way of saying that, in putting together the demand[1] projections, shown in Table 1, the alternatives have been considered as fully as knowledge and understanding of past trends and reasonably informed surmise of their future modification permits. The demand is that for primary major metals after allowing for the fraction of demand that can be met from scrap supplies and comprises the domestic market and exports where these are of significance.

The segments from which demand for most major metals will continue to emanate are, above all, construction, transportation, containers, and durables, but both the relative position of the various metals within each category and the relative significance of each category for the various metals are likely to change. For example, in 1960 about 50 per cent of steel-mill products went to automotive use and construction (residential, commercial industrial, etc.) No feature of the projected growth of the United States economy is likely to reduce significantly the rôle of steel in these two consuming segments, but producer durables (other than transportation equipment), which now absorb not quite 12 per cent of steel, are projected to increase in significance until, by the end of the century, they become a market for 22 per cent. In the case of copper, the substitution of other materials and changes in copper consumption trends are expected to result in a further drop in its use for constructing electric power plants. The use of copper in building construction, on the other hand, is projected to become more prominent since the amount of copper used per dollar of construction appears to have reached a stable level, and the increase in all types of construction activity will thus boost aggregate copper consumption.

How strongly substitutons may affect the relative future growth of competing materials may best be illustrated by the use of materials in the container and packaging industry, a segment of the United States economy, incidentally, that, owing to the American penchant for leaving nothing unpacked or unwrapped, is outranked in value added only by steel and motor cars. The projections are based upon an analysis of recent trends in the various fields in which the specific materials are used, on the apparent relative advantages of each, and on whatever future development can be allowed for statistically. While plastic containers may not have risen by as much as 800 per cent by the year 2000, nor metals by as little as 50 per cent, these seem more likely contingencies than that both of them should grow at the same rate, be this 50, 300, or 1,000 per cent.

These few observations must suffice to convey a flavour of our approach in estimating future demand for the country's various resources and resource products as illustrated for selected metals in Table 1.

---

[1] Demand is used here interchangeably with use, consumption, requirements, in a non-technical sense, to denote the quantities that will be used up under stated conditions which include no substantial upsets in relative prices.

Reserves and Resources

The projections constitute the background against which future adequacy of metal reserves and resources can be gauged. I say "reserves and resources" to distinguish between those mineral deposits—reserves—that can be mined under prevailing economic conditions and with current technology, and those—resources—whose exploitation is not now commercially feasible. Among obstacles to production may be difficulty of access, distance from market, grade of ore, chemical or physical characteristics of the mineral, and others. All of these factors, it must be emphasized, lack relevance unless related to current market conditions, for at some price no deposit is too hard to get to, too far away from markets, or too poor in grade or make-up to be commercially valuable.

A confrontation of projected United States demand and estimated United States reserves and resources is made in Table 2. At the outset a word of caution. The fact that two-digit figures appear in this presentation should not be taken to connote precision. The estimates are of varying vintage (some 10 years old or more) and reliability. They suggest, at best, orders of magnitude and permit, at most, broad-brush judgements. And even such judgements are beset by problems.

TABLE 1. United States Consumption of Selected Metals, 1960, and Projections Up to the Year 2000

				CUMULATIVE: 1960 to	
		1960	2000	1980	2000
Iron	(a)	59.4	161	1600	4160
Manganese	(b)	1.05	2.9	28	73
Chromium (Cr_2O_3) *	(b)	.52	1.9	15	43
Nickel *	(b)	.12	.56	3.7	11.7
Aluminum	(b)	2.06	13.3	73	255
Copper	(b)	1.74	4.6	42	112
Lead	(b)	.64	1.5	15	38
Zinc	(b)	1.05	3.2	28	69
Tin	(b)	.07	.12	1.3	3.0
Tungsten *	(c)	4.6	21	150	460
Molybdenum *	(c)	15.9	152	650	2560
Vanadium *	(c)	2.0	8.5	60	185
Cobalt *	(c)	4.5	19.2	140	430

(a) In millions of long tons. (b) In millions of short tons. (c) In thousands of short tons.
* Figures represent demand for primary metal, but in the cases marked with an asterisk it has not been found feasible to exclude the likely contribution from obsolete scrap. Also, chromium demand is for chromium oxide rather than the metal.
SOURCE: *Resources in America's Future,* pp. 429, 452.

TABLE 2. United States Cumulative Demand 1960–2000 Compared with Estimated United States Reserves and Resources

		Cumulative Demand for Primary Metal 1960–2000[1]	U.S. RESERVES R.F.F.[1]	U.S. GEOLOGICAL SURVEY National Academy[2]	U.S. GEOLOGICAL SURVEY Senate Hearings[3]	U.S. RESOURCES R.F.F.[1]
Iron	(a)	4.2	3.0	5.5[4]	5.5[4]	23
Manganese[5]	(b)	75	0.9	1.0	–	78
Chromium (Cr$_2$O$_3$)	(b)	45	–	0.5[6]	–	4[7]
Nickel	(b)	12	0.5	0.4	0.2	?
Aluminum	(b)	260	13	50[8]	50[8]	98
Copper	(b)	110	50	32.5	32.5	100
Lead	(b)	40	4.5	7.7	10	8–12
Zinc	(b)	70	25	25	25	?
Tin	(b)	3	–	.005	.005	–
Tungsten	(c)	460	71[9]	70	30	[9]
Molybdenum	(c)	2600	2000	1500	1500	?
Vanadium	(c)	190	600	680	45	?
Cobalt	(c)	430	43	50	15	150

(a) In thousand millions of long tons. (b) In millions of short tons. (c) In thousands of short tons.
– Nonexistent or small.
[1] *Resources in America's Future,* Chapter 21 seriatim.
[2] *Mineral Resources, A Report to the Committee on Natural Resources,* National Academy of Sciences–National Research Council, Publication 1000-C, Washington, D.C., 1962, p. 8.
[3] Testimony of Dr. Thomas B. Nolan, Director, Geological Survey, "State of the Minerals Industry", Hearings before the Sub-committee on Mining, Minerals, and Fuels of the Committe on Interior and Insular Affairs, U.S. Senate, 88th Congress, 1st Session, May 9 and 10, 1963, p. 124.
[4] Iron ore.
[5] R.F.F. figure includes manganese content of ore of all grades. Geological survey figure is stated in terms of ore of 35 per cent manganese content and better.
[6] Chromite.
[7] Undetermined, but probably a small portion of this amount is of reserve status.
[8] Million long tons of bauxite.
[9] Substantial part of amount listed as reserves is probably potential ore at present prices.

I have deliberately presented three sets of figures under "reserves" to demonstrate the wide divergencies that may emerge in even a short space of time. The first column lists estimates compiled early in 1962 by the staff of Resources for the Future (referred to as R.F.F. in these statistics), drawn from published material, mostly from the United States Geological Survey and the United States Bureau of Mines, both major divisions of the Department of the Interior. The next two columns show two sets of estimates of the United States Geological Survey. In submitting the second set, the director of the Geological Survey, Dr. Thomas B. Nolan, characterized the estimates as "revised slightly" from the table submitted previously. Some of the revisions, which occurred in the brief span of two years are substantial. Nickel, tungsten, vanadium, and cobalt have all undergone significant shrinkage, one of them— vanadium—to less than one tenth its previous volume, and are substantially lower than R.F.F.'s estimates, On the other hand, the figure for lead reserves was raised by one third. Both lead reserve estimates exceed the R.F.F. figure (which allows, however, for a 20 per cent milling loss, and, on a comparable basis, would thus be 5.6 million tons).

The point I wish to stress is that reserve estimates are subject to uncertainty, not only at a point of time but over time. Discoveries in new areas can radically alter the picture (e.g. manganese in Gabon, bauxite in Australia), and changing economic conditions can make noneconomic deposits commercially useful or relegate what was at one time considered a reserve into the "potential ore" category. Such revisions tend to seem erratic and oftentimes paradoxial. Yet, most are logical enough. Some may even be anticipated. For example, I would have little hesitation to predict that, before long, estimates of United States iron ore reserves will show a substantial increase, since in the past few years significant portions of the low-grade iron-bearing formations in Minnesota, Wisconsin and Michigan—taconites, semi-taconites, and jasperites—have made the transition from potential ore to reserves. Conversely, it is doubtful that even a small fraction of domestic tungsten occurrences can qualify as reserves, except at highly inflated prices.

One problem then arises from insufficiently frequent updating of estimates to accommodate the depletion of operating properties, upgrading to reserve status of previously non-commercial deposits owing to new technology or lasting increases in price, and the development of new general information about the presence or frequency of mineral deposits in an area. Another derives from the sharp price fluctuations to which some metals have been subject (e.g., the price drop in tungsten that occurred in 1957–58). To the extent that these can be clearly discerned as temporary phenomena and one can distill a "normal" price that would prevail in the long run, such fluctuation should not affect estimates of reserve. In practice, it may, however, be difficult to adhere to such a prescription, and some of the more striking differences in Table 2 are undoubtedly owing to just such a situation.

In fact, there is nothing wrong with such fluctuations in reserve estimates, *provided* the authority responsible for making them accompanies the release of the information with the proper explanation and, preferably, a showing of reserves at a schedule of prices. While such a schedule would never be very accurate, it would give a dimension to the reserve estimate that is now lacking. For example, to know that, at a price of $20, United States tungsten reserves are in the neighbourhood of 30,000 tons of contained metal, that at, say, $40 they would rise to 70,000 tons, and at, say, $60 to perhaps 100,000 tons or more, woula make the reserve estimate a much more valuable piece of information than it is now, when it appears capriciously to skip about over what is sometimes a very wide range. As information accumulates and the public is given access to it, one must hope that the simple estimates of to-day will one day be replaced by such schedules of prices and tonnages. And while one is wishing, one might as well "wish big" and suggest that such schedules, in addition, would note the the reasons for higher cost such as lower metal content, poorer accessibility, high-cost process, etc.

Demand Versus Domestic Reserves and Resources

Thus cautioned, let us compare cumulative demand up to the year 2000 with current estimates of United States *reserves*. The over-all conclusion is that reserves approach demand only in the case of molybdenum (where projected demand, incidentally, is likely to have been overstated); and in the case of vanadium, though here all depends on the figure one picks for reserves, i.e., on one's view of the price situation for vanadium and for its associated coproduct, uranium. In none of the major metals do United States reserves, as presently estimated, appear sufficient to go the distance. Because of the limitations of reserve estimates, it would be surprising if it were different, for, in practice, though not in concept, they reflect less an independent estimate of discovered and undiscovered occurrences that can be profitably mined at current prices and technology than findings of mining companies. These are in business to make profits from production, not to develop reserves beyond the amount deemed necessary to support such production for a reasonable length of time. To some extent the supply–demand gaps revealed in our tabulation may therefore reflect the facts of commercial life.

As a second step, we might compare cumulative demand with *resources*, taken here to indicate the sum of reserves and identified potential ore, the latter concept denoting the potential ore for which there exist quantitative estimates. Since all material with any metal content whatsoever is potential ore, the narrowing down to the "identified" level brings potential ore within statistical reach. This comparison changes the picture radically for iron, manganese and copper: resources about equal or exceed demand. But for aluminium, lead, zinc, tin, chromium, nickel and tungsten there remains a wide gap.

A third query then arises: what would be the likely effect of having recourse to domestic material not now in the reserve category? The lack of information on cost/grade relationships—"grade" being shorthand for a wide variety of quality characteristics—allows one to advance only the broadest of judgements. In the case of iron, available evidence suggests that higher cost encountered in mining low-grade domestic material would boost the price of the steel ingot by not more than two or three percentage points (though additional short-run cost might arise from disruptions in the relationship between ore supplies and plant location). A shift to domestic, low-grade sources of bauxite, bauxitic clays and other inferior aluminium-bearing minerals might raise the price of the aluminium ingot by as much as 10 per cent, but in the longer run one would expect this penalty to be reduced, if not eliminated.

On the other hand, as a colleague of mine on the staff of Resources for the Future recently showed, extremely steep price increases are required to call forth production of domestic tungsten from sources other than the few that are favourably situated. And even then the volume of additional production tends to be quite moderate. Similar conditions probably prevail for nickel, chromium and manganese. Price increases associated with low-grade material are likely to to be substantial, though not necessarily as steep as in the case of tungsten.

As for copper, we have a long historic record to go by: a steady decline in the grade of ore mined—from 3 per cent in 1880 to an average of less than 0.8 per cent to-day—has gone hand in hand with long-range stability in price, owing to cost-saving innovations and imports. Can this trend persist as the average grade mined declines further? Here history fails to suggest a clear answer. One can argue that mining involves an irreducible minimum loss that looms larger and larger as the average grade mined declines, and that, as a consequence, the cost must rise. In rebuttal, one can argue that more efficient methods of handling increasing amounts of waste rock will keep the cost from rising, and that a different technology, perhaps in the form of substantially different mining and recovery methods—such as leaching in place, for example—may progressively lower the loss ratio so that cost-boosting forces will be beaten back. The answer lies wholly in the future, but its obvious that the situation differs from that of iron and aluminium, on the one hand, and that of tungsten or manganese on the other.

United States reserves of lead and zinc appear greatly deficient for meeting projected demand, but one cannot tell what this implies for the long-run cost of the two metals, since only very sketchy information on the volume and character of potential ore is available. One must ask, instead, what causes this lack of data, and why one is confronted with fluctuations of reserve estimates without the broader framework of a resource estimate. The answer may lie partly in the geologic circumstances in which these metals occur—*i.e.*, underground (and frequently small) deposits and sharp cut-offs rather than continuity in the shape of extensive halos of low grade; much of the metal occurring in combination with others; many mines, largely of the lead-zinc-precious metal variety in the West, that have not been fully exploited, but are unlikely to be reopened and are not part of the reserve estimate; the ailing state of the lead and zinc industries, which has, in general, depressed the level of exploratory activity and most importantly has kept the investigation of one per cent or leaner ore deposits from taking place altogether.

Recently lead reserve estimates have been substantially raised. The successive upward revisions of the United States Geological Survey's estimate, from 5.6 million in 1957 to 7.7 million tons in 1962 and 10 million tons in early 1963, undoubtedly reflect the discoveries in southeastern Missouri whose extent has now begun to be gauged sufficiently to allow their appearance in the reserve estimates. In other words, reserves in lead have grown, owing to discoveries rather than to shifts in economic conditions. One must add, however, that recent discoveries do not represent a new lead "province". Though there has also been extensive discovery in zinc, reserve estimates have not as yet been affected.

Future Supply Patterns: Five Tonnage Metals

Determinants of the pattern of future supplies will differ for different metals. In the case of *iron*, the most important will be the cost margin, at the steel mill, between imported high-grade iron ore and beneficiated domestic ore. The competitive position, incidentally, will reflect the curious fact that technological changes in steel-making have conferred certain advantages upon, or removed certain handicaps from, beneficiated low-grade ore.

Another factor will be the weight that mine owners—often identical with steel producers—give to the desirability of working off their foreign ore investments as against developing their low-grade domestic holdings. Given three important factors—the magnitude of the funds sunk into foreign ventures (including shipping and other transportation facilities), the locational advantages of much domestic steel-making capacity for foreign ore, and the still not fully developed character of some of the techniques that would provide the key to the utilization of the bulk of America's low-grade iron ore—it is likely that, for some time to come, foreign ores will at least hold their own and possibly further encroach upon domestic material.

The length of the ocean voyage is only one of the cost factors that determine competitiveness, and, especially where subsequent rail shipment is required, the cost of extra water mileage does not stand out as one of the large cost items. Thus, iron ore has come long distances. Liberia, among African iron ore producers, has become an established supplier, and others—such as Mauritania and Gabon—may follow in the future. Chile and Peru have shipped iron ore to the United States.

However, rapidly swelling export capacity in Canada will constitute a formidable competitor, as will further progress in turning out a competitive and abundantly available domestic product. Both will tend to limit severely imports from sources other than nearby Western Hemisphere locations.

The Caribbean is the source of nine-tenths of America's *bauxite* supply. There is no indication that this is about to change, despite the twin facts that aluminium is the most abundant metal in the earth's crust, and that the feasibility of using domestic minerals has been demonstrated. Even a minor advantage in cost is sufficient to favour imports, especially in view of the relative nearness and magnitude of the traditional suppliers and the corporate identity of bauxite and aluminium producers. Reserves in place in Jamaica, Surinam, and British Guiana alone amount to at least 850 million long tons of bauxite, sufficient to produce some 200 million short tons of aluminium. In the light of a projected 40-year demand of 255 million tons of aluminium and the existence of another 700 million tons of potential ore or more in the three countries named, it is not realistic to expect United States aluminium producers to make an eager search for alternative domestic supplies. On the other hand, it is probably wise to prepare for a slow shift from imported bauxite to imported aluminium, or at least alumina.

It is much harder to reach a judgement concerning the future supply pattern of *copper*. Foreign trade is complex. Both imports and exports are large compared to consumption, and a substantial percentage of imports consists of raw copper (ore, blister, matte, etc.) that is refined in United States plants and then exported. These in-and-out movements fluctuate a good deal from year to year. In addition, much refined copper is imported for consumption as well as for re-export. On a net basis, in 1940 the United States turned from an exporter to an importer of raw and refined copper, though recent record exports and moderate declines in imports have reduced the import balance, until, in 1961, there emerged once again a net export (if only of a few thousand tons).

While *net* imports provide the more logical starting point in appraising problems like national security or the balance of payments, in judging the future rôle of imports one must focus on *gross* rather than net imports. These, too, have declined, owing to diminishing imports of refined copper. But raw copper imports have continued to represent a constant share—about 22 per cent—of gross primary supply, and thus, even in 1961, when the small export balance emerged, copper produced from imported ore and concentrates plus imported refined metal totalled nearly 440,000 tons, or more than one third the tonnage refined from domestic ores. Thus, large-scale imports go hand-in-hand with a small or nonexistent net import balance.

How are imports related to the contribution that output from domestic mines has made over the longer term? At different times, domestic output has reached, or just exceeded, one million tons, first in 1929, then in the first half of the 'forties, and, with the major exception of 1959, every year since 1955. The latter is quite a remarkable event, since, at other times, the achievement of the one-million-ton level has been followed by abrupt and steep declines. But the lowest since 1955 has been 800,000 tons in 1959, and the recovery was rapid and thorough.

The figures suggest that, up to World War II, fluctuations in demand severely affected smelter production from domestically mined ores, but that, thereafter, imports have taken most of the buffeting. Can one legitimately project this condition into the future, and is it safe,. therefore, to assume that the decline in both gross and net imports—mainly *via* declining imports of refined material—suggests a new pattern?

I would think not, at least not within the framework of the Resources for the Future projections. For 1980 demand for primary copper has been projected at 2.5 million tons; for the year 2000 at 4.5 million.[2] While domestic copper mining has expanded—and the opening of Arizona's Mission mine in November, 1961, was only the latest, but is not likely to be the last, example of new mines brought into play—it is difficult to imagine that, by 1980, expansion could raise domestic copper mining sufficiently to fill the projected increase in demand of 800,000 tons of metal.

In doubting such expansion, I am guided by the consideration that projected demand for primary copper in the four decades ending in 2000 would cumulate to over 100 million tons. Even if one should judge current estimates of United States reserves to be conservative, one would not want to assume that such tonnage could be met from domestic deposits. Current mining capacity has been reported at 1,318,000 short tons in 1961 and assumed to rise to not quite 1,400,000 by 1966. Let us optimistically assume that future exploration and development might raise this to 1,600,000 tons by 1980 and to 1,800,000 by 2000. And let us assume further that average annual production would amount to 80 per cent of capacity. Then production in the years 1960–1980 would total some 50 million tons. This would equal Resources for the Future's estimate of reserves (which is 50 per cent more generous than that of the United States Geologic Survey) and leave more than half of the projected 1960–2000 demand unmet.

By the end of the century, projected annual demand reaches 4.5 million tons of primary copper; the prospects of supplying more than one third or two fifths from domestic mines are not bright. In view of the drastic difference in grade—deposits in Latin America and Africa running several times the 0.75 per cent at which United States copper is

[2] That these figures are not larger is owing to generous allowances for secondary production that will flow from increased future copper consumption: barring changes in the rate of scrap generation, by the end of the century secondary production would slightly exceed current United States production of primary copper from all sources.

being mined, on the average—foreign sources would seem better equipped to respond to a long trend of rising demand. It is not likely that domestic occurrences of substantially higher grade than now mined have been overlooked; grade of ore mined in the United States will thus continue to decline.[3] The problem this poses is clear. A decline in of less than 3 per cent additional ore, but a decline by 0.1 per cent from 0.75 to 0.65 per cent means that some 20 per cent more ore must be handled. While there may be savings in cost in the transition from underground mining of high-grade ore to open-pit mining of low-grade ore, it is less likely that savings will accrue as open-pit mining tackles ore grades progressively declining below three-quarters of one per cent.

Two important considerations, however, keep one from concluding unhesitatingly that, in the long run, copper imports must increase. The first is that there is far more copper ore with a grade lying between 0.7 and 0.6 per cent than there was between 3.8 and 3.7 per cent, thus giving a very broad base to domestic operations. Secondly, history shows that higher efficiency in combination with the advantage in transportation has maintained domestic copper at a competitive level, despite pronounced inferiority in grade. Much will, therefore, depend on future developments in costs abroad—that is, in Africa and Latin America. If stable political and social conditions permit mining to take place in a regular and efficient fashion, the advantages of the raw material will have a greater chance of being reflected in lower costs. But to the degree that continued investment is made a questionable venture, copper producers may, as has happened, decide that a low-grade ore in a stable political and social environment offers a more promising opportunity for investment than a high-grade ore whose exploitation may be rendered uncertain and costly by external conditions.

What about the future supply pattern of *lead* and *zinc?* Demand has been projected for lead at about 40 million and zinc at about 70 million short tons (both excluding secondary production) for the next four decades. In the last year of that period annual demands for lead would run at about 1.5 million tons, for zinc at about twice that figure, both in terms of recoverable metal content.

If one takes domestic reserve estimates at face value, adequacy appears unlikely: less than 10 million tons of recoverable lead, and some 20 million tons of recoverable zinc, assuming a recovery factor of 80 per cent. The quality of these estimates leaves much to be desired, and the lack of data on potential lead and zinc ore, pointed out above, makes them even less meaningful. But they are hardly so poor as to alter the judgement that the United States economy will have to rely heavily upon imports of either ore or metal. Only major discoveries could alter

[3] Resources down to a copper content of only 0.5 per cent may total 100 million tons, thus doubling the reserve estimate. But this is a purely theoretical figure, deduced from historical and geologic correlations.

this conclusion. Substantial new deposits have been found in recent years, lead in southeastern Missouri and zinc in Tennessee, suggesting that more surprises may be ahead; but the gap between projected demand and reserves is very large, and to the degree that foreign ore is available, the incentive to explore at home is likely to lag.

As has been pointed out elsewhere, the United States government's efforts during the Korean War to subsidize exploration for lead and zinc had most disappointing results. It would be surprising if similar efforts in the future were to be more successful and the United States economy were to become less rather than more dependent upon imports, provided that demand develops along the lines projected in Resources for the Future's study. At the moment, quota restrictions on imports prevent this. But, in the long run, the maintenance of a higher price to producers —designed to call forth additional domestic production—would, unless accompanied by subsidies to users, stimulate substitution. Aluminium and plastic have replaced lead or zinc in a variety of uses in the past, an experience that casts a heavy shadow over the prospect of successful protection and stimulation by import restriction.

In a 40-year perspective, therefore, one would have to anticipate a growing import opportunity. How large? Assuming that supplies of neither lead nor zinc from domestic mines are likely to increase significantly, lead imports might approach 500,000 tons in 1980 and exceed 1,000,000 tons by the end of the century. Even if domestic mining should rise to the high level it held in the 'twenties, the required imports would still amount to 200,000 tons by 1980 and by the end of the century to 800,000 tons. Under parallel assumptions, zinc imports would exceed one million tons in 1980 and some 2.5 million tons in 2000. Since the production of zinc has not declined as much as from historical highs as has that of lead, the reattainment of previous peaks would reduce these estimates but little.

The persistent lag of growth in the consumption of lead, and to a lesser degree of zinc, may raise questions as to the rationale of future growth. While the test lies in the future, it is worth mentioning that the projected growth of demand for lead rests upon a steady advance in the consumption of batteries, principally for motor vehicles, leading to an increase of about 120 per cent in lead consumption for this purpose between 1960 and 2000, and to a much faster growth of lead as a fuel additive, causing a better than tripling of lead consumption in that use between 1960 and 2000. Since the latter consumption is dissipative—in contrast to the steady return to secondary production of used-up batteries—the faster growth in fuel use represents a correspondingly bigger boost for the demand for primary metal.

Die casting, use in brass products, and galvanizing of steel sheet and strip are projected as the areas of fastest rising demand for zinc. The growing construction industry, deriving its momentum from rapid population growth and household formation in the coming decades, is the most important single customer in the demand for galvanized sheet and strip, followed by transportation and producer durables.

Supply of Minor Non-Ferrous Metals

When we come to *manganese, nickel* and *chromium,* problems of the quality of estimates of United States reserves become well-nigh academic, since appreciable domestic supplies of these metals—and to a lesser degree also of *tungsten*—have, in the past, come forth only under conditions of highly favourable prices, generally provided through government purchase programmes. The demand projections, excluding scrap, therefore come close to being the equivalent of import opportunities (Table 1).

In looking ahead for nearly half a century the possibility that a domestic supply source might emerge cannot, of course, be categorically denied. For example, manganese production from steel mill slag heaps or from ocean floor nodules may some day be profitable. Most steel mills do, as a matter of routine, segregate slag that is high in manganese content, which suggests that they keep this potential supply in mind. Manganese production from ocean nodules receives sporadic attention, and when it does, it tends to fascinate the reader. But although the estimates advanced by at least one of the researchers in the field paint an exceedingly attractive picture of low cost, a follow-up in the form of commercial activity has failed so far to materialize—possibly because the requisite scale of operation is so large as to make the investment formidable and the risk high.

To bring into play the more pedestrian domestic on-shore resources —assaying between 10 and 15 per cent manganese—would raise prices to two or three times the current world level, and only an emergency is likely to provoke such action. The decline in domestic manganese ore production (35 per cent or more manganese content) from 364,000 tons in 1957—stimulated by a government price 2½ times the world level— to 39,000 tons in 1961 testifies to this. Thus, the demand for 22 million tons up to 1980 and for the additional 26 million tons up to the end of the century[4] would seem to call in its entirety for imported material.

Domestic production of nickel, chromium, and tungsten would be feasible, in conjunction with manganese and other metals from ocean nodules, and the same doubts obtain. More conventional domestic sources, at or near world prices, are not in sight, even on the most generous interpretation of data. Large-scale government subsidy programmes have obscured the supply picture by recording, for example, a tenfold increase in domestic chromium production during the 'fifties;

[4] The magnitudes are based principally upon projected steel demand, assuming the continuation of present levels of manganese admixture per ton of steel ingot.

currently only a few thousand tons of domestic chromium "make the grade", leaving imports to fill the demand projected at 115 million tons of chromium oxide for the years 1960–2000.

The United States produces no nickel as metal from domestic ores. Apart from a few hundred tons that are a by-product of copper refining, the sole operation now existing derives some 10,000 tons of ferro-nickel from a silicate-ore deposit in Oregon. An unspecified part of production is sold to the United States government under long-term contract. The only other producing facility in the country, capable of turning out about 1,000 tons of metal from local sulphide ore, closed down early in 1961. In recent years, despite encouragement by the government through purchase agreements, domestic primary production has not filled more than 10 to 15 per cent of the country's consumption. The balance is imported or derived from nickel-bearing scrap.

This state of affairs reflects the apparently poor endowment of the country. Reserves in the continental United States are at present believed not to exceed one-quarter of a million tons in nickel content, the equivalent of some two years' consumption. An equal amount is estimated to exist in Alaska. Continuing imports would thus seem the major source of supply.

The effect of price upon tungsten reserves has already been discussed in this article. When, in the first half of the 'fifties, the United States government paid $60 per short ton unit (one ton of material containing 20 lb. of WO_3 or 16 lb. of metal) there were more than 700 individual mining operations, producing as much as 7,000 tons of metal a year. In late 1958, all but two producers had quit the field, and production had dropped to less than 2,000 tons; it has recently been running at about twice that level, and imports have dropped sharply.

Projected consumption is 460,000 tons over the balance of the century. While reserve estimates are not explicitly related to price nor to a detailed schedule as to what portion is in tungsten operations (as opposed to the production of tungsten as a by-product), even the optimistic estimate of 71,000 tons remains too far below projected requirements not to make continuing, perhaps large, imports inevitable.

In both *molybdenum* and *vanadium* the United States is well endowed. In molybdenum, new discoveries and extensions of know deposits of molybdenum and copper should provide the country with sufficient supplies not only to meet rising domestic demand but also to support a large export trade. Estimates of vanadium contained in known United States deposits run at 600,000 tons.[5] The projected use of vanadium in the next 40 years has been estimated at only one-third of this magnitude. Most interest has been centred on winning vanadium as a by-product of uranium mining—and this may be subject to sub-

---

[5] The most recent write-down to 45,000 tons was apparently made under the impact of the closing down of certain uranium operations.

stantial fluctuations—but it can be expected that advancing technology will make vanadium commercially accessible in other minerals, such as titaniferous magnetite and vanadiferous phosphate. All this leaves little doubt of long-term United States self-sufficiency.

The same cannot be said of *cobalt*, of which United States reserves are only moderate: 43,000 tons, plus 107,000 tons of potential ore. This compares with projected 40-year consumption of nearly half a million tons. At present, only one cobalt mining operation exists in the United States, producing cobalt-bearing pyrite from magnetic iron ores in Pennsylvania. Imports supply the bulk of consumption. It is difficult to foresee any significant change in this pattern, especially in view of the metal's importance in defence applications.

Government Support of Domestic Industry

Since in almost no metallic mineral is the United States entirely devoid of at least a moderate or poor deposit, attempts to increase the country's degree of self-sufficiency have never ceased. Whether aiming at strengthening national security or promoting local economic development, the practical objective has been the limitation of lower-priced imports, usually through the imposition of tariffs or quotas, or by lowering the cost to the consumer of the domestic product through subsidies.

One of the dangers inherent in the first attempt is a loss of markets. A continuing high price or major price and supply fluctuations make any material unattractive. The growing potential for substitution between different metals and between metals and non-metals provides ready alternatives. Lead and zinc mining have been the latest beneficiaries of a subsidy programme, which has been added to the more basic existing import quota system. Small producers are paid a portion of the gap between a stipulated "normal price" and the average price as it prevails in the market. The percentage is 75 for lead and 55 for zinc; for both metals the yardstick price is 14.5 cents per pound.

Another operation which did not originate as a subsidizing move but ended up close to being one has been the government stockpile programme. Its principal effect upon the supply pattern has been to bring into being, or keep alive—for various periods and at considerable cost—numerous mining operations whose output, delivered to the government, has included much not otherwise marketable material, which vanished from the scene as soon as the helping hand of government had been withdrawn.

At issue in these attempts is the wisdom of buying insurance against contingent shortage; by stockpiling, by keeping in being uneconomical operations, or in other ways. The record suggests that legislators have tended to believe in it, but have not generally addressed themselves to the question of whether the direct and indirect costs of such programme are lower than would be the costs of restarting or augmenting domestic production if and when required. It is clear, however, that where quotas and tariffs have been voted, they have preferred to let the cost fall, in the first instance, upon the consumer of the metal in question rather than on society as a whole, whereas stockpiling has been financed out of general revenue.

It would be Utopian to expect such barriers to disappear or to be dismantled at a rapid rate. This is all the more true as the domestic industry involved is usually geographically concentrated and thus lends itself to an impressive demonstration of depressed local conditions brought about by foreign competition. Indeed, it is perhaps remarkable that there has slowly developed a substantial amount of immunity to this particular justification for mineral subsidies or import restrictions. For example, neither the small but highly vocal fluorspar industry nor, at the other end of the spectrum, the large iron ore mining industry has succeeded in making the argument stick. The percentage of imported iron ore has climbed rapidly since the 1950's, despite attempts to halt or reverse this situation. A potentially much more effective countermeasure is the continuing development and improvement of low-grade domestic iron-bearing minerals, not too long ago deemed practically worthless, but increasingly entering into the country's iron ore reserves. The 20 billion tons of iron estimated to be contained in these formations would constitute more than enough to feed United States steel mills far into the 21st century.

Apart from the broad research programme carried out by the United States Geological Survey and the Bureau of Mines (both subdivisions of the United States Department of Interior—and, in themselves, perhaps the most important long-term government aids to mining), there have been specific attempts to strengthen the domestic leg of United States metal supply; first, through the fostering of research designed to bring low-grade materials into competitive production and, secondly, through assistance in exploration for as yet undiscovered mineral occurrences. The most recent attempts under the second heading have been the Defence Minerals Exploration programme, initiated in April, 1951, and terminated in mid-1958, and its successor, a virtually identical programme passed by Congress in the second half of 1958 and administered by the Department of Interior's Office of Mineral Exploration. In both instances, the goal has been to stimulate exploration activities through government contributions to specific, privately-sponsored exploration ventures for a long list of named minerals. Government participation varied and at one time went as high as 90 per cent in the case of uranium. At present, 50 per cent constitutes the upper limit.

The main impetus toward broadening the supply base of domestic minerals has come, and presumably will continue to come, from regular activities of government and mining companies, or mining departments of firms in the field of metals, chemicals and other related branches of industry. The vision of the latter, however, as in the past, is more likely to transcend the confines of the United States. They can be expected carefully to weigh development work on low-grade domestic ore against the risks involved in financing high-grade ore projects abroad. A balanced advance along both paths, as we have seen in iron ore and copper, is the most likely outcome. And if the projections of Resources for the Future are anywhere near the mark, then the coming decades should provide room for both domestic output and imports to enjoy the fruits of rising demand.

36. The Aluminum Industry in Australia

Craig Duncan

The development of an aluminum industry in Australia offers an actual example of the role played by geographic factors in mineral utilization, as described by Bateman in an earlier selection. The scale of operation possible was a decisive factor in the utilization of these recently discovered deposits of bauxite.

In recent years aluminum has come to occupy a prominent place among world metals. During World War II strategic requirements led to a rapid increase in ingot capacity, and the transition to peacetime uses brought but a temporary diminution in demand. The war had engendered a wider appreciation of the properties of aluminum and its alloys; production costs had been cut; and, as a result, an acceleration first in American and then in world consumption soon became apparent.

In 1953 aluminum replaced copper as the leading nonferrous metal in the United States. Although the threat to copper was not as readily discernible in world consumption figures, by 1958 aluminum was certainly challenging copper for the leading place.

Confident in the buoyancy of the market and encouraged by the optimistic predictions for the future of the metal, the aluminum industry

SOURCE: *Geographical Review*, LI (1961), 21–46. The author is senior lecturer in the Department of Geography, University of Queensland, Brisbane.

put into effect elaborate plans for expansion. In 1958, for example, two new producers, Ormet and Harvey Aluminum, added 176,500 tons to United States capacity. Along with 154,000 tons of new capacity from the established producers, this increased the country's productive potential by about 20 per cent. Similar, if less spectacular, increases occurred in other countries.

The validity of long-term predictions is still acceptable, so that this rapid increase in production capacity augurs well for the future. For the present, however, and coincident with a general, if mild, recession in North America and a slight downtrend in Europe, overproduction is plaguing the industry. The more ambitious plans for domestic and overseas expansion have been temporarily shelved as producers wait for demand to take up their idle capacity—estimated to be 10 per cent of installed capacity in the United States, 13 per cent in Canada, in early 1960.

It is against this background that the aluminum industry in Australia must be viewed. In keeping with the general world trend, consumption has increased remarkably in the postwar years. During the five years to 1958 consumption of ingot and aluminum shapes more than doubled —from a net of 14,521 tons in 1954 to 31,335 tons in 1958. In Australia, aluminum occupies fifth place by weight (tonnage) among the major metals consumed; in volume (cubic feet) it is outranked only by steel.

Development of the Industry

Until World War II access to the use of major industrial processes was tightly controlled. A succession of aluminum cartels in Europe held control of the Héroult patents; the last of them, the Alliance Aluminum Compagnie, a highly centralized organization formed in 1931, regulated the production, sales, and prices of aluminum and financed a pool of accumulated stocks. In the United States the Hall patents, originally acquired by the Pittsburgh Reduction Company, were held almost exclusively by the Aluminum Company of America (not, it must be added, without some litigation) until the outbreak of World War II. Alcoa, through its subsidiaries, had built an empire that reached into every market for aluminum. It was not until patents were released as a result of wartime emergencies that industries were established, first in the United States and then overseas.

Unhampered access to patents discouraged the establishment of an aluminum industry in Australia. The British Aluminium Company, a member of the European cartels, and the Electrolytic Zinc Company of Australasia had planned to produce aluminum at Risdon, Tasmania, where the latter company had a zinc smelter. However, the war intervened, and nothing came of the venture.

Australia continued to import aluminum even though its supply lines were reduced and indeed threatened in the early stages of the war in the Pacific. Aluminum was a critical material. Consequently, when the Australian Aluminium Production Commission was formed in 1944, it was instructed by the Commonwealth government "to do all such acts and things as are necessary for the production of ingot aluminium," and to do this "with all possible expedition in order to promote the naval, military, and air defence of the Commonwealth and its territories."

Thus, as a result of the exigencies of war, Australia established the key smelting industry. Capital was made available from public funds, and management was vested in the commission as a statutory corporation, or government-financed body. This arrangement did not draw on private supplies of capital for so large an undertaking. Overseas companies, intent on supplying ingot to Australian fabricating industries, naturally had no incentive to establishing smelting plants; in addition the prevailing political climate discouraged any such move. Relatively high establishment costs, a limited market, and high labor costs, often coupled with restrictive practices, were further deterrents to investment in Australia.

The relation of the industry to physical input factors has also conditioned Australian development. Deposits of bauxite, long known to exist within the country, lacked the economic advantages that might have encouraged their use. Neither quality nor quantity was adequate to overcome the economic prejudice against high coastal shipping rates and unreliable coastal services. Bauxite for the Australian smelting industry has had to be obtained from overseas.

However, the whole industrial outlook is undergoing a revolutionary change. In 1955 widespread laterites in the Cape York Peninsula of northern Queensland were identified as bauxite. After two years of intensive prospecting and proving, their extent was roughly determined. The deposits consist for the most part of good-quality ore and promise to transform completely the structure of the Australian aluminum industry. The field is so extensive that large-scale development will not only be feasible but necessary if high establishment costs are to be met.

Access to large supplies of hydroelectric power is a prerequisite to any industrial location of an aluminum smelting industry. On the mainland of Australia unreliable river flows combine with a generally mature topography to reduce to a minimum the number of suitable hydroelectric generating sites. For this reason Tasmania, with its more rugged surface and higher rainfall totals, may be regarded as the only available source of economically suitable hydroelectric power. But even Tasmania's resources are inadequate to accommodate a major industry such as that to be based on the new bauxite discovery. Consequently, if a major project is contemplated, it will be necessary to locate the smelting industry elsewhere.

Bauxite, the Basic Raw Material

One form of bauxite is an aluminous variant of lateritic processes and is therefore found primarily in tropical regions or in areas where the tropical conditions of high mean temperatures, heavy rainfall, and an abundant supply of organic acids are to some extent simulated. Gentle relief is a further requirement, because it makes for sluggish surface and underground drainage, which encourages dissolution and results in the selective precipitation of iron and aluminum compounds. Bauxite usually occurs as a blanket deposit on a appropriate peneplain surfaces or on the level surfaces of basic and intermediate fissure eruptions. Elsewhere, it occurs in pockets and lenses. It is a porous rock, often pisolitic with the pisolites either separate or loosely cemented, a structure that adds considerably to the ease of mining by surface methods.

Alumina (Al_2O_3), which is extracted from the bauxite, is found in two forms. Of these, the trihydrate, gibbsite, is more readily soluble in caustic soda and can thus be extracted at much lower temperatures than the monohydrates, boehmite and diaspore. Both the trihydrate and the monohydrates are found in Australia.

As early as 1900 pisolitic rocks, probably bauxitic, were examined by government geologists in various parts of Australia, but it was not until after World War II that a methodical survey was undertaken. As a result, many of the deposits were found to be within economic mining limits.[1] In 1951 reports of deposits in the Northern Territory led to the locating of several new areas. It was during this period that nearly nine million tons were proved on Marchinbar, one of the Wessel Islands.

The situation before the Cape York discovery of 1955 is summarized in Table I. Altogether these reserves plus other small and often low-grade deposits were estimated to total about 35 million tons, or about half the reserve of the United States. Mining has been on a diminutive scale, and none of this ore has been used for the production of aluminum. The small deposits of Tamborine Mountain in Queensland and those in the Boolarra district of Victoria provide raw material for industrial and pharmaceutical chemicals. The New South Wales deposits at Moss Vale and a low-grade deposit at Gosford are currently being used to control slag fluidity in the open-hearth steel furnaces at Newcastle and Port Kembla. Quantities mined in 1958, mainly for these uses, were 4,054 tons in Victoria, 1,664 tons in New South Wales, and 1,191 tons in Queensland. The total is not large, nor is the use critical. For example, bauxite deposits have in some areas provided excellent road metals.

The search for bauxite continued in the northern areas. The New

[1] Defined as aluminous laterite that contains not less than 30 per cent of available alumina.

TABLE I. Australian Bauxite Reserves, 1953 (*In thousands of tons*) *

Locality	RESERVES		Approximate Al_2O_3 Composition
	Proved	Indicated	
Queensland			
Tamborine Mountain	473	1,020	37.3–41.0
Hampton		250	37.8
New South Wales			
Inverell	9,610	5,960	35.7–42.9
Moss Vale	518	3,600	31.0–53.9
Trundle		40	43.0–55.0
Victoria			
Boolarra	769	116	43.8–53.0
Tasmania			
Ouse	627		38.6–41.0
St. Leonards	142	10	40.9–41.7
Myalla		180	
Northern Territory			
Marchinbar Island	8,980	800	47.7–53.3
TOTAL	21,100	12,000	

* After H. B. Owen: Bauxite in Australia, *Bur. of Mineral Resources Bull.* 24, Canberra, 1954, p. 15.

Guinea Resources Prospecting Company, after examining reports of a further thirty million tons in Arnhem Land, adacent to the Marchinbar discovery, was able to establish the existence in quantity of pisolitic bauxite averaging 48 per cent alumina content on the Gove Peninsula. It also established that many of the lateritic deposits of other areas noted by the Australian Aluminium Production Commission were too high in silica to be of economic value.

Late in 1955 an oil prospecting party identified as pisolitic laterite a surface formation along the west shore of the Cape York Peninsula. Subsequent investigations by the Consolidated Zinc Corporation, operating through a subsidiary, Enterprise Exploration Pty. Ltd., led in 1956 to the announcement that the deposits were "very substantial and of a grade suitable for the manufacture of alumina."

The Cape York bauxite deposits, named the Weipa formation, overlie "a relatively thin series of arkosic sands, sandy clays and silts probably of Tertiary age." They lie on the imperceptibly dipping western flank of the Cape York geanticline. Erosion has removed much of the laterite from crestal areas; streams have dissected the surface so that near the coast wide estuaries separate a series of lateritic plateaus that represent "remnants of the old Tertiary peneplain and occur immediately inland from the coastal plains." Altogether the laterites cover about 500 square miles, of which 200 square miles contain bauxite of economic grade, most of it gibbsite; the less desirable boehmite is in the upper zone.

"The tonnage of metal grade bauxite in the whole of these districts is not accurately known, but it is estimated that the reserves may be more than 3,000 million tons, of which at least 2,000 million tons will be metal grade averaging 55 per cent alumina, 3.5 per cent reactive silica, and 1.5 per cent quartz." So extensive is the bauxitic layer that it may be said to be the largest in the world, estimated to contain about 30 per cent of total world reserves.

The magnitude of the discovery has completely reoriented Australia's potential for production of aluminum. Not only is the rather small but expanding Australian industry assured eventually of a supply of raw material, but the Weipa deposits are extensive enough to warrant large and long-term development, with sales in world markets as the ultimate aim. With a full realization of these possibilities, Consolidated Zinc in 1956 formed the Commonwealth Aluminium Corporation (Comalco) and was joined early in 1957 by the British Aluminium Company as an equal partner. In addition to its considerable technical knowledge, British Aluminium had, through its partnership in the New Guinea Resources Prospecting Company, an interest in the Gove Peninsula bauxite deposits of the Northern Territory. A special mining lease of some twenty-two square miles in this area was granted to Comalco.

Comalco was also granted a "Special Bauxite Mining Lease" by the Queensland Government and was instructed to

conduct such geological and/or geophysical investigation surveys and/or boring pitting and other testing on the Special Bauxite Mining Lease as it considers necessary to determine the scale of its operations for the mining of the designated materials and the capacity of the plant and other facilities to be erected and installed within or near the area for the purpose of treatment of such designated materials and the production of alumina and other products. . . .

Within fifteen years of the date of the agreement, Comalco was further instructed to

make such investigations as may be necessary to ascertain the economic possibility of constructing and operating within the Special Bauxite Mining Lease or elsewhere in the State a large-scale enterprise for the conversion of alumina into aluminium. . . .

Provisions in the agreement act also outlined specifications for town development, water-resource investigation, conservation measures, and plans for the establishment of port facilities. The framers obviously tried to strike a balance between maximizing the development of the resource and retaining, first for Queensland, and then, if this proved impractical, for another location in Australia or its territories, the economic benefits accruing from mining *and* manufacturing. The definition of the "large-scale enterprise" appears, in the circumstances, to be exceptionally modest—"an aluminium smelter of a designed capacity of not less than thirty thousand tons . . . per annum." This is about Australia's present aluminum consumption and is less than the capacity of any of the North American plants. Recently Comalco announced that, regardless of the location of the smelter, alumina works costing about $100 million would be erected on the mining site.

Locating a major reduction plant, estimated to cost $450 million, requires much more prolonged investigation. The most critical factor, a continuous supply of large amounts of inexpensive electricity, is at present occupying Comalco's attention. Power-generation possibilities in Queensland and in the Territory of Papua have been investigated. New Zealand, because of its high undeveloped power potential, is also being considered.

Queensland possesses potential power resources in the rivers of the tropical northeast, but it lacks the extensive storage facilities necessary for the control of the highly variable flows. Consequently Comalco, in meeting the terms of the act, undertook to investigate alternative sources of power before turning to other areas.

At Blair Athol, in east-central Queensland, there are extensive deposits of good-quality coal. A five-year option on the area was taken by Comalco. Exploratory drilling indicated that about 200 million tons of good-quality, steam-raising coal in one continuous seam averaging 78 feet in thickness was to be found. The tonnage that could be extracted by inexpensive open-cut methods is reported as sufficient for a continuous output of 700,000 kilowatts of power for at least 75 years. Although the coal-generated electricity would be more expensive than hydroelectric power, prewar developments in Germany and recent expansion along the Ohio River in the United States would certainly seem to indicate that dependence on a primary fuel is not impracticable. However, an Australian industry based on Blair Athol coal would not enjoy similar locational advantages in relation to markets.

A considerable capital saving to the company would result if the state government put into operation its plans to develop power from another large coal deposit, that at Callide, some 60 miles inland from the port of Gladstone. Perhaps Comalco had this in mind when it announced that it intended to build a modern 40,000-ton smelter on the east coast of Queensland. The date of completion, it was stated, would depend on "a mutually satisfactory agreement between the Government and the company." Subsequently this was referred to as a first-stage smelter, being based on estimates of the markets in Australia alone.

The Purari River in southern Papua offers possiblities for power generation, and sites along its course have been investigated. Frequent floods make control and dam building difficult, and potential sites are often in comparatively inaccessible and geologically immature country. The two areas investigated are more than 200 miles from the nearest possible port, on the leeward side of Yule Island. More promising is a dam site located at Wabo, seven miles above the navigable limit of the Purari River. Investigations indicate a potential output of about 700,000 kilowatts of firm power at a cost that fully justifies the work necessary for a more complete appraisal.

In mountainous and lake-studded southern New Zealand there are promising sites for hydroelectric development. Early in 1960, Comalco negotiated an agreement with the New Zealand government permitting a complete investigation of the Lake Manapouri and Doubtful Sound areas. Construction similar in principle to that at Kitimat, British Columbia, appears to be contemplated. Should Comalco decide to utilize this area, it must undertake to establish initially a plant with an output of 100,000 kilowats. By 1991 the estimated potential of 600,000 kilowatts must be reached. This scheme will require careful investigation in relation to the Australian proposals. No decision has yet been announced, and the company is in the unenviable position of having to placate the various interested parties while trying to arrive at a decision that will enable it ultimately to compete most favorably in the highly competitive world markets.

Stimulated by the Weipa discovery, prospecting for bauxite has extended across Australia. Aluminium Limited of Canada (Alcan), operating through its research subsidiary, Aluminium Laboratories Limited, holds an "authority to prospect" from the Queensland government over a less likely area of 1,250 square miles east of the Weipa lease. Prospecting is under way. Comalco's investigations on the Gove Penninsula have revealed a considerable tonnage of bauxite of economic grade. A subsidiary of Reynolds Metals has completed a photographic reconnaissance of the remote Kimberley coastal area in Western Australia, apparently without locating useful deposits.

The most spectacular discovery resulting from the recent activity has been made by Western Aluminium N.L., a subsidiary of the Western Mining Corporation Limited, whose major operations in the gold fields of Western Australia are rapidly deteriorating. Western Aluminium has been prospecting in the Darling Ranges, near Perth. A recent progress report stated that current drilling "indicates reserves of 37 million tons of bauxite containing 44 per cent, Al_2O_3; of this amount 13 million tons can be mined at 47 per cent Al_2O_3. . . . All Al_2O_3 is in the easily treated trihydrate form. . . . The area drilled so far is a minor part of the area known to contain bauxite."

A trial parcel of 7,345 tons was shipped to the Australian smelter in Tasmania, but of greater significance was the export to Japan of three 10,000 ton shipments, one to each of the major Japanese producers. The producers have indicated that, if tests and price negotiations proved satisfactory, they could take as much as 300,000 tons a year.

The Western Mining Corporation has indicated that it has no definite proposals for developing an alumina industry in Western Australia at this stage, "although the establishment of such an industry is the long term objective of Western Aluminium N.L."

Primary Manufacturing: The Bell Bay Plant

It is appropriate now to turn to that phase of the industry which was initiated with the formation of the Australian Aluminium Production Commission in 1944. The Commonwealth and Tasmanian governments made equal contributions in providing the initial capital of $6.7 million for plant construction, but by the time the plant came into production in 1955, further Commonwealth contributions amounting to $18 million had been made. The British Aluminium Company acted as technical adviser to the commission.

TABLE II. Australian Imports of Bauxite (*In tons*)

Country of Origin	1955	1956	1957	1958
Malaya	19,287	18,765	–	–
Indonesia	–	19,625	45,133	69,472
Others	–	501	14	1
TOTAL	19,287	38,891	45,147	69,473

SOURCE: *Australian Mineral Industry: 1958 Review* [see text footnote 3 above], p. 39.

The investigation of sources of bauxite and plant location occupied the commission in its early stages. Because bauxite yields only about half its weight in alumina, an extraction plant near the ore body was desirable. At Inverell, New South Wales, was a large body of ore that, although considered suitable for alumina production, was inconveniently located for other purposes. On the other hand, bauxite found in Tasmania was conveniently located for processing but lacked the quality of other Australian deposits. Most were exposed to high coastal shipping charges and, at the time, to unreliable services. After due consideration had been given to the relevant factors, it was decided that overseas sources of bauxite should be sought.

The commission had already been committed to choosing a site for the smelter in Tasmania. Many sites were examined, and "after full consideration of all relevant factors, particularly the availbility of adequate power and water supplies, the Commission on the 24th March, 1949, decided upon Bell Bay as the site for both the alumina and reduction plants. . ."

The site was about twenty-five miles from the nearest railhead, but it was suitable for development as a port. Nearby, the Trevallyn Power Station was being constructed, primarily to supply the plant. Gibbsite, with about a 55 per cent alumina content, could be imported from Southeast Asia. Its f.o.b. cost was about twice the ex-mine value of the Australian ores, but this was compensated by the lower shipping costs. Quantities imported are shown in Table II.

Most of the bauxite treated since the plant began operation in 1955 has come from Bintan Island in Indonesia but in 1959 problems of supply were encountered. In addition, the price rose by 28 per cent, and there was every indication that further rise would occur. To ensure continuity of supply and to offset the increases, trial shipments from other areas have been obtained. In current treatment is bauxite from Ramunia, Malaya. A contract has been signed for the supply of bauxite from the Gulf of Kutch region in India. The commission is also closely watching potential sources of supply from the Weipa deposits and from the recently discovered ore in the Darling Ranges.

Processing to produce marketable aluminum is done in three stages. First the alumina is extracted by the Bayer process, and then it is reduced to aluminum by the Hall-Héroult method. Refining or suitably alloying the crude metal is the final stage. Bayer extraction consists in dissolving the bauxite in a caustic soda solution, filtering, and then precipitating the alumina. The caustic soda is prepared from soda ash, an expensive ancillary raw material obtained from South Australia. Limestone used in the calcification of the alumina crystals is obtained from the Bell Bay area.

In reducing the alumina to metal, it is first dissolved with cryolite, and then a powerful electric current is passed through the solution. Oxygen is released, and aluminum metal collects in the bottom of the furnace. The reduction cells must be operated continuously; and the whole procedure is most complex as compared with other smelting processes, having in its functioning at least fifteen difficult operational variables. The cryolite for dissolving the alumina is imported in its natural form from Greenland and, as a synthetic, from West Germany. Pitch, anthracite, and petroleum coke, used for the anode terminals and for the cathode lining of the cells, are obtained from the United Kingdom and the United States. Pastes from these materials are manufactured on the premises. In the casting shop the newly formed ingot is analyzed, alloyed, and shaped for sale as electrical conductivity metal, extrusion billets, standard ingot, and casting alloys.

Annual aluminum production at Bell Bay amounted to 11,370 tons in 1959, an increase of 2,227 tons over 1956, the first full year of operation. Some alumina was exported to Canada early in 1960.

This production, which supplied only 40 per cent of current market requirements in Australia, was not at an economic level, in spite of plant efficiency. Consequently, the ingot was allocated for prior sale in the Australian market, and at a price about $75 a ton above the world price.

In September, 1959, the Commonwealth and Tasmanian governments announced that the capacity of the Bell Bay plant would be stepped up to 16,000 tons. Tacit recognition of the fact that production would still be at an uneconomic level was seen in an agreement between the two partners to negotiate for capital from private sources for further expansion. Moreover, in the early months of 1960 it became evident that the Commonwealth govenment, no longer wedded to principles of state ownership, was only too willing to rid itself of a property which, in the generally prosperous year of 1959, yielded only 1.4 per cent on capital.

In September, 1960, the Commonwealth government sold its interest in the Bell Bay plant to a company in which the Consolidated Zinc Corporation had a two-thirds interest and the Tasmanian government the remaining one-third. Consolidated Zinc announced that it planned to raise production initially to 28,000 tons and ultimately to an amount between 40,000 and 50,000 tons.

Such proposals will require close scrutiny with reference to both the Australian market and the rising cost of Tasmanian power; but the company, obviously intent on building an integrated industry, is also admirably placed if it wishes to rationalize its production in relation to market requirements. The Commonwealth government is reported to have rejected an offer from a Swiss company for its share of the plant. Perhaps it has in mind the highly successful iron and steel producer, Broken Hill Proprietary, in encouraging the expansion of this British-incorporated but primarily Australian-based company.

· · · · ·

Future Possibilities

Further possibilities must be considered in relation to the availability of resources, development capital, and markets.

Extensive deposits of bauxite are being discovered as prospecting is intensified. Export of large quantities to Japan may soon be possible if the Western Australian deposits prove suitable. Japan has also sought bauxite from the Weipa area. The Weipa deposit, however, offers unique resource potentialities that virtually preclude its consideration with the other Australian deposits. This section of the industry could well remain aloof from the more typically Australian aspects, which must have as their main purpose the satisfaction of basic needs within the country and which, because of the lack of readily available development capital, must consider exportable surpluses at the primary rather than the secondary level.

Although Australian capital is contributing increasingly to the development of the Australian industry, it is from overseas that the main stimulus must come. Comalco is studying the feasibility of constructing a "large-scale enterprise" with overseas markets as the main outlet. It does so realizing that there is no easy entree to a world industry which is well supplied with raw materials and which is, temporarily at least, oversupplied with production capacity. Herein lies the most critical challenge to large-scale development of the Weipa bauxite deposit. Recent developments may be interpreted in terms of this situation. In September, 1960, British Aluminium and the Consolidated Zinc Corporation, in a joint statement, announced that "the interests of all concerned in the early achievement of further aluminium production in Australia would be best served by the discontinuing of the present joint association in Comalco."

Viewed in the light of world aluminum developments, the policies of these two major companies were obviously in conflict. British Aluminium, through its American parent, was fully aware of the difficulties associated with the sale of aluminum both in the United States and abroad. Perhaps Reynolds Metals was irked by the restrictions placed on development in Queensland. Moreover, Reynolds Metals does control larger reserves much closer to the American smelters, and economically these would warrant prior consideration before it turned to the Australian deposits.

As compensation for its withdrawal from Comalco, British Aluminium was granted control of the Gove Peninsula lease and the Commonwealth government's interest in the New Guinea Resources Prospecting Company. The company thus acquired rights to the Purari River system for hydroelectric development. Hence British Aluminium, with command of the Gove Peninsula bauxite deposit, with rights to extensive hydroelectric power resources in New Guinea, and with access to the considerable technical and capital resources of its own and the parent company, will be in a position to develop, when expedient, an aluminum industry in Australia.

The Consolidated Zinc Corporation, perhaps because of a closer identity with Australian interests, appeared to be more ready to further the immediate development of a major Australian aluminum industry. Through Comalco, it now controls the Weipa deposit and is in a position to negotiate further with the government of New Zealand should it require access to the power resources of the southern lakes of that country. However, in its present form Comalco does lack access to the capital resources necessary for the development of a large-scale enterprise. Should the company seek another partner in order to gain access to capital and, if necessary, technical assistance, it may not have to look far. The Kaiser Aluminum and Chemical Corporation is reported to be undertaking a study of the Australian industry "with the possibility of forming a subsidiary Kaiser Company to manufactur alumina in Australia." This may be but a prelude to more extensive development.

An alternative, and one which is becoming more apparent as the pattern unfolds, does present itself. Given a less ambitious initial program,

Comalco might construct its Queensland plant, which, in conjunction with Bell Bay production, could be geared to meeting Australian needs in the near future. Modifications of the Bell Bay plant to enable it to utilize Weipa bauxite have been proposed. Any surplus ingot could be sold on the world market, and compensation for uneconomic overseas sales during the formative years could be obtained by inflating the domestic price in a protected market. Such a pattern is not uncommon in Australia and would enable the company to draw on the resources of the domestic-oriented industry in order to promote, at the right time, the large-scale development that is its ultimate aim. The undertaking would undoubtedly prove beneficial at the present stage but would provide little recompense for the ultimate scale of development.

Australian capital, eager to participate in an expanding industry, has, for obvious reasons, contributed most readily at the fabricating level. Because of the more immediate prospect of return, investment will continue to be at that level even though Australuco, owned by Aluminium Limited of Canada and British Aluminium (possibly two uneasy partners today), continues to dominate the fabricating industry.

At various levels, imports will, in the immediate future, play a necessary role. Although bauxite requirements can be supplied by the near neighbors of Australia, Comalco may soon be in a position to provide the ore from its Weipa deposit. At the fabricating level, varying quantities of imported ingot, semifabrications, and assembled products will continue to supplement domestic production, but without usurping its privileged position. In satisfying the unpredictable upsurges in consumer demand, and in catering for the "fringe" requirements, imports have a status which, if unenviable, is vital to the structure of the Australian industry.

Australian markets for aluminum and aluminum products, under the present conditions of a rapidly developing economy, are particularly receptive to continued expansion. Prospects over the next decade may be regarded with considerable optimism. One writer has suggested that an eventual rise in Australian production to one hundred thousand tons would not be unrealistic. Whatever the amount, expansion is inevitable.

While the domestic market for aluminum may remain the preserve of the Australian producer, the world market will continue to be competitive. Full consideration of its characteristics is beyond the scope of this paper. Successful entry by an Australian producer will demand that all factors of production be evaluated against world standards and conditions. Among them the immaturity of locational relationships must be considered, and these will undoubtedly be subjected to increasingly critical scrutiny.

37. Exploring the Diamond Coast

William Bascom

There is always a certain amount of romance and glamour in prospecting for diamonds, even on the barren, forbidding desert coasts of Southwest Africa. Because of the value of these stones, whether gems or industrial diamonds, several new and unusual prospecting techniques have been developed.

The southwest coast of Africa is dry and desolate. It is a land of stark rocks and wandering dunes; its shores are pounded by great breakers and swept by cold currents; its weather alternates between wind and fog and blasting sun. Traditional inhabitants, aside from an occasional bushman, are ostriches, jackals, and gemsbok, who roam landscapes as unforgiving as any on Earth. Yet it has one saving grace in the eyes of man. There are diamonds! This is the diamond coast.

There is something curiously stirring and romantic about a diamond. The flash of fire in these greasy crystals promises instant wealth and leads men to take insane risks. So the discovery of a single diamond inevitably causes a diamond rush—no matter how forbidding the country.

Diamonds were first found in Africa in the Orange River in 1867 and this soon led to the discovery of the diamondiferous volcanic pipes at Kimberley. But these were a thousand miles east of the scene of this story, beyond the mountains of Central Africa. In the late 1800's these inland deposits were organized into a large and stable industry by Cecil Rhodes, who set up the famous De Beers mining and selling organization.

During the same period the barren west coast was generally ignored except for a small guano industry on some offshore islands. Africa was so large and so little known that international boundaries were vague. In 1863 rumors of mineral wealth inland had led a German trader named Adolph Lüderitz to make a trading agreement with a native chief and then to seek help from his home government. Germany had been a late starter in the race for colonies, and Bismarck seized the chance to declare that all the territory between the Orange and the Kuenene Rivers was under the Kaiser's protection. The new country was German South West Africa. However, in order to protect the natives properly they first had to be subdued, and this required that a military railroad be constructed from Lüderitz Bay to the interior.

In August 1908 a native track worker named Zacharias Lewala, who

SOURCE: *Geotimes*, IX, 2 (September, 1964), 9–12. The author is President of Ocean Science and Engineering, Inc., Washington, D.C.

had worked in the diamond mines at Kimberley, took a stone to his foreman, August Stauch, saying "Master, this is a diamond." Although the find was reported to the railroad authorities, they, and the citizens of Lüderitz, laughed at the thought of diamonds lying on the surface of the ground a thousand miles from Kimberley. Stauch left his job, obtained prospecting permits and began to search. He soon found abundant diamonds littering the floors of several valleys. The first incredulous public reaction turned into a diamond rush when a government geologist confirmed the find.

Lüderitz boomed and the German government moved rapidly to set up its own diamond sales agency (Diamant Regie) to compete with the De Beers group. To make sure that no stones went elsewhere, a huge area that included the diamond deposits was declared forbidden territory. The Sperregebiet, as it was called, extended some 80 km inland along 600 km of coast. It was patrolled by soldiers, mounted on camels, who were permitted to shoot at any diamond poachers who survived the desolate desert. Even for those who survived both, the chance of finding diamonds outside the original area was very small. The area is still under rigorous security control. No aircraft may fly over it, or boat land, or car drive through; all persons leaving are subject to X-ray examination and search.

The nakedness of the rocky valleys of German South West Africa is astonishing, and the roads run mostly on barren rock. Except for an occasional wandering barchan dune there is rarely as much as a foot of loose material on the valley floors. Most of the sand and fine material has been moved away by blasting winds that have left only polished rock surfaces, large pebbles, and diamonds. It is no wonder that in the early days diamonds were mined by a line of natives moving over the ground on their hands and knees, picking up diamonds and putting them into match boxes slung around their necks.

A series of these valleys, roughly parallel, extends generally SSW from the area of the original find toward the ocean where they end in south-facing bays. As the diamonds obviously did not originate in the Pre-Cambrian schists in which the valleys are carved and as the material in the valley floor was moved by winds blowing inland, a few people guessed at once that these diamonds had come in from the sea. In 1915 a Methodist reporter named William Everleigh wrote: "As the gems are found along the coast and on the islands off the coast it is not unreasonable to infer that they also lie in the sand of the sea bed."

But there were certain difficulties about working in the sea. Before World War I the Germans had the mainland, and the British owned the offshore islands. Gunboats of both sides patrolled the area, anxious to prevent an international incident, and several would-be undersea diamond prospectors were driven away. After World War I the extensive German mines were taken over and combined into a single unit:

Consolidated Diamond Mines of South West Africa (known generally as CDM), now controlled by the De Beers group. Over the years the deposits in the thin, wind-blown sendiments were worked out and new ones of a different character were developed.

The new play began south of the Orange River in what is now the Republic of South Africa. Diamonds had previously been found in isolated spots along the coast, but in 1927 the first big find was made in Namaqualand. A new rush was on, and it attracted a famous geologist, Dr. Alexander Merensky, who had done some thinking about the origin and distribution of the alluvial diamonds. He believed the diamonds had been deposited during a time when a warm current flowed along the coast and that the warm water had made it possible for a certain kind of oyster to live there. So Merensky, who had prudently obtained financing in advance, began buying up claims well above sea level where he found oyster shells. These claims formed an elongated pattern, as indeed an old beach deposit should, which became known as the 'oyster line.'

In the first week of digging, while Merensky and his associates were living in a small tent camp, they recovered hundreds of carats of large diamonds from beneath a single rock. The theory about the oysters and the warm current was subsequently shown to be entirely wrong—but like certain other geological theories it had proved adequate in the circumstances, and Merensky, like Stauch before him, retired a rich man.

However, it was not until the 1930s that the present CDM mine, immediately north of the Orange River in South West Africa, was found by a systematic search instituted by order of Sir Ernest Oppenheimer. This deposit, now the world's largest gem-diamond mine, was methodically explored by a series of prospecting trenches dug perpendicular to the shoreline and spaced 1 km apart. These trenches, whose walls stand vertically, are 1 meter wide in alluvial gravel that may be as much as 10 meters deep. All the material extracted was processed on the site in portable diamond-recovery plants and a careful record kept of the depth at which stones were found and their relation to the beach stratification.

In places there is as much as 15 meters of dune sand overburden above the gravel, so a single prospecting trench, often over 500 meters long, becomes a major excavation. As a result of this sampling program the extent of the diamondiferous gravels is well known. At a production rate of 100,000 carats a month there are nearly 20 years of mining ahead.

The trenching revealed two distinct terraces. Near the Orange River the inshore terrace is 30 to 40 meters above the sea and 2 km from the present shoreline; a lower terrace, halfway to the sea, is 5 to 10 meters above sea level. Some 50 km north the two inexplicably converge at the same level and 15 km farther on, disappear.

Generally the productive terraces trail off seaward in the direction of Chameis Bay. On each terrace there are well-developed shoreline features including rounded and undercut sea cliffs about 5 meters high, wave-cut terraces with lines of potholes, and beach deposits of alternating sand and shingle. Generally the best diamonds are found in the heavy mineral sands at the base of the sea cliffs and in the potholes. When the area is mined, cracks in the schist are scrupulously cleaned with brushes by Ovambo laborers. These men are paid cash rewards for the stones they find in this fashion and occasionally make several months' pay in a few moments. Last January one pothole less than a meter in diameter was found to contain several hundred stones averaging half a carat. Other nearby potholes had few stones.

Generally the larger stones are found near the mouth of the Orange River where the median size produced by CDM is about 1.5 carats. Fifty km north the median size is 0.8 carats; 150 km north it is 0.2 carats. This strongly suggests that the stones came down the river and were distributed to the north by the prevailing longshore current. This current is caused by incomplete refraction of waves from the Antarctic seas to the southwest. These large, long-period waves not only tend to put the bottom material into suspension but also impart a component of motion to the north. This effect is sufficient, in time, to account for small diamonds being moved as much as 400 km to the north of the river mouth. Occasional northwest storms reverse the flow of current; that explains existence of diamonds in the State Alluvial Diggings only a few kilometers south of the river.

Several objections have been raised to the theory that the stones came down the river. The most curious is that no diamonds have ever been found either in the river bottom or on its old terraces for hundreds of miles above the river mouth. But more than 800 km inland, in the Vaal and the Orange rivers, which drain the diamond-pipe areas, alluvial mining has been carried on for nearly a century. Another objection to the river-origin theory is that the color and character of the diamonds found in the raised beaches and under the sea are quite different from the inland stones. As an experienced diamond-sorter can tell at a glance which of a dozen mines any parcel of diamonds comes from, this is an important piece of evidence.

Moreover, the coastal alluvial diamonds are nearly 90 per cent gems but those found inland are only about 20 per cent gems. As the industrial stones have exactly the same physical properties as the gems, any theory must explain the absence of the industrials in marine deposits. To add to the puzzle, the inland pipes are Cretaceous in age and the marine alluvium is very recent.

The absence of adequate explanations led to an equally favored second theory: the diamonds originated in diamond pipes close to the coast, either on land or under the sea, and the Orange River mouth happens to be close to one or more such pipes. This theory accounts for both the size distribution and the difference in the kind and quality of stones. However, there is no direct evidence of such pipes and undersea geophysical surveys have not detected any pipe-like formation. As diamonds are also found at the mouths of the Buffels and Oliphants rivers it strains credulity to require a pipe opposite each river mouth.

Such are the main lines of thought about the source of the stones; they were first presented over 40 years ago, and there have since been many variations, subtheories, and arguments on each side.

The geological controversy, still unsettled, had pretty much died down, and CDM was happily mining its treasure in the raised beaches when a new character appeared on the scene.

In 1961, Samuel V. Collins, an undersea-pipeline man, arrived at the CDM town of Oranjemund to inspect the site of a proposed fuel pipeline through the surf. He at once became convinced that the diamond deposits extended under the sea and that it would be possible to mine them. He set up the Marine Diamond Corporation and obtained a concession from the government of South West Africa to mine diamonds offshore of CDM's diamond area No. 1. The first move was to convert a salvage vessel to a sampling ship and begin prospecting in a new way. The *Emerson K* developed a technique for air-lifting samples of bottom material to the deck where it could be screened and sorted.

The first few voyages produced few stones, but there was always a crowd waiting at the quay in Cape Town when the ship returned, eager for news of any find. When the sampling program discovered the long-expected diamond gravels, Sammy Collins became a popular hero. He increased his concessions and built several mining barges—two of them now dredging the bottom of Chameis Bay and recovering 15 to 150 diamonds an hour each. Virtually all are gem stones with a median size of a little less than half a carat (the value of such uncut stones is about $25 a carat).

By 1963 the undersea mine had sufficient production to interest the De Beers group, and an arrangement was made that provided for a scientific examination of the Collins concession to establish its value. Ocean Science & Engineering was engaged to make the new exploratory effort, and our South African subsidiary, directed by David Smith, began work at once on two major jobs. The first to make a geological-geophysical survey of the undersea concession area. The second was to sample the sea floor systematically in places where the geophysical work indicated unconsolidated sediments that might include diamondiferous gravels.

A small freighter, the *Xhosa Coast*, was converted for exploration. With our subcontractor, Alpine Geophysical Corporation, we installed a precision radar for position fixing and a "sparker" for determining the thickness and structure of the bottom sediments.

No one can tell in advance how well any geophysical system will work in a new area. The sub-sea rocks may not be good sound reflectors and the records may be uninterpretable; in shallow water the first returns are buried in the outgoing signal; layers thinner than the wave length cannot be discriminated; thin clay beds mask the bedrock surface beneath, and so on. Moreover, reports of severe weather and huge winter swell documented with photos of Collins Barge 77 bucking very rough seas—and of the same barge high on the rocks at Chameis after a severe July storm—made us apprehensive. But once such an adventure is begun there is no turning back.

The first step was to establish precision survey points on the shore. In some places survey monuments were easily relocated but in other areas, particularly the Namib Desert, there was nothing. Absolutely nothing. For the Namib is one of the world's great sand piles. It is made of material moved along the coast by the current, brought ashore by the waves, blasted inland by the winds. To this has been added the sandy material that moved up the diamondiferous valleys near Lüderitz. This fantastic mass of sand extends 100 miles along the coast and nearly that much inland. It rises 600 ft. above the sea at a very steep angle of repose along many miles of coast. The only way past the sand is along the beach—at low tide, of course—and early prospectors who took that route with camels knew it as 'the great wall.' They worried considerably about being caught against the steep sand slope by a rising tide.

Our helicopter was a great improvement on a camel but there were plenty of other difficulties. In the morning the fog was so thick the radar could not see through it; when it cleared about 10 a.m. the rising heat waves made it impossible to see points on the desert floor (you see violent wiggles or a mirage); and after 4 p.m. the wind created a daily sandstorm. But precision surveys were essential, and we used the helicopter to transport theodolites and tellurimeters. Each survey point was equipped with a radar transponder, which produced a brilliant blip on the ship's radar and permitted it to navigate accurately. The *Xhosa Coast* cruised back and forth along the coast for many months recording the reflection of sound by the undersea rocks and sediments. When the records were interpreted and plotted, the result was a very satisfactory detailed chart of the sub-sea structure of an area of more than 5,000 square miles.

Armed with these charts, a sampling program was devised whose objective is to determine the diamond content of a small part of this vast area. This meant a method had to be developed for obtaining large uncontaminated samples of possibly diamondiferous gravels at specified points. Enter the *Rockeater*.

Rockeater, once a small freighter, has been converted to an underwater mineral sampling ship—as far as we know the first in the world. It has unusual features including a derrick mounted above a center well at the point of minimum motion. It is capable of core-drilling hard rock with diamond bits to 5,000 ft, or it can bring up unconsolidated materials from depths of 500 ft by means of dredge pump or air-lift. The material recovered passes through a screening plant designed to permit analysis of the oversized and undersized materials. Material in the diamond-sized range is processed in a heavy media plant and jigged to a concentrate that is finally hand sorted for diamonds.

Rockeater has automatic steering controls, hydraulic mooring and lifting winches, precision radar-sonar equipment, and many other devices that make it one of the most sophisticated exploration ships ever built. It gives an answer direct, in diamonds, on the site so the senior geologist aboard can establish the value of a sample immediately.

It is encouraging to know that after a half century of exploration the diamond coast is still yielding new deposits. However, the search grows increasingly difficult and new technologies must be continually brought to bear. Diamonds are expensive because they are hard to find!

X. OCEANOGRAPHY

As we know, the land surface of the world is more than one quarter of the total. All the rest is water covered, with an estimated total of 300 million cubic miles of water filling the oceans of the world. The surface of the sea has been studied for many centuries, but relatively little is known about the great depths, the sea floors, and the nature of life in the great water masses. Recently, there has been greatly increased interest in oceanography, which in the narrowest sense is not geography. Nevertheless, since geographers have great interest in oceanography and all studies of the seas, new knowledge in the area proves—or may prove—to be of tremendous value to mankind. These selections touch several aspects of oceanography, or what might be called "sea geography," indicating some of the problems and benefits the sea may bring.

38. Inexhaustible Riches from the Sea

George A. W. Boehm

Our knowledge of the sea and especially the sea bottom is very limited. The following is an optimistic view of the abundant resources of the sea, and of the practical possibilities of acquiring them from our use. Although one may not go as far as the author in forecasting permanent habitations at depths in the ocean, it would be well to remember the amazing pace of present-day technological development and recognize that what is forecast here becomes more likely every day.

Men of vision have long recognized that a great untapped storehouse of natural wealth lies in and beneath the waters that cover 70 per cent of the earth. But only recently has a concerted effort begun to exploit these resources. There is a world-wide surge of scientific interest in understanding the oceans and finding new ways to recover from them a vast abundance of food and minerals.

Much has been accomplished within the last decade. Marine fisher-

SOURCE: *Fortune*, December, 1963, pp. 133 ff. At the time he wrote this article, the author was an associate editor of *Fortune* magazine, through whose courtesy it is reprinted here. He is the author of *The World of Math*.

men have doubled their annual catch. Oil, gas, and sulfur have been pumped in steadily swelling torrents from the sloping sea floor under shallow waters. An enterprising Texan has begun to dredge diamonds off the coast of South Africa. Engineers have been devising equipment to mine an inexhaustible supply of industrially important metals from valuable deposits that have much of the ocean bottom. And scientists are beginning to study a host of antibiotics and other drugs that are secreted by sponges and other marine organisms.

But the science of oceanography, though vigorous, is still relatively young, and it still has a long way to go in building up an accurate knowledge of the oceans and all that they contain. The bottom is no better mapped than was the North American continent before the Lewis and Clark expedition. Even major shipping lanes are largely uncharted. Three years ago, for example, a U.S. Coast and Geodetic Survey ship on her way from the Panama Canal to Key West discovered a 6,000-foot mountain rising from the bottom of the sea to within 90 feet of the surface; its existence had never before been suspected. Currents that could serve as express highways for shipping and that profoundly influence the movements of fish are likewise poorly charted. Biologists still know so little about the breeding and migratory habits of most fish that only infrequently can they offer fishermen economically useful scientific advice. The art of designing and engineering equipment capable of withstanding the rigors of the ocean is scarcely beyond its infancy.

But if the current burst of interest is any indication, many of these gaps in knowledge and technique are sure to be filled within the next few decades. Virtually all the leading maritime nations—notably the U.S.S.R., Japan, Britain, Germany, and the U.S.—are expanding their research programs. In the U.S. the Kennedy Administration recently outlined a program that would involve spending $2.3 billion on oceanography over the next ten years. It is to be a coordinated effort involving the Navy and fourteen federal agencies, with some contracts going to such research centers as the University of California's Scripps Institution of Oceanography at La Jolla; Woods Hole Oceanographic Institution on Cape Cod; the University of Miami's Institute of Marine Science; and Columbia University's Lamont Geological Observatory. The money and scientific manpower that are to be committed are hardly impressive, to be sure, when compared to what has been allotted for space exploration. Many scientists deplore the fact that, in fiscal 1963, a meager $124,500,000 went for oceanography, against more than $5 billion for space. They feel that it is far more urgent for man to become familiar with a major portion of his own planet than it is to explore the moon.

Nevertheless, the oceanographic program can afford a fairly deliberate pace—at least, in its present early stage. It is not a crash project calling for a rushed and costly solution of engineering problems. Ocean research is a long-range investment in scientific knowledge. In terms of the exploitation of resources, the payoff in this decade may not be very great. It is enough that the growing store of knowledge be brought fully to bear years hence when the world's population will have doubled and many of the high-grade mineral resources on land will have been depleted by a voracious technology.

The Age of Aquaculture

A deeper understanding of marine resources will basically alter man's attitude toward the ocean. Up to now, as Harris B. Stewart Jr. of the Coast and Geodetic Survey observes, man has used it as a nomad uses the grassland or a primitive hunter the forest. While the raising of crops and livestock has been elevated almost to the state of an exact science, most fishermen practice a haphazard art with equipment that has not been radically improved for decades.

The new attitude that is evolving has been labeled "aquaculture." The term implies cultivating and managing the resources of the sea the way farmers and foresters husband the resources of the land. Rather then simply gathering the fruits of the water, man will involve himself in the natural processes that create resources and will do his best to regulate them to his advantage.

The aquacultural approach has led scientists to speculate about ways to herd fish, increase the stock, build up the productivity of the water, and even influence the accumulation of mineral ores. Eventually much of this research will be concentrated at the marine equivalents of agricultural experiment stations. Their forerunners are already springing into existence. The largest is the State of California's ten-year-old Institute of Marine Resources, with headquarters at Scripps. Some small countries with limited land resources—notably Israel and Ethiopia—are now setting up similar marine institutes.

The most promising places for practical aquaculture are bays and estuaries, where the waters are fairly well fenced in and are easily accessible from land. Rudimentary attempts at near-shore cultivation proved richly rewarding as far back as the days of ancient Rome, when oystermen began providing hard rubble for the shellfish to grow on. Today, perhaps the most impressively productive of such enterprises is mussel culturing in the Gulf of Taranto, Italy, where the annual yield averages 108,000 pounds of meat per acre.

There are also opportunities for aquaculture in the shallow water on the continental shelves, which, added together, have an area equal to that of all Asia. Scientists will have to understand the nature of these environments as intimately and as intuitively as an Eskimo understands his world of ice and snow. One pioneer is already at work: The French oceangrapher Jacques-Yves Cousteau has been colonizing the ocean floor. This year seven of his associates lived in cylindrical steel huts resting on the bottom of the Red Sea. Five of the men lived for a solid month at a depth of fifty feet; the other two spent more than a week at eighty feet. Supplied with a continual flow of air from the surface, all worked a six-hour day that included hard physical labor. Cousteau believes that men can live in such colonies at the limits of the continental shelf as far down as 600 feet. Other scientists have warmly applauded his daring experiments, and now the U.S. Navy Medical Research Laboratory is planning to provide living quarters for a group of volunteers in 200 feet of water off Bermuda.

With its strong technological flavor, aquaculture will give industry more of an interest than it has had up to now in the exploitation of ocean resources. A few companies have already demonstrated interest in oceanography (although not yet to the point where they are eager to invest substantial amounts of their stockholders' money). According to a preliminary survey by the National Security Industrial Association, private companies now employ about 500 marine scientists and deploy 65,000 gross tons of ships and other craft suitable for ocean research. But so great is the economic potential that it is only a matter of time before industry must get deeply involved. The ocean is an inexhaustible, self-replenishing storehouse of most of the basic materials that a modern economy needs. Dissolved or suspended in the water or lying on the ocean floor are countless tons of all the natural chemical elements; the production of plant matter equals the growth on all the croplands, meadows, and forests; and the community of animals easily outweighs all the creatures who live on the land.

The Pyramid of Life

The main problem is to exploit these resources in ways that make economic sense. On land most of the organic matter exists in the form of trees, shrubs, grass, and other macroscopic, long-lived organisms. But in the sea, where the turnover of life is frantically rapid, well over 90 per cent of the living material consists of microscopic plants and animals that grow rapidly and soon die or are eaten. The basis of life in the ocean is a very thin soup of these tiny plants and animals, collectively known as plankton, which inhabit the sunlit upper layers of water. They are the foundation of a living pyramid. That is to say, they are the staple food of small fish (and, oddly enough, the gigantic blue whale), and these small fish are in turn eaten by larger fish. Thus wherever the water is fertile, as it is where nutrients well up from below, plankton abound and so do fish.

At each step up the pyramid a great deal of material goes to waste, whether it be an animal plankton engulfing a plant plankton or a large fish eating a smaller one. The predator reconverts, on the average, only about 10 per cent of its prey into living matter. Thus it takes roughly 1,000 pounds of plant plankton to produce one pound of medium-size fish, and 10,000 pounds to produce a pound of large predator, such as a tuna.

The wastefulness of this natural economy has given rise to the notion, widely popularized, that man might short-circuit the process by going directly to the bottom of the pyramid and straining plankton from the water for use as food or fertilizer. The trouble is that the high cost of pumping and sieving would make plankton a luxury product (and a barely palatable one, to boot). Unless some wholly revolutionary technique is developed, man will have to continue to depend on fish to do the job of concentrating the nutrients of the sea into usable form.

It might be possible, however, to give the fish a helping hand by stimulating the growth of plankton in certain locations—a procedure that would be somewhat analogous to fertilizing a pasture. So ocenographers are investigating several schemes for stirring up parts of the ocean so as to bring to the surface nutrients that make plankton flourish. One way would be to anchor buoys with rough chains in a swift current in order to create turbulence. Another approach, favored by scientists at Woods Hole, is to install a vertical pipe that would raise water from lower levels through a physical process that depends on slight temperature and salinity differences. A National Academy of Sciences committee has suggested setting a large heat source—perhaps an atomic pile—on the bottom to start vertical convection currents. None of these ideas seems economically feasible at present, but with refinements in technology they may someday prove important to aquaculture.

Dreams of Gold

The fact that seawater itself is rich in suspended or dissolved minerals has inspired proposals to "mine" it by chemical processing. But the commercial possibilities seem limited, at least for the near future. To be sure, common salt has been produced by evaporation for many centuries and in many parts of the world, and in recent times potash has also been recovered. Since 1924 the Ethyl Corporation has been extracting bromine, and since 1941 Dow Chemical has supplied the nation with magnesium made from seawater in a single Freeport, Texas, plant. Someday it may pay to get rubidium and cesium from the ocean, but the market for these metals is still small. Other possibilities include sulfur, boron, strontium, and fluorine, for which economical processes have yet to be developed. Virtually all other minerals exist in such slight concentrations that it would be scarcely worthwhile to pump the water to recover them, even if processing cost nothing. If, on the other hand, water were being pumped anyway—e.g., for a desalting plant—

the economic balance might shift so that it would pay to extract some other minerals.

Dreams of extracting great mineral wealth directly from the water have always died hard. Shortly after World War I the great German chemist Fritz Haber conceived the idea of paying his country's war debts by recovering gold from the ocean. He worked for years without coming anywhere close to his goal.

Practical oceanographers prefer to focus on those minerals that are to be found in economically exploitable concentrations. They have long been aware that the bottom of the sea contains ore deposits comparable with those on land. The very oozes and clays that form much of the sea floor might well be worth mining as aluminum ore or as raw material for portland cement. But the most promising form of mineral wealth in the sea simply lies in chunks on the bottom. It has been known for almost a century. About 1870 the British oceanographic vessel *Challenger* dredged up from the bottom of the ocean lumps of a strange mineral that looked like fire-blackened potatoes. Assays later showed that these nodules were exceptionally rich in manganese oxide and contained substantial amounts of other metals—chiefly iron, copper, cobalt, and nickel. At the time manganese nodules were regarded as freaks, and mining companies took little interest.

During the recent International Geophysical Year, however, further dredging in deep waters revealed that much of the ocean floor is literally cobbled with nodules. Those that have been hauled up range in size from microscopic bits to one that weighed almost a ton.

Underwater Vacuum Cleaner

Individual nodules grow in layers like onions and at an incredibly slow rate, generally no faster than one millimeter in a thousand years and in many cases much more slowly. Yet as worldwide surveys have shown, there are so many nodules forming all the time that they could supply all man's needs for their major metallic constituents, and still the total growth would easily exceed the rate of depletion.

So far no one has actually mined manganese nodules commercially, although several companies are investigating ways of dredging and refining them. The preeminent authority on the subject is engineer John Mero, formerly on the staff of the University of California, who recently joined Newport News Shipbuilding & Dry Dock Company as a consultant. The company is loathe to discuss its plans, but it seems obvious why it has hired Mero. He has stated repeatedly that the best way to mine nodules is to suck them off the bottom with a sort of hydraulic vacuum cleaner. Newport News Shipbuilding manufactures hydraulic pumps.

According to Mero's economic analysis, manganese nodules will have to be mined on a large scale—with a dredge capacity of at least 5,000 tons per day—so that capital costs will not eat up the profits. A single dredge of this size could supply the U.S. with 50 percent of the manganese, all the cobalt, and 10 percent of the nickel it needs. From a ton of nodules Mero would expect to get $45 worth of metal at a processing cost of $22. Dredging the material and transporting it to shore would cost from $3 to more than $10 per ton depending on its location and depth. The easiest nodules to mine are on the relatively shallow Blake Plateau off the Carolina coast, but unfortunately they are low-grade. The biggest deposits of the most valuable nodules (those especially rich in nickel) lie in extremely deep waters in mid-Pacific.

Others who have looked into the possibilities of manganese nodules are generally not so optimistic as Mero. For one thing, they anticipate mechanical difficulties in pumping nodules from depths as great as a couple of miles. But the continuing rapid depletion of high-grade ores on land is bound, sooner or later, to make nodule mining an attractive commercial venture.

An entirely different kind of nodule, rich in phosphate rather than metals, also promises to be worth mining. In fact, not long ago the Collier Carbon & Chemical Corporation, a Union Oil subsidiary, leased rights from the U.S. Department of the Interior to dredge phosphorite nodules from Forty Mile Bank, a rise forty miles due west of San Diego. The nodules are very nearly comparable to high-grade phosphates mined on land.

None of the phosphorite nodules have yet been mined commercially, for Collier shelved its plans and gave up its lease. But surveys indicate that the reserve off southern California may be about a billion tons— plenty to provide California agriculture with phosphate fertilizer for decades to come.

Most nodules are found in deep water, but submarine prospectors have been discovering other mineral deposits in extremely shallow water on so-called "drowned beaches." These were exposed in ages past when water was heaped on the land in glaciers and the sea level dropped. Then they were covered with sediments carried down by turbulent rivers from the interior of the land. When the glaciers waned, the sea level rose again, drowning the sedimentary deposits. Today they lie on the shelving ocean bottom just off shore.

Rich tin ores lie on drowned beaches and submerged river valleys off the coasts of Thailand and Indonesia. Gold occurs in sands and gravels near Nome, Alaska. Sam Collins, a forty-nine-year-old oil-drilling and pipeline contractor from Texas, has struck it rich in a brand-new mining business: scooping diamonds from the floor of the ocean. With financial backing from the de Beers organization, Collins is averaging almost $200,000 worth of diamonds per month dredging gravel in shallow water off the coast of South-West Africa.

A Cure for Kwashiorkor

While far sighted oceanographers seek ways to locate and exploit new resources, such as nodules, one important branch of ocean study is concentrating on a more immediate goal, the more efficient and effective use of a familiar resource—i.e., fish. At present, seafood makes up very little of man's food. Increasing its proportion even a small notch would make significant gains on the world's most serious dietary deficiency. The main problem isn't a lack of calories. It is that in many areas people don't get nearly enough of the well-balanced proteins contained in meat, milk, eggs, and fish. In parts of Asia, Africa, and Latin America, where the diet is largely rice, manioc, and other starchy foods, 100 million suffer from a wasting protein-deficiency disease, known in children as kwashiorkor. And perhaps half a billion more the world over are sapped of vitality by lack of protein.

Meat, milk, and eggs are inherently expensive foods, but potentially, at least, marine fish offer a reasonably cheap solution to this nutritional problem. The world's catch, which now stands at about 45 million tons, has doubled within the last decade and could be increased still further simply by the adoption of slightly more efficient methods. In countries like India and Ceylon, where the government has helped fishermen buy powerboats, the catch per unit of human effort has risen sharply. Japanese and Russian fishermen are backed up by efficient fleets of tankers and processing ships.

Much more could be done if fishermen did not concentrate so much of their efforts on just a few species and if they would fish the entire ocean. Today a mere dozen species account for fully 75 percent of the U.S. catch. Harold S. Olcott and Milner B. Schaefer of the Institute of Marine Resources point out that vast expanses of the sea are never visited by commercial fishermen and that in areas where salmon and tuna are being depleted such species as hake and squid are being ignored. Olcott and Schaefer say that broadening the scope and variety of fishing could multiply the world catch as much as five times.

But first there is a marketing job to be done. Recognizing this, scientists have devised new ways to preserve fish and "sell" it to people, and indirectly technology is creating new markets for species that have never before been fished to any great extent. Until recently, for instance, Alaskan shrimp were largely ignored because they had to be peeled by hand, but the invention of an automatic peeler made it feasible to gather the shrimp, and today there is a 30-million-pound market.

The freezing of fish has expanded markets for many varieties, but frozen fish is expensive to preserve, store, and transport, and it is not the answer to the nutritional problem in underdeveloped nations. Two new procedures are now being investigated: freeze-drying and irradiation. In freeze-drying the fish is frozen and simultaneously the water is removed so that it can be kept indefinitely without costly refrigeration. Atomic radiation destroys bacteria and keeps fish from spoiling for periods up to several years.

Fish into Fish Flour

But perhaps the best solution is to do away with the fish as a recognizable entity and concentrate its protein content. This is done by grinding up the whole fish—guts, eyes, head, tail, bones, and flesh—then removing water, fats, and odorous fractions by chemical treatment. The final product, called "fish flour," is a bland, light-colored powder that keeps indefinitely without refrigeration. It can be mixed with flour for bread, used to fortify soups and cereals, or made into a milk substitute. Experimental feeding of it to kwashiorkor victims in Latin America has produced speedy cures. Fish flour can be produced for about 15 cents per pound, and since it averages about 80 percent protein (as against 20 percent for fresh meat), it is the nutritional equivalent of meat at 3 cents per pound.

Fish flour has been manufactured in several countries, including Norway, Sweden, South Africa, and the U.S., but so far with indifferent commercial success. The story of fish flour in the U.S. has been strange indeed. The Viobin Corporation has a modern plant in New Bedford, Massachusetts, and another one nearing completion in Greenport, Long Island. Together the two plants will be able to convert 170 tons of fish per day into thirty-four tons of flour. So far, however, the product has been fed only to mink, piglets, and lambs. The reason is that the Food and Drug Administration has ruled that fish flour is aesthetically unacceptable for human consumption in the U.S. because it contains guts, bones, heads, and tails. Ezra Levin, the chemist who heads Viobin, has pointed out indignantly that the FDA's stand is inconsistent, since the agency permits the sale of whole sardines and also gelatin made from bones and hides. But the FDA remains firm despite the efforts of Sen. Paul Douglas of Illinois and others to have the ruling changed. Meanwhile a committee of the National Academy of Sciences has in principle endorsed fish flour as human food. And there, in midair, the matter rests.

There is another reason for encouraging fishermen to catch a wider variety of fish. Some species of today's commercially valuable fish are in danger of depletion, while worthless fish threaten to take over the ocean. "We are picking the flowers and leaving the weeds to flourish," says Columbus O'D. Iselin, senior oceanographer at Woods Hole.

What Happened to Cannery Row?

As weeds in a garden can crowd out flowers, so weeds of the sea helped to wipe out what was once one of the most profitable of all fisheries:

the California sardine industry. Cannery Row in Monterey (the subject of John Steinbeck's novel) is now just a dismal stretch of boarded-up factories; as late as the mid-Forties they were processing over half a million tons of sardines almost every year.

Some of the oceanographers working for the California Cooperative Oceanic Fisheries Investigation have reconstructed the events leading up to this disastrous decline. Apparently in 1944 relatively cool water swept down from Alaska and reduced the spawning rate of sardines. The water stayed exceptionally cool for several more years and, what with overfishing, the sardine population dwindled, and it never recovered, because by the time the environment improved in 1957, the feeding grounds had been preempted by a kind of anchovy that has a limited market as a food fish in the U.S. Had the anchovies been fished intensively during the lean years, Cannery Row might still be thriving.

Fortunately such disasters are becoming rarer as better conservation methods are devised and applied. Some of the world's fisheries are coming under management spearheaded by a tight little community of perhaps 200 experts: marine scientists from universities and government, representatives of industry, and "fishery diplomats." They circulate among a number of international agencies that keep track of the population of certain fish in specified areas and then recommend regulations as to the quantity of fish the participating countries should catch.

Almost every major fishery in the Atlantic and the Pacific is covered by such organizations as the Inter-American Tropical Tuna Commission, the International Commission for Northwest Atlantic Fisheries, and the International Pacific Salmon Fisheries Commission. Some have research staffs of their own; others rely on scientific reports from member nations. Wilbert M. Chapman of the Van Camp Foundation, who has served on a number of commissions, comments: "If politicians and legal people can just be kept out, fishery people can cooperate in regulating themselves to preserve stocks."

The trouble is that the politicians do not always keep out. Some of the local and national regulations are eminently in accord with sound conservation practice, but others seem to have been laid down by nautical Luddites. Salmon fishermen in Alaska, for example, are forbidden to use fish traps, which are by far the most efficient gear for harvesting salmon, and the size of their boats is limited to a mere fifty feet. "The effect of these restrictions is to conserve not fish but the jobs of the least efficient fishermen," says Richard H. Fleming, head of the department of oceanography at the University of Washington. As a result salmon, once a common food in the Pacific Northwest, has become as expensive as choice beef. Worse yet, in the international market U.S. salmon fishermen cannot compete with the Russians and Japanese, who use the latest fish-finding and fish-catching gear and large modern boats that can process fish while at sea. "Some of our foreign competitors could use our ships as lifeboats," says Dayton L. Alverson of the U.S. Bureau of Commercial Fisheries.

Fish Forecasting

Fishery management has the same aim as forest management: to harvest as much as possible without, in the long run damaging the resource's ability to renew itself. The key concept is "maximum sustained yield" —i.e., the rate of exploitation that the resource can tolerate without diminishing. This kind of conservation calls for carefully regulated harvesting, rather than hoarding. Foresters know now that periodic thinning out improves a stand of trees; similarly, a fish population may be all the healthier if it is reduced so that the survivors have plenty of food.

The most efficient way to manage a crop of fish would be to harvest them just at the end of the period of most rapid growth, before increasing mortality among the mature fish cuts into the total weight of the population. Albert C. Jones of the University of Miami's Institute of Marine Science is now trying to determine the optimum time for harvesting shrimp. His task is complicated by the fact that shrimp near southern Florida spawn at different time of the year and migrate from open sea to estuaries and back to sea. Thus there is no one time when all the shrimp in a given area will be at the stage most desirable for harvesting. Yet logic dictates that there must be an optimum time for the population as a whole, and if Jones can find out enough about the spawning and migratory habits of shrimp, plus the growth and mortality rates at different stages of their lives, he may be able to advise the shrimp industry as to the best time to concentrate its efforts.

One factor that makes fishery management so much more complex than forestry is that the size and location of the crop are likely to fluctuate wildly and unpredictably. Climatic and water conditions are chiefly responsible. Since medieval times the Norwegian herring fishery, for example, has undergone huge and irregular cyclical changes. Lately, the catch has varied from well over a million tons in 1956 to 69,000 tons in 1961.

Another factor that makes fish populations difficult to predict is the interaction of different species with each other. It is not enough, for example, to know how many halibut have spawned in a particular area; also to be taken into consideration are the whereabouts and prevalence of salmon, which, it is believed, like to devour halibut larvae. Ideally, scientists want to know the entire life cycle of all commercially valuable fish, their predators, their prey, and the fish that compete with them for food. So far there are many more questions than answers. No one, for example, has a clear idea of the migration habits of so common a fish as the skipjack tuna.

Nevertheless, biologists have had considerable success in predicting fish populations. The Bureau of Commercial Fisheries at Woods Hole, for example, makes reliable forecasts of the abundance of haddock and other ground fish so that fishermen and processors can plan their operations a year in advance. The bureau has also been able to correlate the appearance of skipjack in mid-Pacific with water temperatures measured off Hawaii.

The most elaborate forecasting service is run by the Japanese Government. Daily maps of water conditions throughout most of the Pacific are drawn up from reports supplied by scores of fishing boats. These maps indicate, among other things, where nutrients are being stirred up from the depths, causing plankton to flourish and fish to congregate.

Burbank of the Sea

The peculiar habit shared by salmon and a few other marine fish of returning to spawn in the very streams where they were hatched suggests that it may be possible to improve them genetically like any domestic animal. Lauren R. Donaldson of the University of Washington is doing just that with Chinook salmon. Since 1949 he has been selecting his breeding stock with an eye toward several factors that make for desirable fish. His goal is a fish that matures early, lays a lot of eggs, has healthy offspring, resists disease, and has a hefty, meaty body.

In a few years of shrewd selective breeding, Donaldson has produced some truly remarkable salmon. Ordinarily the Columbia River Chinook returns to spawn when it is four years old, but most of Donaldson's fish spawn at three and many males as early as two. Moreover, his precocious youngsters are full-size, weighing as much as thirty-five pounds. Donaldson plans next to work on steelhead trout, another fish that breeds in streams and matures in the sea. "I'm using the ocean like a pasture," he explains, pointing out that the fish return to his breeding ponds like a herd of cows wandering back to the barn.

Donaldson's venture opens a promising new vista for aquaculture. And his use of the pasture simile brings home the fact that aquaculture will introduce a brand-new element into the questions of national sovereignty and personal and corporate ownership of ocean resources.

The time-honored three-mile territorial limit is no longer sacrosanct. At a United Nations meeting on the law of the sea held five years ago in Geneva, both the U.S. and Britain took the position that the limit should be extended to six miles, with exclusive fishing rights covering an additional six miles. They suggested also that nations which have for a long time fished these waters should retain their historic rights.

Other nations favor wider territorial limits. The Soviet Union, Canada, the U.A.R., and other countries claim control of the sea within twelve miles of their coasts. Ecuador, Peru, and Chile have staked out exclusive fishing rights to 200 miles.

A new law of the sea is taking gradual form. There is pretty general agreement, for example, that a nation should have control of resources on the ocean bottom out to the end of the continental shelf, which in many cases extends more than 100 miles out to sea. Ultimately large areas of the ocean may be put under control of an international organization, which will have the power to grant leases for the exploitation of resources so that a nation or a corporation that spends effort and money to develop a resource will be assured of the benefits.

It seems certain, then, that ocean resources will be brought under much tighter control of nations and individuals. "The only reason the doctrine of freedom of the sea has worked," says Richard Fleming, "is that nobody really wanted to own the resources of the sea before. Up until now the situation has been much like that which existed in the early days of the West, when open-range lands with no fences were the rule. It was only later when the land itself became valuable that ownership and law enforcement of that ownership came into existence."

39. Secrets of the Restless Tides
C. P. Idyll

The causes, character, and distribution of tides are fairly well known and constitute a basic element of physical geography. Nevertheless, many unanswered questions remain concerning some of the more unusual aspects of tides. Even today, although there is awareness of the great power potential of tidal flow, nothing, or at best very little, has been done to make effective use of this power source. Many questions concerning tidal characteristics are answered in this selection.

The moon has been credited by poets and necromancers with all manner of strange powers. It is said to drive men to love or madness; its light transmutes homely objects into magical things; it is supposed to affect the weather and the germination of seeds sown in the earth. Fishermen

SOURCE: *Think,* XXV, 11 (November, 1959), 32–35. Reprinted by permission of *Think* Magazine; copyright 1959 by International Business Machines Incorporated. The author is chairman of the Division of Fisheries, Institute of Marine Science, University of Miami, Florida.

even claim that a catch spoils faster by moonlight than under the heat of the sun.

All of these assertions of the moon's power, momentous and trivial alike, are open to more or less doubt. What cannot be challenged successfully, however, is the immense power that the moon exerts on the seas.

For sheer power—inexorably, day in, day out, over the millennia of time—tides have no match. The tides of the Bay of Fundy alone move 100 billion tons of water in and out twice every day—some 70 times the daily volume of the Mississippi River at New Orleans.

Nearly everyone knows that the moon somehow controls the tides, but many fail to realize that the sun, too, brings its influence very much to bear on daily tidal movements.

But then, if the moon and the sun shine over the whole world, why are the tides in Fundy 50–plus feet in range while those in many Pacific islands measure a few inches? Why, again, do most of the coasts of the Atlantic Ocean have two well–marked high tides a day while many areas along the Gulf of Mexico have only one? Why do most tides march along later every day by about 50 minutes while those of Tahiti are so unvarying that popular belief says you can almost set your watch by their steady pulse?

First, let us apply ourselves to the basic question of how the moon and the sun exert their influence on the seas.

One of the fundamental forces of the universe is the mutual attraction of masses of matter. All bodies, whether earthly or cosmic, exert a pull on each other. If the masses are small the attraction is slight; if they are large the pulling force is also large. In other words, the attractive force is in proportion to the combined masses of the object. Gravity, of course, is merely this attracting force between the earth and the apples or the airplanes suspended uneasily above it.

But to understand fully why water on the surface of the earth moves in response to the attractive force of the moon, we have to realize that *each particle* in the adjacent objects feels the pull of gravity. Hence, every molecule of the earth is pulled as if by invisible wires toward the moon. Particles of rock, of grass and of you and me come under this influence to the same extent as particles of water, but none of these is as free to react to the moon's pull, so the result of this force is evident only in the sea.

The tendency of objects to be attracted to each other is greater the closer they approach, and this tendency grows rapidly weaker as their distance apart increases. To put it more exactly, the force of the attraction is inversely proportional to the square of their distance apart. The attraction is only ¼ as great when the distance between the objects is doubled; it is reduced to $\frac{1}{16}$ when the distance apart is 4 times the original separation.

We have been talking mostly in terms of the moon's influence on the tides, and the implication is, then, that this is stronger than the effect of the sun. This is so, and results from the moon's relative nearness to the earth.

Let us make three improbable assumptions. Suppose first that the whole earth is covered with a continuous ocean; next that the moon does not move, the earth does not rotate around its own axis and thus always presents the same face to the moon; and finally that the sun does not exist. Then the water would be heaped up permanently at the part of the ocean nearest the moon. There would then be no tidal currents.

Now let us suppose that the earth is released from its unnatural stillness and begins again to rotate around its axis. The elevated part of the ocean would now swing around the earth, following the moon, and tidal currents would again be set up. Now, if we again bring the sun into the picture, its attraction would cause a second smaller tidal current to pass around the earth. If we now allow the continents and islands to resume their rightful places, we complicate, but do not basically change, this fundamental pattern of tidal movement.

Why Some Tides Are Higher

With these points of reference we can account more easily for the greater heights of tides at certain times. The high "spring" tides occur at the time of the full or new moon, when the influences of the sun and moon augment each other. At the neap tides, the influences of the heavenly bodies partially cancel out each other. Spring tides, of course, can occur at any time of year; their name comes from an old English verb, *springan,* meaning rise.

There are two spring tides and two neap tides each month, as the sun and the moon alternately come into line with the earth and separate a quarter of a circle apart.

Spring tides are not all the same height, nor do the neaps all have the same range. Spring tides at new moon, when the moon and the sun are both on the same side of the earth, are larger than the spring tides produced at the full moon, when the moon and sun are lined up, but on opposite sides of our globe.

Winds also have an effect on the height of tides. A steady onshore wind will produce higher than expected tides, while a hurricane can drive the seas to devastating levels.

Now let us consider the interesting problem of why some regions of the world have enormous tides exceeding 50 feet, while others have a range of only inches.

The Atlantic end of the Panama Canal, for example, has tides of only a foot or so, while 40 miles away, in the Pacific, 16–foot tides occur.

The highest tides occur in bays which get progressively narrower as they go inland, so that the water surging up the bay is compressed and is forced to rise to accommodate the fluid mass crowding inward. Such areas are characteristically shelving too, so that the space for the water is decreased in still another dimension.

This reduction of the cross–section of the tidal entrance is not the main reason for high tides, however. Familiar with the flat surface of the sea, we tend to think of the oceans as being held each in its own big, single basin. This is far from the truth, since the seas are divided into many basins of various shapes and depths.

The familiar phrase "restless sea" takes on a new significance when we learn that the water in each of these basins is in constant back–and–forth motion, like the water being sloshed in a wash tub. This oscillation is not only continuous, but its timing is steady, so that the water rises and falls on the edges of the basin with a definite period. At the edges, too, the rise and fall is at its maximum, while in the center of the basin, the node, the up and down movement is zero, or nearly so.

The motion of a child's "teeter-totter" is perhaps another clarifying analogy, the fulcrum going neither up nor down, but the ends rising and falling rhythmically. Thus, areas with the greatest tides are on the edges of one of these big sea basins, with the gigantic sloshes driving salt water to unusual heights. If one more circumstance is added so that the period of oscillation is about 12 hours, coinciding with the timing of the cosmic influences, then we get the really notable tides like the 50–footers in the Bay of Fundy. In such cases the oscillation gives the tide an extra boost, much as a person on the ground can send a child in a swing up higher by proper timing of his push.

For someone who has spent his life on a coast with twice–daily tides, it is confusing to visit areas like much of the Gulf of Mexico or the Mediterranean where there is only one tide in 24 hours. Then, there are areas which have two tides a day, but where one is of smaller magnitude than the other.

In many cases there is only one tide a day because the oscillations—the sloshing of the water back and forth in the ocean basins—of more than one tidal current cancel each other out and eliminate the second tide which would be expected. Secondly, reflected waves, water bouncing off a nearby shore, may be just so timed that it cancels out one or even both of the daily tides.

The tidal motions of the sea's waters are the result of the centrifugal force created by the spinning of the earth and the attraction of the sun and the moon. Just how this combination of forces will be manifested—whether, for example, one or two tides a day will occur—depends to a considerable degree on the size and shape and bottom characteristics of the particular ocean basin.

Where diurnal tides occur, the highs are an average of 12 hours and

25 minutes apart, corresponding to the progressively later rising of the moon day by day. This interval is not exact, but varies over a period of days.

Tidal Waves and Tidal Bores

Tidal waves and tidal bores are sometimes confused, but are in fact quite different phenomena.

A tidal bore is the high forefront of an incoming tide, which occurs in certain parts of the world. Ordinarily, tides creep up relatively slowly, advancing at a quite unspectacular rate—rather like a clock whose hands move so slowly as not to be noticed. But the next time you look at the clock it is, perhaps, an hour later; the next time you glance at the tide it may have put tons of water over what was formerly miles of sand flats.

In special places, on the other hand, the coming of the tide is a boisterous, exciting event, with the water racing along at the clip of a running man. Tidal bores are fronts of water created when a tide in a narrow channel and with a big range is checked in its flooding by a sand bar or similar obstruction. When it is released it rolls up the channel with speeds sufficient to catch and drown many an unwary loiterer on the flats. The Tsientang River of China has bores of 8 to 11 feet in height—occasionally as big as 25 feet—traveling at 13 knots. The bore of the Fundy tides is deeply respected by those living in the area, and they run their lives with tidetables in their hands, to avoid being caught.

Those misnamed phenomena, tidal waves, are spawned by cataclysmic upheavals of the earth. Earthquakes and volcanic eruptions sometimes send enormous walls of water racing around the globe, with disastrous results to coastal areas.

Moon Madness

It is often stated, sometimes jestingly, sometimes in all seriousness, that the moon drives men to madness. "Madness" has never been identified in sea animals, but something akin to it is caused by moon–dominated tides. People living on the seaside in Southern California, for example, marvel at the precisely timed, frantically conducted spawning run of the grunion, the small silvery fish which regulates its egg–laying to coincide precisely with the spring tides of certain times of the year.

From March to August, these little fish appear in multitudes on the sandy beaches. Spawning occurs at very precise times in relation to the tidal cycle, taking place only during a few hours on the three or four nights following the full or new moon. This means that it occurs only on the highest tides of the cycle. The fish actually leave the water briefly for the spawning act. The female burrows frantically into the damp sand, tail first; the male then twines himself around the half–buried female, and the eggs and sperm are cast out simultaneously. The fish then flop into the sweep of a receding wave, back into the sea. The fertilized eggs remain buried in the sand for two weeks, until the next series of high tides will have enough reach to wash them out of their nests. When the salt water covers the eggs, they hatch quickly.

A host of other marine creatures have a rhythm timed to the sea's movements. Such fixed animals as barnacles, oysters, and mussels, which are periodically exposed on the flats, wait for the tides to bring them their food, and their activity is timed to the tides' oscillation.

The vision of billions of tons of water surging back and forth over the surface of the earth once or twice a day has excited many a man into wondering if tides might not provide enormous amounts of power.

The potential is there, certainly. If tides all over the world were harnessed, they could produce about 2,000,000,000 horsepower annually —about half the world's needs.

In actual fact, the areas of the world which offer favorable conditions for obtaining power from the tides can be counted on two hands—with fingers to spare. These conditions are a considerable tidal range and a large basin behind a narrow opening to the sea. Tides must rise not less than 10 feet to be useful as a power source, and 20 feet is a much more realistic minimum.

Thus, the only regions to be seriously considered as potential tidal–power localities are: the Bay of Fundy on the New Brunswick–Maine border; the Brittany coast around St. Malo, France; the Severn estuary on the west coast of England; Penzlinskaya Bay in Siberia; Cook Inlet, Alaska; and the San Jose and Decada Rivers in Argentina. Full use of all of these would produce, instead of half the world's power needs, perhaps 0.2 per cent. And to reduce still further this potential, some of these locations are at the moment economically unfeasible because they are too far from power–using areas.

Tidal power, nevertheless, is still a solid prospect for beefing up the power total of certain favorably located areas.

The Passamaquoddy Scheme was a serious attempt to harness the 25–foot tides of the Bay of Fundy. This was developed into the ad-vanced planning stages in the early 1930's, but in 1936 Congress put a stop to the work, amid a good deal of clamorous and bitter argument. One serious second thought concerned the effect of the dam on the rich fishery resources of the area, including the herring runs. The idea seems too good to die, however, and in 1956 Congress revived it by author-izing $3,000,000 for a new survey, while Canada appropriated $300,000 for a study on her side of the line. A report of a 3–year study is due this fall to both governments.

Engineering advances of recent years have been encouraging enough to get another long-considered tidal power project actually under way. This pioneer scheme is that of the Rance River, 2 miles upstream from St. Malo, on the Brittany coast. The Rance estuary has been one of the areas studied longest, since it fulfills tidal power conditions well. The maximum range is 37 feet, and a narrow opening leads to a 7¾-square-mile basin behind.

A Permanent Life

The Rance River project involves the building of a dam 2,329 feet long and 157.4 feet wide. The dam will rise 5 feet above the highest tides. Work began on the dam in 1956, and 8 to 10 per cent of the turbines are scheduled to begin operation in 1960. The remainder will be working by 1963 if plans proceed as conceived. The cost of the project will be about $100 million, but the tidal power plant should have a permanent life and should save France a half–million tons of coal a year.

If the Rance River scheme works, the French will think seriously about an even bigger tidal power scheme, which envisions enclosing the whole bay of Mont Saint Michel near the site of the Rance project. Here, 41–foot tides race into a basin of around 300 square miles. A 20–mile dam could produce about half of France's present electricity consumption.

The Range River and Mont Saint Michel projects will be watched with great interest, and if they succeed we may see others looked on with less skepticism.

The tides can be considered from many points of interest. We may look at them with the eye of the engineer, envisioning thousands of horsepower energy. We may have the uncomplicated viewpoint of the seaside dweller, who times his activities to the tidal cycles, or the inquisitive outlook of the biologist who studies the influence of the restless waters on sea creatures. Whatever our interest, we cannot but marvel at their timing and their lifelike breathing motion.

XI. SPACE

The space era, opening with the launching during the International Geophysical Year, 1957–1958, of artificial satellites by the Soviet Union and the United States, has added new dimensions to man's insatiable search for knowledge about the vast reaches of space. Manned space flights and the scientific instrumentation of unmanned space vehicles traveling beyond the earth's atmosphere have revealed more information about the nature and structure of the universe than it was possible to obtain in any earlier period of history. Although our egocentric notions of the earth and its solar system as the dominant part of the universe have long been abandoned in favor of scientific fact and theory, we have only started exploration of the vast areas beyond our own system.

40. Basic Factors in Manned Space Operations
Hubertus Strughold

In this analysis of the factors and problems confronting man in further exploration of space, Dr. Strughold presents what might be called the geography of space, or "spatiography." From this it is quite evident that effective space operation is much more than powerful boosters facilitating the escape from the earth's gravitational field, and that an understanding of the actual and functional characteristics of differing areas and dimensions of space is essential to further successes.

Physical Environment of Space Operations

The physical environment of the space between the celestial bodies in our solar system is radically different from that found on the earth's surface. The decisive difference is the absence of an atmospheric medium. Space is an environment of emptiness, an almost perfect vacuum. To realize the full significance of this fact for human space flight, we need only examine the atmospheric functions for life in general and for manned flight in particular. Then we must ask ourselves what happens when these functions are missing. The linking question between

Source: *Air University Quarterly Review*, X, 2 (Summer, 1958), 29–46. The author is with the School of Aviation Medicine, U.S. Air Force.

the two is where above the earth's surface do these atmospheric functions come to an end and, consequently, the conditions of space begin. From the answer we will get a clear picture of the physical environment of manned space operations, and how deep this environment reaches down to the earth's surface.

The Atmospheric Environment

The atmosphere as a functional medium for life and for manned flight does not extend as high as its material expansion. The region around 600 miles out, or 1,000 kilometers, is generally accepted as the material limit or border of the earth's atmosphere. This estimate is based on the occurrence of collisions between the air particles. Only as far out as such collisions occur can the atmosphere be considered a continuous medium. Above 600 miles the separation (free path) of the air particles has become so spacious that intermolecular collisions become very rare. Instead the air molecules and atoms move out toward space, with high kinetic energy imparted by their last collision. The heavier ones follow an elliptic trajectory, fly many miles high—as a kind of microrocket—then fall back into the atmosphere. Others with very high kinetic energy, essentially the light elements hydrogen and helium, may even escape forever into space.

Thus we observe above the 600-mile level a kind of spray zone of free-moving air particles, the so-called "exosphere," for which an extent of about 600 miles is also assumed. Above about 1,200 miles, or 2,000 kilometers, the exosphere gradually thins out into the near vacuum of space, with a particle density of about 1 gas particle per 1 cubic centimeter.

The Space Environment

These gas particles in interplanetary space, which are essentially in an ionized state, consist primarily of hydrogen. One cubic meter contains about one million hydrogen particles and very many less particles of oxygen, potassium, sodium, silicon, calcium, etc. Also about 11 million electrons are found in 1 cubic meter, or 11 in 1 cubic centimer.

This interplanetary gas is only a part of the so-called "interplanetary matter." Other components are dust particles essentially of cometary and meteoric origin, micrometeorites, and meteorites. In addition to these very thinly dispersed matter, interplanetary space is permeated by electromagnetic and corpuscular radiations of both solar and cosmic origin. These will be discussed in more detail later.

The significance of this physical environment of space for manned space operations can best be understood by contrasting it with the atmosphere as a functional medium for manned flight. We shall see that these functions of the atmosphere for manned flight do not terminate at the 600-mile material limit. Rather they end at different altitudes and all much lower than 600 miles; some end even within the stratosphere. These various altitude levels are called the "functional borders" between atmosphere and space, or the "functional limits" of the atmosphere. At and above them we find spacelike or space-equivalent conditions with regard to certain functions. The concept of the functional limits of the atmosphere, and especially that of space equivalence within the atmosphere, permits a determination of where space begins for the flyer.

. . . . .

SUMMARY OF ATMOSPHERIC ZONES / The atmosphere as a material continuum reaches up to 600 miles, but as a functional environment for flight it extends only to 120 miles. Space as a physical environment, with practically all of its space characteristics, reaches down to 120 miles altitude. With some of its physiologic effects, space extends down as low as 63,000 or even 50,000 feet. This means that there is a transition zone between atmosphere and space where the functional and physical environments overlap. The well-known classification of the atmosphere in terms of physics must therefore be supplemented by a space-medical one. Based upon the foregoing considerations we can divide the whole atmosphere into four zones: (1) the physiological zone—from sea level to 10,000 feet; (2) the physiologically deficient zone—from 10,000 to 50,000 feet; (3) the partially space-equivalent zone—from 50,000 feet to 120 miles; and (4) the totally space-equivalent zone—from 120 miles to about 600 miles.

For the flyer the atmosphere beyond 120 miles is no longer tangible. It is imperceptible. Here it turns into a pseudoatmosphere. The area around the 120-mile level is therefore the final functional limit of the atmosphere. Beyond this final functional limit the laws of aerodynamics lose their meaning and those of celestial mechanics or astrodynamics become fully effective.

Such is the picture of the physical characteristics of upper atmosphere and of space, which we obtain by contrasting them with those found in the lower regions of the atmosphere. These characteristics may be briefly summarized: In space there is no oxygen or air pressure to keep a man alive, no atmospheric material for the pressurization of the cabin, and no natural protection against meteorites or solar and cosmic radiation. In space we are exposed to the whole range of the electromagnetic radiation spectrum of the sun, from soft X-rays of about 10 angstrom in wave length, ultraviolet rays, visible rays, heat rays, and radio waves up to about 10 meters in wave length. We encounter the whole range of cosmic ray particles in their original, primary form and the energy with which they enter our solar system. And there is no material medium in space to support a flying vehicle. But this picture of the physical environment of space would not be complete if we did not consider the variations found in some of its characteristics.

Variations in Space Characteristics

REGIONAL VARIATIONS / First, certain regional variations are found in the vicinity of the earth. Space around the earth is considerably different from that found in interplanetary space just as the climate around a house differs somewhat from that found in a nearby open field. The side of a house protects us from wind, rain, or snow and it offers shadow on a hot, sunny day. Similarly the solid body of the earth protects us from half of the meteorites and cosmic ray particles. Thermal and visible radiation in the vicinity of the earth is strongly influenced by the earth's own and reflected radiation. The regional distribution of the cosmic rays is to a high degree determined by the earth's magnetic field.

Since these rays are charged particles (except the neutrons), they are channeled into the polar regions by the earth's magnetic field. And in the equatorial regions the low-energy particles are deflected back into space. Solar corpuscular rays are concentrated in the polar regions also, as evidenced by the geographic location of the northern and southern lights (aurora borealis and aurora australis). These displays are caused by light emission from the air molecules and atoms, brought into excited states by the bombardment of solar ray particles.

Recently a high-intensity radiation belt consisting of protons and electrons beginning at an altitude of 600 miles above the equator has been discovered by J. van Allen by means of the satellites Explorer I and III. Its location is also related to the earth's magnetic field.

So far we have confined ourselves to the space in the vicinity of the earth and to the area of the earth's orbital distance from the sun. We find regional variations in the properties of space on a much larger scale when considering the whole distance range from Mercury to Jupiter or Pluto. These variations are the result of the differences in solar radiation which follow the inverse-square law in relation to distance from the sun. The differences in the radiation climate of space are enormous and involve all four important sections of the solar electromagnetic spectrum: infrared rays as the main heat rays, visible rays or light, chemically active ultraviolet rays, and X-rays.

Heat rays. As is generally known the intensity of the heat-carrying rays (essentially infrared) is measured by the solar constant. This is the amount of heat irradiated upon unit of area per unit of time. At the top of the earth's atmosphere this value is roughly 2 gram-calories per 1 cm^2 per 1 minute. At noon on the earth's surface it is never higher than ½ of this value because of heat absorption by atmospheric water vapor and carbon dioxide. At the orbital distance of Venus the solar constant increases to 2½ times its value at the orbital distance of Earth. At the orbital distance of Mercury it increases to 6 times as much. At the distance of Mars it decreases to less than ½, at Jupiter's distance to $\frac{1}{25}$, and at the mean distance of Pluto it drops to $\frac{1}{1600}$ of the terrestrial value. These variations in the thermal irradiance from the sun in different parts of the space in our solar system are of tremendous importance with regard to the climatization of the space cabin.

A vehicle designed for an operation into the region of Venus is not fitted for an excursion to Jupiter. And a spacecraft entering the intramercurian space would inevitably run into a kind of solar heat barrier, as symbolized by the legendary flight of Icarus and as actually demonstrated by a real object named Icarus. This Icarus is an asteroid discovered by Walter Baade at Mount Palomar in 1949, about 1 mile in diameter. It makes a trip around the sun in 409 days. The orbit is so eccentric that at the perihelion the asteroid is only 16.8 million miles from the sun, halfway between Mercury and the sun. At that distance, its surface temperature for a few days must be above 500° C. At its aphelion—in the region between Mars and Jupiter—the surface temperature of Icarus should drop below the freezing point of water.

There are three other asteroids—Hermes, Apollo, and Adonis—which undergo similar but not quite so drastic temperature changes along their eccentric orbits, and which have their perihelion between Venus and Mercury. The most spectacular examples in this respect are, of course, the comets, which—hibernating in the remote regions of Jupiter and Pluto as icy mountains of dirt, frozen water, ammonia, and methane —come to life by exhibiting gigantic tails caused by solar radiation as soon as they approach closer than three astronautical units to the sun.

It must be added that solar thermal radiation has also a decisive influence upon the atmospheric temperatures of the planets.

Light. Another important property of our environment is visible radiation or light. In space the sky is dark everywhere because of the absence of a light-scattering atmospheric medium. The illumination from the sun varies considerably with the distance. Solar illuminance is usually expressed in foot-candles.* At noon on a sunny day at middle latitudes at the bottom of the atmosphere, solar illuminance is roughly 10,000 foot-candles. At the top of the atmosphere it is 13,000 foot-candles. This light intensity in space increases to 26,000 foot-candles at the solar distance of Venus, and to 78,000 foot-candles near Mercury. It decreases to about 4,500 foot-candles at the Martian orbit, to 590 foot-candles at Jupiter's orbit, and to about 8 foot-candles in the remote region of Pluto.

This consideration of the heat rays and the visible rays or light indicates that we observe enormous regional variations in the sun's thermal effectiveness and illuminance within the space of our planetary system.

Ultraviolet and X-rays. The same can be said of the ultraviolet part

---

* Foot-candle (unit of illumination) = one lumen per square foot. Lumen = luminous flux emitted through a unit solid angle (one steradian) from a point source of one candle.

and the x-ray range of the solar spectrum. Even for the orbital region of the earth, considerable gaps exist in our knowledge of these phenomena. These may be bridged eventually by recordings in artificial satellites.

It may be added that the chemically very active ultraviolet is held responsible for the different chemical composition of the atmospheres of the inner planets and the outer planets. The former are basically oxygen atmospheres, the latter are hdyrogen atmospheres.

TEMPORAL VARIATIONS / The regional differences in the radiation climate in our solar system are not static. Rather they show temporal variations because of variations in the activity of the sun. The latter are frequent and occur in the form of giant flares and eruptions. These phenomena on the sun's surface, associated with sunspots, are characterized by intensified electromagnetic radiations (ultraviolet) and by the ejections of huge amounts of ray particles (electrons, protons). As already mentioned, the latter make themselves noticeable in gigantic polar lights within our atmosphere at altitudes from 600 miles down to about 60 miles. During the period of such solar events, according to Hermann Schaefer, the radiation intensity in the extra-atmospheric polar regions of the earth may reach values a thousand times higher than during the time of a quiet sun.

It is generally known that the sunspot cycle is of an 11-year duration. The consideration of this temporal pattern may be important for scheduling space operations.

Also a man in a space vehicle may encounter a suprise when he runs into the path of a disintegrated comet. Such a path is characterized by streams or swarms of macrometeorites, micrometeorites, and dust, all remnants of the perished comet. If the earth crosses one of these paths we observe the spectacle of a meteor shower.

Space as a physical environment is essentially a radiation environment with very thinly dispersed matter. In contrast, the atmosphere is essentially a material environment with attenuated radiation. Emptiness permeated by radiations of a broad intensity range and temporal fluctuations and spiced with meteoric pepper is the environment with which an astronaut is faced unless he is protected. Space medicine, in close cooperation with astronomy and space technology, must and will provide this protection.

Classification of Space Operations

The successful development in rocketry since the ending of World War II represents an achievement of revolutionary significance in the history of mankind. It has opened wide the gates into space. The conquest of space, however, will take the course of a step-by-step evolution just as did progress from the first simple, manually operated electrostatic machine to the huge electric power plant of today. Paralleling this step-by-step evolution of space flight, the medical problems will become more numerous and complex.

We shall discuss primarily the various stages of manned space operations that are already realized or may be expected in the immediate or remote future. Secondly, we shall briefly outline the increasing complexity of the medical problems associated with the technological developments in space flight. This will afford a panorama of the grandiose adventure into space as visualized by the space doctor. Too, it may show us where we stand today and what is about to come.

Bases for Classification of Space Operations

A classification of the various kinds of space operations can be based on the properties of the environment, the characteristics of motion, and the destination of the flight.

FROM ATMOSPHERE TO SPACE / At about ten miles altitude the atmosphere begins to become partially space-equivalent. This condition progresses to total space equivalence at about 120 to 140 miles, if we ignore some peculiarities found in the vicinity of the earth. This is an important fact, because the lower portion of the partially space-equivalent zone is already the routine zone for high-performance jet planes; and rocket-powered craft, as well as the ultrahigh balloon flights, penetrate in rapid progression higher and higher into these regions. These kinds of space-equivalent flight represent the transitional stage from present-day flight operation to true space operations or astronautics. True space operations are conceivable only above the mechanical border of the atmosphere, i.e., above 120 or 140 miles. This region is therefore the dividing line between aeronautics and astronautics. Here we leave behind us the realm of aerodynamics and enter that of celestial mechanics, or the region of Kepler's laws.

SPATIOGRAPHY / To define or classify by categories the possible space operational developments beyond the aerodynamically effective atmosphere, we need a topographical description of extra-atmospheric space— a kind of geography of space or a "spatiography," which subdivides free space into certain areas, using certain "borders" or differences in the environmental properties as demarcations. At first glance such an attempt seems difficult in an environment where emptiness is the rule and where concentration of matter in the form of celestial bodies is the exception. However, there are several possibilities. The simplest procedure is to use the orbits of the moon and planets as topographical demarcation lines, and to speak of cislunar space, translunar space, cismartian space, transmartian space, and cisvenusian and transvenusian space, as suggested by Krafft Ehricke. Thus cislunar space is the region between the moon's orbit and the earth's orbit. In all these cases, the earth is the point of reference. If the sun is the point of reference, the prefixes "intra" and "extra" are common in astronomy. The intramercurian space, for instance, is the area between the orbit of Mercury and the sun. All these orbits are theoretical topographical lines distinguished by the astronomicl fact that they are the paths of celestial bodies. They offer a simple and easily understandable means of subdividing interplanetary space.*

ENVIRONMENTAL CONDITIONS OF SPACE / Of practical and vital importance to the astronaut are differences in the environmental conditions of space itself. To begin with, the space in the vicinity of a celestial body is different from free interplanetary space. It shows peculiarities caused by the mere presence of the celestial body, by the optical properties of its surface, and by forces originating from it and extending into space. In the vicinity of the earth, for instance, we are protected from half of the meteorites and cosmic rays by the solid terrestrial body beneath us. The thermal space environment near the earth is strongly influenced by radiation—both the earth's own and that which it reflects. Also the sunlight reflected from the earth's surface and clouds must be taken into account. A special peculiarity in the vicinity of the earth is the regional distribution of solar and cosmic ray particles, which are channeled into the polar regions by the geomagnetic field. The space around the earth up to a distance of about one earth radius or 4,000 miles—where all the above-mentioned peculiarities are conspicuous—Krafft Ehricke calls "terrestrial space." "Circumterrestrial space" would be another appropriate name. Similarly we can also speak of Martian space, Venusian space, and lunar space.

GRAVITY-BASED SPATIOGRAPHY: GRAVISPHERES / Large spatial areas may also be conveniently designated according to the gravitational forces of celestial bodies. The astronomer is primarily interested in the field concept of these forces and in the mutual gravitational attraction of celestial bodies in order to explain their orbital motions, the occurrence of perturbations, and tidal effects. A space vehicle, however, has practically no gravitational field of its own, its atractive force being in the order of one billionth of one g. In space flight, gravitational attraction is consequently such a one-sided affair that only the gravitational force of the attracting celestial body need be considered.

The question now arises as to how far into surrounding space this force—or more precisely, the gravitational control of a celestial body over a space vehicle—extends. Here we arrive at an important concept in astronautics, the "sphere of gravitational influence," which may better

---

* Ignoring the galactic movement of the sun, which "interplanetary space" may be assumed to accompany *in toto* as a frame of reference.

be defined as the "sphere of predominant gravitational attraction." The earth's sphere of predominant gravitation attraction extends about one million miles from the earth's center. Beyond this distance the gravitational attraction of the sun becomes predominant for a space vehicle. After crossing the neutral zone outward from Earth a vehicle would be "captured" by the sun and follow a path around it comparable to the heliocentric orbits of the planets. The earth could continue to exert some influence upon the vehicle's orbit but only in the form of perturbations. Theoretically the earth's gravitational field extends to infinity.

Within the sphere of the earth's predominant gravitational influence the moon exerts a gravitational subsphere of its own, and the balancing line between the two bodies lies at a distance of about 24,000 miles from the moon, or from the earth about nine tenths of the distance to the moon. The earth and the moon, like the other planets and their satellites, move together in the gravitational confine of the sun. Because of the importance of the spheres of predominant gravitational attraction in astronautics, it might be advisable to call them "gravispheres," in analogy to "atmosphere." The atmosphere is an extension of a planet into its surroundings in the form of gaseous matter. The gravisphere then is an extension of a planet into its surroundings in the form of dynamical gravitational forces. Thus we can speak of a terrestrial gravisphere, lunar gravisphere, Martian gravisphere, Venusian gravisphere, etc., and finally of the giant solar gravisphere which blends far beyond Pluto with the gravitational no man's land between the stars. The spatial extension of the gravispheres of the other planets is, of course, different from that of the terrestrial gravisphere, depending on their gravities and distances from the sun. This subdivision of our solar space is based exclusively on dynamics.

CHARACTERISTICS OF MOTION / The dynamical aspect of space leads us logically to the characteristics of motion in space operations. Basically all space operations consist of three phases: the active (power-on) phase during launching, the passive (power-off) phase of coasting, and the atmospheric re-entry phase.

Coasting: orbital velocities. Here we are concerned only with the coasting phase, because this kind of motion gives space flight a unique characteristic. Above the mechanically effective atmosphere (140 miles), coasting can take place in a closed path or orbit (circular or elliptic) round the earth only if the vehicle has the required velocity. Such velocities—the so-called orbital velocities—are reached when the gravitational (centripetal) attraction of the earth is balanced by the inertial effects of the vehicle acting in the opposite direction. The result is the state of weightlessness. Near the earth's surface—if the earth had no atmosphere—the orbital velocity would be 17,668 mph. With increasing altitude the orbital velocity decreases because of diminishing geogravitational attraction. The moon, 240,000 miles away from the earth, has an orbital velocity of 0.7 mi/sec. But it should be emphasized that, in contrast to the decrease of the orbital velocity with altitude, pushing or projecting a vehicle into a higher orbit requires a higher amount of initial energy. Consequently a greater projection velocity is required to attain the higher potential energy of the higher orbit in the gravitational field.

The orbital velocities just explained are examples of the first category of astronautical velocities. This category can also be applied to orbital flights around the moon, around other planets, or around the sun. The orbital velocity of the earth around the sun, for instance, is 18.6 miles per second.

Escape velocities. If the kinetic energy or projection velocity of a vehicle is high enough, the vehicle may leave the earth's sphere of predominant gravitational attraction in an elongated ellipse and enter the area in space where the sun's gravitational attraction prevails. The velocity required for a rocket to cross this balancing borderline is called the "velocity of escape." This velocity brings a vehicle into an open hyperbolic path with regard to the earth, but into a closed, circular, or elliptic orbit with regard to the sun—a heliocentric orbit.

The escape velocity from the earth belongs to the second category of astronautical velocities. To escape from the earth into the sun's gravisphere requires a velocity of 25,000 mph or 7 mi/sec. Escape into the moon's gravisphere requires only slightly less. Escape from the moon requires 1.5 mi/sec, from Mars 3.1 mi/sec, from Venus 6.3 mi/sec, and from Jupiter 37 mi/sec. The escape velocity from the earth is the prerequisite for lunar and interplanetary space operations. These operations may bring the astronaut into regions of space with ecologically different radiational properties or to other celestial bodies with strange atmospheric environments.

Evolutionary Stages of Space Operations

Space operations may be classified in accord with the properties of the environment, the characteristics of motion and pertinent velocities, and the destination of the flight. The evolution of human flight—as it is today, as it may be tomorrow, or as it might be in a more or less remote future—we may then see in four stages:

1. For the past fifty years we have been in the stage of atmospheric flight. Its characteristics are very well known: propeller and jet propulsion; the lower regions of the atmosphere as the flight zones; pressurized cabins; subsonic and supersonic speeds; generally normal gravitational conditions; distances of geographic dimensions; and flight durations of fractions of a day. Status of the craft: airplane.

2. We have now entered the next stage: space-equivalent flight. The characteristics are jet and rocket propulsion; the partially space-equiva-

lent regions of the atmosphere; sealed cabins; supersonic and hypersonic speeds; the gravity pattern—multiples of g, reduced g, and nullified g; operational range of geographic dimensions; flight duration from minutes to several hours. Status of the craft: airplane plus projectile. The craft of the century series and especially those of the X-class—like the Bell X-2 and the North American X-15—are the prototypes belonging to this stage of space-equivalent flight or space-equivalent operations.

3. As soon as it is possible to push a manned vehicle into an orbit with orbital velocity, we will have manned orbital flight or manned satellite flight. The characteristics are totally space-equivalent regions of the atmosphere or circumterrestrial space; sealed cabins; orbital velocities in a geocentric orbit or in the earth's gravisphere; the gravity pattern—multiples of g and long durations of nullified g. Status of the vehicle: biosatellite. The smaller research satellites with and without animals in the International Geophysical Year are the first step in the direction of manned satellite operations or circumterrestrial space operations.

4. The final stage will follow as soon as the attainment of escape velocity makes escape operations possible beyond the gravitational control of the earth. The characteristics of gravispheric escape operations are similar to those of satellite operations except that the vehicle now enters the gravispheres of other celestial bodies and may circumnavigate the moon or other planets, or may even land on them. In this final stage of space operations the vehicle will have attained spacecraft status.

There may be some transitional stages between these four basic stages of space operations, such as satelloid flight, i.e., a powered satellite (as suggested by Krafft Ehricke) for flights in the regions below the mechanical border of the atmosphere.

This classification gives a realistic perspective of the stage at which we stand today and of the developing possibilities we may expect in the future. The timetable of that development will be determined by space technology, but in any event space medicine must and will be prepared to meet and cope with all these possibilities.

Medical Problems in Space Operations

The medical problems in space operations are manifold. Some of them are fully encountered in the preliminary stage of space-equivalent flight. They become more and more complex in advanced operations, and the accent of importance may shift from one to another in different space operations.

In the space-equivalent phase of space operations, the regeneration of the cabin's air will offer no problem. Cosmic rays and meteorites are of no concern. The accent may rest on the increased importance of the gravity pattern—acceleration during launching and deceleration during reentry—and on the landing maneuver.

In manned satellite operations involving hundreds of revolutions, the regeneration of the cabin's air by physicochemical means and other climatic measures will demand increased considerations. The same may be said about zero gravity, day-night cycling, and some psychological problems. Cosmic rays and meteorites too may enter the picture. Return from the orbit will be a problem of primary concern in addition to those already mentioned.

In gravispheric escape operations into heliocentric orbits and via transfer orbits into the gravitational territory of another planet, the time element becomes dominant. In these operations new methods for regeneraion of the air by means of natural or artificial photosynthesis may have to replace the chemical type. Recycling of body wastes will be necessary to ease logistics. The long duration of the flight will increasingly pose psychological problems resulting from isolation and confinement. And finally, landing on another planet may open the gates to a new astrobiological world with a strange climate and perhaps with strange flora and fauna. But the astronaut's first concern must be for his survival on his return from this particular celestial body—unless he should find staying there less strenuous than the return trip to that far-distant blue and green planet "Terra" orbiting between Venus and Mars.

XII. THE FUTURE
OF PHYSICAL
GEOGRAPHY

41. Studies in Physical Geography
National Academy of Science

This final selection provides not only a summary of the various aspects of physical geography, but also offers a prognosis of future developments. One of the more important points is that as man acquires more extensive knowledge of all physiographic elements, he will increasingly be able to alter or control the long-dominant physical environment in order to meet his needs more adequately.

The Problem Area

Physical geographers study the physiographic-biotic systems as determined by natural and cultural processes [1] and the spatial distribution of this system. Many other fields of inquiry either directly or indirectly impinge upon this area of study. Nevertheless, the physical geographer expects to provide a focus for the interpretation of the physical and biological world as a foundation for human activity, spatially considered.

To perform this essential task with competence and insight, the physical geographer must be a specialist. He must be so if he is to be able to select from the mass of specialized inquiry the specific parameters, hypotheses, or approaches which are most appropriate to the relation between man's spatial behavior and his environment. However, the environment of man is not a fixed or given quantity. It is in part a function of man's perception, in part a set of forces which man must

---

[1] "Process" denotes a succession of physical, biotic, or cultural events dependent on characteristic energizing agents. Thus the physical process of erosion is associated with gravity, hydraulic agents, and atmospheric movement; the vegetative process is associated with the forces of organic genesis, growth, and decay; and technological processes are associated with man's capacity to capture energy from his physical and biotic surroundings and to direct it toward his purposes. (Ackerman, 1958, 5.)

SOURCE: *The Science of Geography,* National Academy of Science–National Research Council, Publication No. 1277, 1965, pp. 14–23.

modify, and in part the static setting in which he is momentarily placed. The judicious selection of significant descriptive and dynamic parameters of the natural environment through fundamental inquiry is the task of the physical geographer.

A beginning point for physical geography continues to be the study of the distribution of forms and processes in the natural environment. Divided into subspecialties, the field appears to encompass a broad array of major fields such as meteorology, oceanography, hydrology, geomorphology, pedology, and ecology, to each of which the word geography is suffixed. Physical geography once did literally encompass the entire field now thus subdivided. Today, rather than encompassing them, physical geography both draws from and makes common cause with these disciplines in an effort to describe the behavior of air, water, soil, and biota at the surface of the earth, and to explain the covariant distribution of diverse elements of the environment on a particular part of the earth's surface.

Physical geography places particular stress upon the system relations among air, water, soil, and biota, upon their distribution into space, and upon their relation to man. The analysis of these complex relations is made manageable because processes involving air and water can often be modeled as closed systems. Where such systems can be recognized, the condition or state of the system may be measured in terms of temperature, available moisture, organic material, landform change, or other parameters. If the system is cyclical, like the hydrologic cycle or if it approaches a steady state as in some river channels, the special role of man in the environment may often be appraised by measuring sequential changes in these parameters. Such changes may be associated with historical changes in land use and development or they may be induced by artificial manipulation of the existing environment. Thus, concepts of the interrelation of many elements in the environment, their distribution in space, and their behavior as systems provide fundamental bases for physical geographic study. They are logical beginnings for an understanding of the man-environment system.

Current Activity

Study of physical geography formed the backbone of geography from its beginning until early in the present century. Geographers were universally concerned with descriptions of the atmosphere, the oceans, and the land. Where natural phenomena appeared to impinge directly upon human affairs, geographers were especially interested in the relation between the two, although the study of the earth itself in the presence or absence of man provided a valid area of inquiry. Then for about 30 years geographic interest in the physical earth appeared to wane. The waning trend is now reversing.

Although the activities described below do encompass workers in a variety of specialities in a number of different geographic regions, communication among many of them is very active. In addition many investigators share common concepts and approaches. In both climatology and physiography, dynamic equilibria and analyses of transport processes are receiving strong emphases. Similarly, current work in plant geography emphasizes the relation between plant distribution and the dynamics of surficial earth processes.

Physiography

Quantitative observations of landforms and surficial earth processes provide one of several foci of current research in physiography. These processes involve the movement of water, ice, wind, and soil in different climatic and geologic environments. Research has been concerned with the evolution and maintenance of specific landforms dominated by one or more of these forces. Thus clusters of activity center around the study of such features as rivers, glaciers, coasts, or hillslopes and the processes acting upon them. Although the dual threads of process and measurement are not equally well developed in each of these areas, significant activity is apparent in all four. The geographic contribution in these areas varies considerably. It looms quite large in coastal studies and, particularly in Europe, on studies of slope processes.

The range from theory to field observation is at the moment perhaps best integrated and most comprehensively covered in the study of glaciers. Recent theoretical formulations of the mechanics of glacier flow have revolutionized the analysis of glaciers themselves and of glacier response to climate. These analyses have provided a framework for observations of the movement of glaciers and for the correlation of such observations with climatic data.

In the study of rivers, correlative measurements of river hydraulics, alluvial forms, and drainage basin characteristics have begun to provide a more complete picture of the behavior of the entire drainage system in response to climatic and geologic controls. Extension of these findings has suggested theoretical hypotheses of the probable characteristics of alluvial landforms assuming the operation of specific physical constraints related to transport of sediment and water.

A comprehensive program of coastal studies at the Coastal Studies Institute, Louisiana State University, Baton Rouge, emphasizing historical, geomorphic, and sedimentary relationships is demonstrating the value of concentrated attack upon a single class of geographic problems. These studies include observations of coastal processes involving waves, wind, and rivers, and their effect on beaches, bars, deltas, dunes, cliffs, mudflats, and other coastal features. The association of current processes and resultant stratigraphy and form are particularly valuable in developing a sound foundation for interpretation of coastal evolution. At their best these inquiries utilize techniques in archaeology, botany, and history and thereby demonstrate one of the stimulating facets of modern physiography. It draws from and contributes to cultural, historical, and economic geography. Study of coasts from tropical to arid regions has begun to show both the universality of some coastal features and also the extreme complexity of the processes causing their evolution. This system involves the interaction of climate, vegetation, and coastal morphology. At the same time, laboratory and field studies of the mechanics of coastal processes provide principles and data which can be utilized in both physiographic and sedimentation studies.

Careful measurements of hillslope forms were pioneered by Strahler and his associates. Although the number of studies remains small, significant efforts at observation and measurement of slope processes are also under way. A few, particularly those in arctic and periglacial regions where hillslope processes operate rapidly enough to be easily measured, begin to provide data with which to evaluate the relative magnitude of such forces as solution, running water, and mass movement in different regions. These more detailed studies can also be used in comparisons of denudation rates in different regions, a subject of interest to both geophysicists, and to cultural geographers concerned with land erosion resulting from the activities of man.

From a regional standpoint, the far north continues to provide perhaps the most fruitful environment for regional studies in physical geography. In Canada, the United States, England, and Sweden, universities and governmental agencies are providing fundamental knowledge of many aspects of the northern physical environment. These studies range from analyses of glacier mechanics and response to climate, noted earlier to geomorphic interpretations of modern and fossil landforms. A striking feature of much of this work is the close association of geographer, physicist, biologist, climatologist, archaeologist, and geologist. Originally dictated in part by expensive logistic problems, as in polar research, this collaboration has proved most fruitful.

Climatology

By contrast with geomorphology, climatic research has not undergone an extensive recent renaissance among geographers. Climate is recognized as of great importance to man, and is the most variable of the components of the natural environment. A large fraction of professional geographers expresses a teaching and research interest in climatology, but relatively few significant research papers have been produced in recent years. Some notable exceptions are exemplified by the work of Thornthwait on the heat and moisture balance of the earth's surface and Curry on the relation of climatic probabilities and agricultural practices. Several studies have also led to better definition of climatic elements and climatic zones.

Possibly the most stimulating recent work in climatology has dealt with synthetic climatology or "climatonomy," and dynamic climatology. Synthetic climatology attempts the quantitative explanation of local and regional climate using as a basis turbulent transfer theory and other fundamental physical principles. Dynamic climatology uses the recent explosive growth of general circulation theory and large-scale machine computation to describe and explain the broad features of the climate. The research in these fields has not yet entered into the mainstream of geographic thought about the man-environment system. This gap in communication among geographers provides an attractive opportunity for constructive action.

Two other largely unexploited areas of climatic research—the microclimatology of cities and historical climatology—are especially significant in studying the man-natural environment system. With increasing urbanization, city microclimates merge into a macroclimate that is man-made. The concomitant air pollution then becomes an ominous as well as significant factor. The literature on this problem is of great interest to the geographic profession but needs interpretation and utilization. On the other hand, a most fruitful collaboration of climatologists and historians with peripheral sciences is adding detail and certainty to our knowledge of past climates. This research has a significant relation to historical geography.

Physiography and Biotic Geography

A close association of plant geography and physiography continues to flourish at several centers. Studies by Sauer and others elucidate the fundamental relation between vegetation, geology, and geomorphic processes on the coast. These inquiries and those of atoll research workers demonstrate how vegetation adjusts to storms, to tides, and to variations in geology. In a completely different environment, Goodlett's floristic geographic studies with Hack and others place renewed emphasis upon mapping and analysis of spatial distribution as a means of shedding new light on the relation between geomorphic processes and the distribution of vegetation. Studies of the distribution of forest species have shown marked covariance with hydrologic and lithologic factors. In addition, studies of the species distribution of the modern flora have a significant by-product in providing a model of relation between pollen assemblages and distribution of vegetation to interpret past landscapes.

A strikingly successful liaison of botany, geomorphology, history, and economics is illustrated in the study of the origin of the coastal area of eastern England known as the Broads. Collaborative efforts in the far north, as noted elsewhere, have provided insight into the interaction of process and vegetation. A similar close interrelation is observable between distribution of tree species on flood plains and the dynamics of floods, spring flows, winter ice cover, and disposition of sediment in a humid temperature environment. Although these and other studies in plant geography are closely related to work in ecology, the latter has perhaps given greater emphasis to physiologic and organic aspects of vegetation and has been less concerned with distribution and physiographic process.

The physical and biogeographic effects of man's wholesale modification of his environment provide new impetus to both biologically and physically oriented studies of the landscape.[2] For example, water control structures, by altering the regimen of streams, produce significant changes in water quality, channel morphology, and vegetation in both upstream and downstream reaches of natural channels. Similarly, sequential changes associated with large-scale construction operations on the land produce initially large concentrations of sediment to streams. Upon completion of construction large areas are covered by impermeable surfaces and streams are starved of sediment. This sequence of events may cause decreased channel conveyance, increased flooding, vegetative growth in channels, reduced oxygenation of bottom waters, and changes in fish population and microbiota. Later runoff from roads and streets may vary in both quality and quantity from its former condition; the nature of these changes is known in detail in only a very few places. In most areas information, if it exists, is primarily qualitative.

Physical Geography and Other Subjects

Renewed interest and inquiry in physical geography have been closely associated with significant expansion of research and research techniques in allied fields. Analyses of the behavior of rivers have accompanied theoretical and laboratory studies of fluid dynamics, sediment transport, and energy changes associated with mobile boundaries. A close working relation between field observation and laboratory experiment has revealed fundamental relations between flow, sediment transport, bed configuration, and channel form. New instrumentation permits field measurement of simultaneous changes in parameters.

Advances in theoretical statistics, techniques of sampling, computer simulation, and computer analysis of data have been readily applied to physical geography. The National Research Council–Earth Sciences Division Symposium in 1963 on computers in geography and geology demonstrated that programs have been developed to compute trend surfaces, evaluate sampling programs, correlate data distributed in space, and simulate diffusion processes in physical and other geography. Statistical analysis of tree ring data, for example, has called into question previously reported cyclical patterns in some physical geographic data. Correlation studies of tree rings have also demonstrated the need for

[2] Landscape—the visible surface of the earth, including cultural alterations thereof.

examining closely the relation between weather conditions and rates of tree growth, and lag-time between tree response and variations in weather elements.

One of the most interesting and productive symbiotic relations between physical geography and other fields has developed where the only record of history is that reposing in the landscape, in recent stratigraphic evidence, in floral or faunal gene pools, in archaeological sites, or other similar phenomena.

Archaeological sites provide one of the most significant meeting grounds of modern physical geography and other disciplines. Virtually all field observational disciplines seem to meet at such sites. Here the tools and insights of the physiographer, cultural geographer, botanist, pedologist, zoologist, anthropologist, historian, and archaeologist contribute to the understanding of both local history and the evolution of man and society. The recognition that much of the evidence is physical and stratigraphic has led to a progressively closer alliance of physical geographers, cultural geographers, and archaeologists. Careful reconstruction of the climatic and physiographic environment is essential if historical generalizations relating to man and his environment are to be valid. This subject interdependence has been clearly recognized in many recent excavations in the Middle East, although contributions by geographers have been limited.

Cytogenetic studies are contributing significantly to cultural geography and to cultural history with information on the genetic composition and origin of cultivated plants. Results from these studies provide unique keys to the history and sequence of contacts among diverse cultures in many parts of the world. These relations in turn shed light on the way in which different peoples have come to terms with their environment and on the sources of inspiration and ideas which aided them in doing so.

With improved dating methods, the tie between archaeologists and physiographers and the other fields also is being strengthened. As the physiographer helps to reconstruct the environment of the past, he enhances the archaeologist's interpretations. At the same time, as the latter refines his time scale, the physiographer is provided with new and powerful tools for measuring rates of surficial earth processes. Present knowledge of these rates is universally meager yet of fundamental importance to any understanding of surficial earth processes in terms of basic geophysics or as a reference level in evaluating the effects of changes in land use or climate.

Some Areas of Future Emphasis in Research

Three major opportunities confront research workers in physical geography: (1) further reorientation of study toward a dynamic systems concept of physiographic processes; (2) much increased observation of surficial processes, particularly in conjunction with theoretical work; and (3) study of the interrelation between physiographic processes and man's activities.

The study of the earth for its own sake and the study of the spatial aspects of man's use of the earth are inextricably bound. By definition such studies are fundamental to an analysis of the man-environment system. A view of this area of inquiry may be obtained from a consideration of a hierarchy of basic problems. Although some current work mirrors this hierarchical structure, the need for studies at several levels in the hierarchy is critical. It must also be recognized that past processes in a given region may have differed markedly from present processes.

Reformulation of Basic Hypotheses

Several approaches to these major problems can be considered. First, in physiography, general principles of landform development, such as those proposed years ago by William Morris Davis and Walther Penck, must be reformulated so as to evaluate all the physical and biological factors entering into the basic hypotheses. Presumably such evaluations will be easier if quantitative relations can be established to describe the system. Such a fundamental formulation must take into account the wide spectrum of possible combinations of climatic and physiographic parameters found in nature.

Already an excellent beginning in this direction has been made. A significant approach to the dynamics of process has been provided by recent concepts of equilibria and cycles. Cycles are best exemplified in models of the heat balance or hydrologic budget of drainage basins and other regional systems of the earth's surface. To the extent that soil and water systems can be postulated to operate at a steady state, it is possible to evaluate input, output, and changes in storage within the system. Concepts like dynamic equilibrium and steady state, or the maintenance of particular landforms as a consequence of the continuous interaction of specific processes and rock materials, are powerful tools in physical geographic studies. The concept of a budget or balance affords a simple mechanism for evaluating the dynamic and spatial relationships between different quantities. The concept of a threshold of erosion, for example, provides a criterion that can be verified and that can be used to evaluate changes in surface from accompanying known or predicted changes in external forces.

These concepts of the physical environment, drawing upon new findings from diverse sciences, are modifying the tradition tendencies to treat environment as a static sum of landforms and averaged climatic data rather than as a complex multivariate system. This reorientation of physiographic study of the natural environment is essential if it is to be truly related to economic analysis, resource management, and other problem areas of geography—an association providing a major opportunity and responsibility of physical geography.

Observation of Earth Surface Processes

A second need is for clear and accurate descriptions of surficial processes. These processes include movement of soil and rock by running water and mass movement, transport of moisture from the atmosphere to soil to plants and back to the atmosphere, disintegration of rock and circulation of solutes, and movement and mixing of diverse materials in the atmosphere. The collective action of these processes, their space distribution, and their relation to human activity are the physical geographers' foci of attention. Of particular importance is an evaluation of the comparative importance of different processes under different climatic and geologic regimes.

Considering the variety and extent of observations to be made, it is not surprising that the characteristics of the environment of man at the surface of the earth—the interface of the atmosphere, soil, and ocean—are still poorly known. In generalized terms, the mechanisms at work, their relation to vegetation, and the manner in which they mold the landscape are scarcely described or understood over much of the earth's surface. Yet these observations are not only absolutely essential for further theoretical progress in the science, they are also vital to the most effective progress in many of the arts by which man manages or develops resources, or otherwise transforms his environment.

The need here is for the observation of physiographic units as interconnected systems, using the newer conceptual tools and statistical aids. A great many data have been and are being collected on hydrology, erosion, vegetative cover, and climatic elements; but measurement and analysis of their performance as local or regional systems are rare indeed. Such studies are essential if physical geography is to contribute most effectively to an understanding of the earth and to the progress of society.

The Interrelation between Physiographic Process and Man's Activities

In addition to the studies of process, an increased understanding must be sought about the way in which the natural environment is modified by man and the consequences of such environmental change. Satisfactory answers to such questions require detailed knowledge of both process and form at times and in regions where man has markedly altered the land and where he has not. A better description and understanding of the relation between organic and inorganic systems is particularly needed.

It is now obvious that man's activities have greatly increased his power within a relatively few years to alter the natural environment, both because of the rapidly rising world population and because of the great impact of technologic development. For example, the changes collectively described by the term "pollution" and the regulation of streams by reservoir or other means have greatly changed surface and ground water characteristics in the parts of the world where most people live.

As another example, the already profound effects of modern earth-moving techniques appear certain to be deepened in the near future as the employment of nuclear explosives comes into use. Finally, chemistry and machine technology have been responsible for vast increases in agricultural productivity in many regions of the world, and their application is spreading more widely with each passing year. Although most investigators recognize that agriculture alters soil properties, few studies have been made of the nature, permanence, or importance of these changes.

An increasing variety of phenomena related to physiographic events is being examined from cultural points of view. Illustrations are found in recent studies of the nature of human perception of the natural environment and of the role of economic, historic, and psychological factors in adjustment to specific environments like flood plains. Yet response to environment cannot be evaluated definitively in the absence of accurate, detailed knowledge of the environment itself.

It is time that the physiographically powerful forces produced by man's culture be recognized as one of the parts of the system that the physical geographer studies. Yet, such fundamentals as the relation of the threshold of erosion to landscape changes, the frequency of sequential events such as drought-fire-mudflows, or snowfall-snowmelt-avalanches, the variable composition of dissolved and clastic load in rivers, the response of biota in rivers and lakes to temporal changes in physical factors, and the chemical and physical effects of cultivation on soils remain inadequately understood. The past concentration of physiographic effort on arid regions, artic regions, and the marine coastal environment needs to be supplemented by much expanded study of the natural environments in which most of the world's people live. Indeed, considering its basic nature, such study is long overdue.

Correlation of This Book with Representative Texts

FINCH, TREWARTHA, ROBINSON, AND HAMMOND *Elements of Geography,* 4th ed. McGraw-Hill, 1959	JAMES *A Geography of Man,* 3d ed. Blaisdell, 1966	KENDALL, GLENDINNING, AND MAC FADDEN *Introduction to Geography,* 3d ed. Harcourt, Brace, & World, 1962	MC INTYRE *Physical Geography* Ronald, 1966

Text chs.	Related Selections in *Physical Geography*			
1	1, 2, 40, 41	1, 10, 11, 29, 38, 41	10, 18, 27, 41	1, 2, 39
2	3, 4	2, 26, 27, 35	1, 2, 10, 11, 40	40
3	5	14	40	3, 4, 5, 6, 7, 8, 9
4	8	8, 13, 19, 37	15, 28, 29, 30, 31, 32	4, 14, 20
5	6, 7	7, 20, 22	10, 11	17, 18, 19, 20, 21, 22
6	9, 13, 19	21, 23	12, 13, 14, 15, 16	13, 23, 24, 25, 26
7	8, 20	15, 24, 25, 31, 32	10, 11, 12, 13, 14, 15	10, 11, 12, 13, 14, 15, 16
8	7, 21	20, 23, 24	3, 4, 5, 6, 7, 8, 9	29, 30, 31, 32
9	5, 19	27	4, 5, 6, 7, 8, 9, 10	27, 28, 34, 38, 39
10	4, 9	4	13, 14	
11	10, 11, 12	12	4, 12, 20, 21	
12	10, 11	27, 40	13, 23, 24, 25, 26	
13	14		17, 18, 19, 20, 21, 22, 23	
14	15, 16		21, 41	
15	13, 14		19, 26, 27, 28, 30	
16	12		3, 15, 19, 21	
17	15, 28		26 23, 24, 25,	
18	38, 39		19, 21	
19	29, 30, 31, 32		28, 38	
20	17, 19, 20, 22		33, 34, 35	
21	13, 23, 24		33, 35, 36	
22	25, 27		36, 37	
23	33, 34		31, 32, 36, 38	
24	35, 36, 37			
25	18		3, 16, 19, 21, 26, 31, 32	
26	15			
27	25, 26			
28	31, 35, 36			
29				
30				
31				

	MILLER AND LANGDON *Exploring Earth Environments* Crowell, 1964	STRAHLER *Physical Geography* Wiley, 1962	TREWARTHA, ROBINSON, AND HAMMOND *Fundamentals of Physical Geography* McGraw-Hill, 1961	VAN RIPER *Man's Physical World* McGraw-Hill, 1962
Text chs.	Related Selections in *Physical Geography*			
1	1, 2, 39, 40, 41	1, 2, 40, 41	1, 10, 40, 41	1, 41
2	3, 4, 5, 6, 7, 8, 9	40	11, 13	40
3	3, 4, 5, 6, 7, 8, 14	1, 2, 40	12, 14	12, 13, 14
4	10, 11, 14, 16	1, 2, 40	14, 15	10, 11
5	12, 13, 14, 15		12, 13, 16	2, 5
6	13, 23, 24, 25, 26	39	15	7, 16
7	28, 38, 39	3, 5, 6, 7, 8	2, 5	4, 8
8	29, 30, 31, 32	3, 4, 5	6, 7, 8	17, 18
9	27, 29, 30, 32, 38	4, 28, 38, 39	4, 9	19, 20, 22
10	13, 19, 20, 21, 22	5, 6, 7, 8, 9, 30	5	23, 24, 25, 26
11	16, 33, 34, 35, 36, 37	5, 6, 7, 8, 9	3, 4, 13	7, 13, 14
12	31, 34, 35	3, 4	8, 14	33, 34, 35, 36, 37
13		3, 13	19, 20	29, 30, 31, 32
14		5, 6, 9, 20, 21	21	38, 39, 40
15		4	28, 38, 39	
16		13, 23, 24, 25, 26	29, 30, 31, 32	
17		13, 23, 25	17, 19, 20, 22	
18		10, 11	18, 23, 24, 25, 26	
19		10	33, 34, 35, 36, 37	
20		1, 10		
21		15		
22		12, 14		
23		12, 13, 14, 32		
24		12		
25		14		
26		4, 12		
27		15		
28		12, 14		
29		15		
30		10, 11, 14		
31		10, 11, 33		